Logic 2

B, R

THE AXIOMATIC METHOD

An Introduction to
Mathematical Logic

PRENTICE-HALL INTERNATIONAL, INC., *London*
PRENTICE-HALL OF AUSTRALIA, PTY., LTD., *Sydney*
PRENTICE-HALL OF CANADA, LTD., *Toronto*
PRENTICE-HALL FRANCE, S.A.R.L., *Paris*
PRENTICE-HALL OF INDIA (PRIVATE) LTD., *New Delhi*
PRENTICE-HALL OF JAPAN, INC., *Tokyo*
PRENTICE-HALL DE MEXICO, S.A., *Mexico City*

THE AXIOMATIC METHOD

An Introduction to Mathematical Logic

A. H. LIGHTSTONE

Associate Professor of Mathematics
Carleton University

Prentice-Hall, Inc.
Englewood Cliffs, N.J.

Library of Congress Catalog No. 64–16439
Printed in the United States of America
05502 C

Preface

This book is written primarily for the student of mathematics who possesses some measure of mathematical ability, has a working knowledge of the axiomatic approach to mathematics, and in particular has been exposed to the axiomatic method as applied to the study of modern abstract algebra.

It is the axiomatic method itself that is under scrutiny here. Consider the statement: "Euclid's fifth postulate is a *logical consequence* of his other four postulates." There are two possible interpretations of this statement, depending upon the viewpoint. To a working mathematician, a proposition is a logical consequence of a postulate-set if the given proposition is true about each mathematical system for which the postulates are true. To a logician, a proposition is a logical consequence of a postulate-set provided that the given proposition can be deduced from the postulate-set by applying the laws and procedures of a particular system of logic. Notice that in the latter approach mathematical systems—the realizations of the given postulate-set—are not involved.

On the one hand, then, the axiomatic approach is concerned with mathematical systems and with demonstrating that given propositions (i.e., *theorems*) are true in these mathematical systems. The other side of the axiomatic method is the purely logical side in which the theorems of the system are established by applying a completely formalized *Theory of Deduction* to the given postulate-set. There is a striking difference in viewpoint: the first approach emphasizes the mathematical systems characterized by the given postulate-set, whereas the second approach considers only the logical apparatus, which is applied directly to the postulate-set. A theory of deduction may be regarded as a *black box*: feed in a set of propositions (the given postulate-set), turn a crank, and out come the theorems of the system.

Our plan is to study both approaches to the axiomatic method and to demonstrate that they are indeed two aspects of the same thing. To be precise, we shall prove that, under a suitable theory of deduction, each logical consequence of a given postulate-set under the first interpretation is also a logical consequence of the given postulate-set under the second interpretation.

We begin with a review of the fundamental ideas involved. First, a presentation of the main notions of symbolic logic, then an outline of the fundamental concepts of set theory. Though the material contained in Part I is elementary, it is vital to the rest of the book and should be well digested. Chapter 1 sets up the usual language of mathematics by introducing the logical connectives, in particular the universal and existential quantifiers. In spite of the importance of quantifiers, it is usual that a senior undergraduate, or even a beginning graduate student, has had little or no experience at handling quantifiers. For this reason, a deliberate effort is made in the early chapters of this book to provide practice in analyzing propositions which involve quantifiers.

Chapter 2 presents the basic notions required to construct the fundamental mathematical entity known as an algebraic system. The vital concepts of ordered n^{tuple}, operator, and relation are built up in terms of the notion of a set, which is presented at the intuitive level. The chapter also contains a section that outlines, briefly, the theory of cardinal numbers. This material is used in certain sections of Chapter 6 and the Appendix. On a first reading, this section and others, as indicated by a star may be omitted.

Part II presents the usual approach to the axiomatic method; it is shown that the first step in applying the axiomatic method is to characterize a family of algebraic systems. The next step is to establish true propositions about each algebraic system in the family. An effort is made to point out the method of demonstrating a theorem—namely, by showing that the given proposition is true about each algebraic system in the family characterized by the given postulate-set. To illustrate these points, familiar examples are drawn from modern algebra. Although the material is self-contained, it is assumed that the reader has already been exposed to these algebraic theories, so that attention can be concentrated on the method itself.

The customary approach to the axiomatic method having been discussed, it is time to consider some logic. Of necessity, a theory of deduction is completely formalized; for this reason, Part III must necessarily be much more difficult—from the student's viewpoint—than the preceding chapters. Fortunately, it is possible to introduce the basic notions of logic in a relatively uncomplicated setting, by considering the theory of deduction for a quantifier-free language. In Chapter 4, then, we present the logical system known as the *Propositional Calculus*. This chapter is important, because it constitutes an introduction to the concepts and techniques of mathematical logic. This material must be mastered before the student goes on to Chapter 5, which is concerned with the important theory of deduction called the *Predicate Calculus*, or the *Lower Predicate Calculus*. Both theories of deduction employ syntactical transforms to simplify the presentation and enable important logical notions to be developed in a series of small steps. The reader will note that Chapter 5 follows closely the pattern of Chapter 4.

Chapter 6 extends the study of mathematical logic initiated in the preceding two chapters by establishing the important *Extended Completeness Theorem*, following Henkin's proof. It follows from this result that Part II and Part III are two aspects of the same thing in the sense that the theorems of a mathematical theory considered in Part II are precisely the logical consequences of a postulate-set, as defined in Part III. This is the fundamental thesis of this book.

Finally, as an illustration of the power of mathematical logic, there is an appendix that contains a discussion of *complete theories*. This appendix draws heavily on the ideas and methods of Abraham Robinson, a pioneer in the application of Logic to Algebra.

A. H. LIGHTSTONE

Contents

part I Review of fundamentals

part II The axiomatic method

part III Mathematical logic

part I

Review of fundamentals

I

Symbolic logic

1. The Logical Connectives

Symbolic logic has its roots in the study of language. Any developed language, English say, possesses a number of words and phrases with a distinct function—namely, special words and phrases that are concerned directly with the truth or falsity of the sentences in which they occur. In particular, these special phrases indicate that the truth of the sentence depends upon the truth or falsity of certain other statements. Such words or phrases are aptly called the *logical connectives.* Some of the more important logical connectives are: not, or, and, if . . . then, if and only if.

Let us see how "and" functions as a logical connective. Consider the sentence: "It is cold, and the sun is shining." This sentence is obtained by joining the two sentences: "It is cold"; "The sun is shining" with the word "and". The resulting sentence, called a *compound* proposition, is true, provided that each of the two component sentences is true.

Clearly, symbolic logic is concerned only with declarative sentences that possess definite and unique truth-values; any sentence of this type is called a *proposition.*

DEFINITION: A proposition is a declarative sentence which is true or else is false (but not both).

Thus, a proposition that is known to be not true must be false, and a proposition that is not false is true. Also, a proposition that is true is not false, and a proposition that is false is not true.

Let us consider the logical connective "or". This word is unusually sensitive in the sense that its meaning changes with the context. It is possible to interpret the compound proposition "p or q" in two ways:

(1) "p or q or both"
(2) "p or else q"; i.e., "p or q, but not both"

The first sense of "or" is called the *inclusive* "or", whereas the second interpretation of "or" is known as the *exclusive* "or". In mathematics it is customary to interpret "or" in the inclusive sense. Thus, in mathematics "p or q" means "p or q or both".

Now consider the logical connective "if and only if", which is conveniently abbreviated by "iff". The compound proposition "p iff q" is regarded as true, provided that "p" and "q" have the *same* truth value.

The logical connective "not" has the function of changing the truth-value of a proposition to which it is attached. Thus, the compound proposition "not p" is true in case "p" is false and is false in case "p" is true.

In order to avoid the ambiguities mentioned above, and to emphasize the intended meaning of the logical connectives, it is customary to introduce special symbols to denote the more important logical connectives. The symbols are as follows: $\sim$ (not), $\wedge$ (and), $\vee$ (inclusive "or"), $\underline{\vee}$ (exclusive "or"), $\leftrightarrow$ (iff), $\rightarrow$ (if . . . then).

The logical connectives are really functions with one or two arguments ($\sim$ has one argument; the other connectives have two arguments). The value of each of these functions is either "true" or "false." If "T" denotes "true," and "F" denotes "false," then the logical connectives are conveniently defined by means of a truth-table that spells out the truth-value of a compound proposition in each of the possible truth-value cases.

For example, to define "$\vee$" we let p and q be any propositions, and consider the truth-value of "$p \vee q$" in each of the possible truth-value cases. There are four truth-value cases:

1. "p" is true, "q" is true
2. "p" is true, "q" is false
3. "p" is false, "q" is true
4. "p" is false, "q" is false

TABLE 1-1

	p	q	$p \vee q$
1.	T	T	
2.	T	F	
3.	F	T	
4.	F	F	

TABLE 1-1a

	p	q	$p \vee q$
1.	T	T	T
2.	T	F	T
3.	F	T	T
4.	F	F	F

The four truth-value cases are gathered together in Table 1-1, above. It remains to insert the truth-value of "$p \vee q$" in each of the four cases. For example, a "T" has been entered in line 3 of Table 1-1a, under the heading "$p \vee q$". This means that "$p \vee q$" is true in case "p" is false and "q" is true.

The remaining connectives are defined by truth-tables in a similar way. We present the truth-table definitions of $\sim$, $\vee$, $\underline{\vee}$, $\wedge$, $\leftrightarrow$.

TABLE 1-2

p	q	$\sim p$	$p \vee q$	$p \underline{\vee} q$	$p \wedge q$	$p \leftrightarrow q$
T	T	F	T	F	T	T
T	F	F	T	T	F	F
F	T	T	T	T	F	F
F	F	T	F	F	F	T

Finally, we consider the important logical connective $\rightarrow$. Bearing in mind the meaning of the compound proposition "if p, then q", we note that this proposition is true where "p" is true and "q" is true; furthermore, our proposition is clearly false where "p" is true and "q" is false.

TABLE 1-3

	p	q	$p \rightarrow q$
1.	T	T	T
2.	T	F	F
3.	F	T	
4.	F	F	

So, we obtain the partial truth-table for $\rightarrow$, displayed in Table 1-3. There are exactly four ways of completing this truth-table: they are displayed in Table 1-3a.

TABLE 1-3a

p	q	a	b	c	d
T	T	T	T	T	T
T	F	F	F	F	F
F	T	F	F	T	T
F	F	F	T	F	T

But a is "$p \wedge q$", b is "$p \leftrightarrow q$", and c is "q". Noting that "if p, then q" is not rendered by any of "p and q", "p iff q", "q", we conclude that d is the only possible interpretation, from our logical standpoint, of "if p, then q". This means that the truth-table definition of $\rightarrow$ is as follows:

TABLE 1-3b

p	q	$p \rightarrow q$
T	T	T
T	F	F
F	T	T
F	F	T

In mathematics, then, the compound proposition "if p, then q" is regarded as true, provided that "q" is true or that "p" is false.

EXERCISES

Denoting the propositions "I study" and "I shall pass" by "s" and "p", respectively, express each of the following compound propositions symbolically

1. It is not the case that I do not study.
2. I do not study, and I shall pass.
3. I shall pass if I study.
4. I shall pass only if I study.
5. I neither study, nor shall I pass.
6. Either I study, or I shall not pass.

Assuming that "l" stands for the proposition "logic is easy", and "m" stands for the proposition "mathematics is easy", express the following symbolic propositions in English:

7. $\sim m \wedge \sim l$
8. $l \rightarrow m$
9. $l \leftrightarrow m$
10. $\sim l \rightarrow \sim m$

11. $(\sim l \wedge \sim m) \vee (l \wedge m)$

12. $\sim (l \rightarrow m)$.

13. Define the logical connective "neither . . . nor".

14. Define the logical connective "only if".

15. Define the logical connective "not both of".

16. Show that the propositions "if *p*, then *q*" and "*q* if *p*", are the same.

17. What do we mean by asserting that propositions *p* and *q* are the same?

18. Is "This statement is false" a proposition?

2. Truth-Table Analysis

Consider the compound proposition: "If logic is difficult, and if mathematics is difficult or logic is not difficult, then logic is not difficult". What is being said? Perhaps, by studying this proposition and by absorbing its meaning, you can determine just what it states. There is, however, an easy and mechanical method of solving this problem. First, we express the given proposition symbolically. Let "*l*" denote the proposition "logic is difficult", and let "*m*" denote the proposition "mathematics is difficult". Then, the given compound proposition is expressed symbolically by

$$[l \wedge (m \vee \sim l)] \rightarrow \sim l.$$

Notice that we are free to assign truth-values to *l* and *m* as we wish; for this reason, we say that *l* and *m* are *independent* propositions. Next, we compute the truth-value of the given compound proposition in each of the four truth-value cases. The calculations are conveniently displayed in a truth-table, as in Table 1-4.

TABLE 1-4

l	m	$[l$	$\wedge$	$(m$	$\vee$	$\sim l)]$	$\rightarrow$	$\sim l$
T	T	T	T	T	T	F	F	F
T	F	T	F	F	F	F	T	F
F	T	F	F	T	T	T	T	T
F	F	F	F	F	T	T	T	T
1	2	3	4	5	6	7	8	9

Note that the body of this table consists of four lines, one for each of the possible truth-value cases. The essential thing we are after in constructing a truth-table is to obtain the truth-value of the given proposition in each of the truth-value cases. We shall always insert the resulting column of "T"s and "F"s under the *main* connective of the given proposition, "→" in this example, and we shall call this column the *main* column of the truth-table. Thus, the vital information contained in a truth-table consists of the columns under the independent propositions and the main column. In fact, we shall regard a truth-table as consisting of columns headed by the independent propositions, the main column, and any other columns that are required to compute the main column.

It should be pointed out that Table 1-4 is *not* read from left to right, as most tables are. To show how this table is to be read, let us consider how it was constructed. The first step in constructing this truth-table is to fill in columns 1 and 2, so that each possible combination of truth-values of the independent propositions is displayed. In a very real sense, these entries are part of the "heading" of the table, rather than being part of the "body" of the table. The second step consists in computing columns 3, 5, 7, and 9; this is easy. Third, we compute the truth-values of "$m \vee \sim l$", inserting this information in column 6 directly under "$\vee$", the main connective of the proposition involved. The fourth step consists in computing the truth-value of "$l \wedge (m \vee \sim l)$", which is easily accomplished, since the truth-values of the two components of this proposition are displayed in columns 3 and 6; the resulting truth-values are entered in column 4, directly under "$\wedge$"—the main connective of "$l \wedge (m \vee \sim l)$". Finally, we compute the truth-values of "$[l \wedge (m \vee \sim l)] \rightarrow \sim l$"; this proposition has the form "$A \rightarrow B$", where the truth-values of A are listed in column 4 and the truth-values of B are listed in column 9. Hence, the entries in the main column are obtained by considering the entries in columns 4 and 9. In this way, we obtain column 8, which is entered under "→", the main connective of "$[l \wedge (m \vee \sim l)] \rightarrow \sim l$".

TABLE 1-5

l	m	C
T	T	F
T	F	T
F	T	T
F	F	T

Denoting this proposition by "C", we have shown that Table 1-5 is a truth-table for C. But it is easy to find a proposition that is false when "l" and "m" are both true and is true in all other cases. Such a proposition is "$\sim l \vee \sim m$". It follows that the given compound proposition possesses the same meaning as the much simpler proposition: "logic is not difficult, or mathematics is not difficult". Thus, the given compound proposition asserts "logic is easy, or mathematics is easy".

Since the essential feature of a proposition consists of the "T"s and "F"s that appear in the truth-table for the proposition, we may as well regard the proposition as being merely a name of this same truth-table. By listing the various possible truth-value cases always in the same order, we can reduce a truth-table to its main column. For this reason, we shall regard a proposition as being a name of a column of "T"s and "F"s appearing in a truth-table.

What have we gained? Clarity for one thing. It is a simple matter, now, to compare two propositions: simply construct their truth-tables! The truth-table *is* the proposition. Furthermore, if two propositions possess the following properties:

(1) they involve the same independent propositions
(2) they take the same truth-value for each combination of truth-values of the independent propositions

then we know that these propositions are names of the same object—namely, a column of "T"s and "F"s—and so are equal. For example, the propositions

$$\text{“}[l \wedge (m \vee \sim l)] \rightarrow \sim l\text{”} \quad \text{and} \quad \text{“}\sim l \vee \sim m\text{”}$$

possess these properties; hence, we write

$$[l \wedge (m \vee \sim l)] \rightarrow \sim l = \sim l \vee \sim m.$$

This is the first occurrence of the symbol "=" in this book, which deserves some comment. Here, and throughout this book, we agree to write "$a = b$" only if "a" and "b" refer to the same object or are different names for the same object. Notice the use of quotation marks! Usually, we refer to an object by writing down a name of the object. In case we wish to discuss the *name* of an object, rather than the object itself, we require a convention to indicate that we are *not* referring to the object. This is achieved by inserting quotation marks around the name in question. For example, consider the following sentences:

(1) The Amazon is the longest river in South America
(2) The first letter of "Amazon" is the first letter of the alphabet

In (1), the name "Amazon" is used to refer to an object—namely, a certain river. This, of course, is the usual use of names. In (2), it is the name, rather than the object possessing the name, that is mentioned. Therefore, in (2) we place quotation marks around the name. In this way, we distinguish between *using* a name and *mentioning* a name.

In later chapters, we shall find it vital to distinguish clearly between *use* and *mention*. At first sight, the distinction may appear subtle, largely because we are accustomed to *using* words and symbols and have little experience at discussing; i.e., mentioning; words and symbols. However, in exploring mathematical logic and the foundations of mathematics, we shall find it helpful to consider as entities in themselves the symbols that are used to express mathematical thought.

Another subtle point worth mentioning here is the distinction between the following, where p and q are propositions:

(1) $p = q$
(2) $p \leftrightarrow q$

At first sight, (1) and (2) may appear to be the same. At a closer look, however, we see that (1) and (2) differ in the following way: (1) is a statement *about* the propositions p and q, whereas (2) is itself a compound proposition.

The point is this. At one level we have the fundamental objects treated in symbolic logic—namely, propositions; for example, "$p \leftrightarrow q$" is a proposition. We may also wish to discuss propositions—to make statements *about* propositions; this activity is on a higher level of abstraction than the former. For example, "$p = q$" is an assertion about the propositions p and q. To summarize, we recognize that it is one thing to assert particular propositions; it is a different matter to make statements *about* propositions.

In a similar way, there are two levels of activity in mathematics. At the first level, we have mathematics itself; here, people *do* mathematics. At the second level, we have statements *about* mathematics; this discipline is known as *metamathematics*. Here, the subject of discussion is the activity at the lower level. To illustrate the distinction between mathematics and metamathematics, a statement about theorems of mathematics, comes under metamathematics and is called a *metatheorem*. In Chapter 6, for example, we shall establish the following

METATHEOREM: Let $\mathscr{T}$ be any theorem about fields of characteristic zero; then there is a prime number p such that $\mathscr{T}$ is true in each field with characteristic greater than p.

A simpler example of a metatheorem, is the following:

METATHEOREM: Each theorem possesses a proof.

EXERCISES

1. (a) Construct a truth-table for the compound proposition

$$[(p \wedge q) \vee p] \to \sim q.$$

   (b) Construct a truth-table for the compound proposition $p \to \sim q$.
   (c) Show that $[(p \wedge q) \vee p] \to \sim q = p \to \sim q$.

2. Show that $(p \wedge q) \vee p = p$.
3. Is it true that $A = B$ whenever $A \rightarrow C = B \rightarrow C$?
4. Find propositions A, B, and C such that $A \rightarrow C$ and $B \rightarrow C$ are names of the same column, yet A and B are names of different columns.
5. Construct a truth-table for the compound proposition
$$[(p \rightarrow r) \wedge (q \rightarrow r)] \rightarrow (p \leftrightarrow q)$$
6. What property do the propositions $p \vee \sim p$ and $(p \rightarrow q) \vee (q \rightarrow p)$ have in common?
7. (a) Simplify the proposition: "This course is easy, or the instructor is not kind and the course is not easy, if and only if the instructor is kind and the course is easy".
(b) Deduce from (a) a disguised way of saying: "The instructor is not kind".
8. Simplify the proposition: "If I study or mathematics is easy, then it is not true that I study and mathematics is difficult".
9. Show that $\sim (p \wedge q) = \sim p \vee \sim q$.
10. Show that $\sim (p \vee q) = \sim p \wedge \sim q$.
11. Show that $p \rightarrow q = \sim p \vee q$.
12. Show that $p \leftrightarrow q = (p \rightarrow q) \wedge (q \rightarrow p)$.
13. Show that $p \leftrightarrow q = (p \wedge q) \vee (\sim p \wedge \sim q)$.
14. Show that $p \rightarrow q = \sim q \rightarrow \sim p$.
15. Show that $(\sim p \rightarrow q) \vee (p \wedge q) = p \vee q$.
16. Show that $(p \leftrightarrow q) \rightarrow (\sim p \wedge q) = (\sim p) \leftrightarrow q$.
17. Show that $(\sim p) \leftrightarrow q = \sim (p \leftrightarrow q)$.

3. Propositions Constructed from Independent Propositions

Our purpose in this section is to construct and name all the propositions that can be expressed in terms of two independent propositions. A more ambitious project would be to construct and name all the propositions that can be expressed in terms of n independent propositions, where n is any natural number. We shall not attempt this; however, we shall compute the number of distinct propositions that can be expressed in terms of n independent propositions.

First, let us show that n independent propositions, where n is any natural number, can be assigned truth-values in 2^n distinct combinations. Observe that the number of combinations of truth-values among $k + 1$ independent propositions is exactly double the number of combinations of truth-values among k independent propositions, because each combination of truth-values of k independent propositions gives rise to two combinations of truth-values of $k + 1$ independent propositions: one with the $k + 1$st proposition true and the other with the $k + 1$st proposition false. Obviously, one independent proposition can be assigned a truth-value in exactly two ways; therefore, two independent propositions can be assigned truth-values in $2 \cdot 2 = 2^2$ ways; therefore, three independent propositions can be assigned truth-values in $2 \cdot 2^2 = 2^3$ ways; consequently, we see by mathematical induction that n independent propositions can be assigned truth-values in 2^n ways whenever n is a natural number.

It is now an easy matter to calculate the number of distinct propositions that can be expressed in terms of n independent propositions. Think of what is involved in constructing the truth-table of a proposition: first, we list all the truth-value cases; next, we compute the corresponding truth-values of the given proposition, which means that we adjoin a column of "T"s and "F"s to the table. We have previously observed that the given proposition *is* this column. The question we face, then, is how many distinct columns can we construct? There are 2^n lines in the truth-table, so in forming a column we must make 2^n entries. Each entry is a "T" or an "F". Since we have two choices for each of 2^n entries, we see there are $2^{(2^n)}$ distinct columns of "T"s and "F"s; hence, there are $2^{(2^n)}$ distinct propositions that can be expressed in terms of n independent propositions.

It is easier to understand the above argument if we consider a special case: consider, for example, the case of two independent propositions. The truth-table that we are concerned with has four lines; therefore, we must determine the total number of distinct columns that we can construct in which each column has four entries. There are two choices, "T" or "F", for the first entry. Corresponding to each of these choices, we have two choices for the second entry, then two choices for the third entry, and finally two choices for the fourth entry. Therefore, we can form $2^4 = 16$ columns of "T"s and "F"s. Note that the sixteen propositions formed from p and q include the propositions p and q, themselves.

Before actually constructing and naming the sixteen propositions that can be expressed in terms of two independent propositions, let us consider the much simpler problem of constructing the propositions that can be formed from a single proposition, say p. First, we note that there are exactly two truth-value cases: p may be true, or p may be false. So the body of our truth-table consists of two lines. We now ask how many distinct columns we can construct in this table. There are two choices for the first entry and two choices for the second entry; therefore, there are $2^2 = 4$ columns. The four columns are exhibited in the Table 1-6; each line of the table represents a

TABLE 1-6

p				p
T	T	F	F	T
F	T	T	F	F

truth-value case. We must now decide on suitable names, in terms of p, for each of the three columns not named. Of course, we could invent a separate symbol to denote each column, but this turns out to be unnecessary, since the logical connectives already available suffice. Clearly, "$p \vee \sim p$" is true whether p is true or false; also, "$\sim p$" is false when p is true and is true when p is false; "$p \wedge \sim p$" is false whether p is true or false. Hence, the completed truth-table is shown in Table 1-6a.

TABLE 1-6a

p	$p \vee \sim p$	$\sim p$	$p \wedge \sim p$	p
T	T	F	F	T
F	T	T	F	F

Let us consider, now, the very important task of listing the sixteen propositions that can be constructed in terms of two independent propositions, say p and q. Remember that when we enter "T", say, in a column, we are asserting that for that truth-value case the proposition concerned is true.

We now exhibit the sixteen columns constructed by assigning truth-values to the four truth-value cases, in all possible ways:

TABLE 1-7

p	q	1	2	3	4	5	6	7	8	9	10	11	12	13	14	15	16
T	T	F	F	F	F	T	F	F	T	F	T	T	F	T	T	T	T
T	F	F	F	F	T	F	F	T	F	T	F	T	T	F	T	T	T
F	T	F	F	T	F	F	T	F	F	T	T	F	T	T	F	T	T
F	F	F	T	F	F	F	T	T	T	F	F	F	T	T	T	F	T

Again, it is possible to introduce sixteen connectives, one for each column; but let us show instead that the three connectives $\sim$, $\vee$, $\wedge$ are sufficiently expressive when combined together, to produce names for all sixteen propositions. We list suitable names of the sixteen columns:

1. $p \wedge \sim p$
2. $\sim p \wedge \sim q$
3. $\sim p \wedge q$
4. $p \wedge \sim q$
5. $p \wedge q$
6. $\sim p$
7. $\sim q$
8. $(p \wedge q) \vee (\sim p \wedge \sim q)$
9. $(p \wedge \sim q) \vee (\sim p \wedge q)$
10. q
11. p
12. $\sim p \vee \sim q$
13. $\sim p \vee q$
14. $p \vee \sim q$
15. $p \vee q$
16. $p \vee \sim p$.

There are other names for these columns. For example, column 13 has the name "$p \rightarrow q$", whereas column 8 also has the name "$p \leftrightarrow q$".

In the following section, we shall develop a systematic method of naming a given proposition.

EXERCISES

1. Show that "$(\sim p \wedge q) \vee (\sim p \wedge \sim q)$" is a name of column 6.

2. For which columns are "$(\sim q) \rightarrow p$", "$q \leftrightarrow \sim p$", "$q \rightarrow (p \wedge q)$" suitable names?

3. (a) Calculate the number of different combinations of truth values that can be assigned to three independent propositions.
(b) Calculate the number of distinct propositions that can be expressed in terms of three independent propositions.
(c) Calculate the number of distinct propositions that can be expressed in terms of four independent propositions.

4. Construct truth-tables for the following propositions:

$$[p \vee (q \wedge r)] \leftrightarrow [(p \vee q) \wedge (p \vee r)]$$

$$[p \wedge (q \vee r)] \leftrightarrow [(p \wedge q) \vee (p \wedge r)]$$

$$(p \rightarrow q) \rightarrow [(r \vee p) \rightarrow (r \vee q)]$$

What property do these propositions have in common?

5. Compute the truth-value of "$[(p \to q) \vee (\sim p \wedge q)] \wedge (r \to q)$", given that
   (a) "p" is true, "q" is true, "r" is false
   (b) "p" is false, "q" is true, "r" is false
   (c) "p" is false, "q" is false, "r" is false
   (d) "p" is false, "q" is false, "r" is true

6. Construct a truth-table for each of the following propositions:
   (a) $[(p \to r) \wedge (q \to r)] \to (p \leftrightarrow q)$
   (b) $[(p \to q) \wedge (q \to r)] \to (p \to r)$

4. The Disjunctive Normal Form

In Section 3 we saw that any proposition that involves only two independent propositions can be expressed in terms of the connectives $\sim$, $\vee$, $\wedge$. Let us establish now the even more surprising fact that any proposition at all can be expressed in terms of these connectives, no matter how many independent propositions are involved. Suppose that the independent propositions are $p_1, p_2, \ldots, p_n$, so there are 2^n truth-value cases. Furthermore, suppose that we are faced with a given proposition, expressed in terms of our n independent propositions. This means that we know the column of truth-values involved, so that we can state the truth-value of the given proposition in each of the 2^n truth-value cases.

We shall now construct a name of this column. There are two cases: either each entry in the column is "F", or there is at least one "T". In the former case, $p_1 \wedge \sim p_1$ is a suitable name of the column. In the latter case, we construct a name of the column as follows. We begin by selecting a truth-value case such that the corresponding entry in the given column is "T"; let us now construct a proposition that is true in exactly this particular truth-value case. This is a simple matter, since the proposition "$q_1 \wedge q_2 \wedge \ldots \wedge q_n$" is true iff each of the propositions $q_1, q_2, \ldots, q_n$ is true. Let q_1 be p_1 if p_1 is true in the particular truth-value case we are looking at, and let q_1 be $\sim p_1$ if p_1 is false in this particular truth-value case. Choose $q_2, \ldots, q_n$ according to the same prescription. Then, the resulting proposition "$q_1 \wedge q_2 \wedge \ldots \wedge q_n$" is true in exactly this truth-value case. Now, do the same for each other truth-value case such that the corresponding entry in the given column is "T". Finally, join all the resulting propositions with "$\vee$". The proposition we have constructed, is true if one or more of its constituents is true and is false if none of its constituents is true. This is precisely what we are after. We shall call any proposition obtained in this way the *disjunctive normal form* of the given proposition, since it is a disjunction of conjunctions.

To illustrate the above construction, let $n = 3$, so that we have three independent propositions p_1, p_2, p_3. There are eight truth-value cases. Let us find the name, according to the above construction, of the column F, T, T, F, F, F, T, F. The entry in the main column is "T" in the second truth-value case; a proposition true in exactly this truth-value case, is "$p_1 \wedge p_2 \wedge \sim p_3$". The entry in the main column is "T" in the third truth-value case;

TABLE 1-8

	p_1	p_2	p_3	?
1.	T	T	T	F
2.	T	T	F	T
3.	T	F	T	T
4.	T	F	F	F
5.	F	T	T	F
6.	F	T	F	F
7.	F	F	T	T
8.	F	F	F	F

a proposition true for exactly this truth-value case, is "$p_1 \wedge \sim p_2 \wedge p_3$". Finally, the entry in the main column is "T" in the seventh truth-value case; a proposition true for exactly this case, is "$\sim p_1 \wedge \sim p_2 \wedge p_3$". Forming the disjunction of the three propositions just constructed, we obtain

$$(p_1 \wedge p_2 \wedge \sim p_3) \vee (p_1 \wedge \sim p_2 \wedge p_3) \vee (\sim p_1 \wedge \sim p_2 \wedge p_3).$$

This proposition is true if any of its three constituents is true; hence, it is true in the second, third, and seventh truth-value cases. Also, this proposition is false if each of its three constituents is false. But each of the three constituents is false in the remaining truth-value cases; therefore, the proposition we have constructed is false in the remaining five truth-value cases. This establishes that our proposition is a name of the given column; thus, we have expressed the given proposition in terms of the connectives $\sim$, $\vee$, $\wedge$.

In fact, we have achieved much more than our stated goal! More important than the fact that any proposition can be expressed using only three connectives, is the fact that we can now write down a name of a given proposition by following the simple and mechanical procedure outlined above. In a subsequent section, we shall put this ability to use.

EXERCISES

1. Write down the disjunctive normal form of each of the following columns associated with the three independent propositions p_1, p_2, and p_3 of the example in the text:

(a) F, F, F, T, T, F, F, F
(b) T, F, F, F, F, T, F, F
(c) F, F, T, F, F, F, F, F

2. By first computing the truth-table, obtain the disjunctive normal form of the following propositions; in each case use the minimum number of independent propositions:
   (a) $p \rightarrow q$
   (b) $(\sim p) \rightarrow q$
   (c) $(p \vee q) \rightarrow r$
   (d) $(p \rightarrow q) \rightarrow r$
   (e) $p \rightarrow (q \rightarrow r)$
   (f) $[(p \vee q) \wedge (p \vee \sim r)] \leftrightarrow p$
   (g) $(p \rightarrow q) \leftrightarrow (q \rightarrow p)$
   (h) $[(p \wedge r) \rightarrow q] \wedge \sim r$
   (i) $[((\sim p) \leftrightarrow q) \vee r] \wedge ((\sim q) \wedge p)$
   (j) $(p \rightarrow q) \rightarrow (r \leftrightarrow \sim p)$

3. Devise a procedure that, when applied to the disjunctive normal form of a given proposition, will produce the truth-value cases in which the proposition is true.

4. It is of theoretical interest to introduce a logical connective—namely, "/"—to denote column 12 of Table 1-7; this means that $p/q = \sim(p \wedge q)$. Show that
   (a) $p/p = \sim p$
   (b) $(p/p)/(q/q) = p \vee q$
   (c) $(p/q)/(p/q) = p \wedge q$
   (d) $p/(q/q) = p \rightarrow q$
   (e) $[(p/q)/(p/q)]/(r/r) = (p \wedge q) \rightarrow r$

5. Now show that any proposition can be expressed in terms of /, no matter how many independent propositions are involved. (This connective is called *Sheffer's Stroke*, after the logician who first realized its importance).

6. By the *conjunctive normal form* of a proposition, we mean the proposition constructed as follows: Select a truth-value case in which "F" appears in the main column; write down the proposition "$q_1 \vee q_2 \vee \ldots \vee q_n$", where for each k, $q_k = \sim p_k$ if p_k is true in this truth-value case; otherwise $q_k = p_k$. Do the same for each truth-value case in which "F" appears in the main column. Finally, form the conjunction of all these propositions. The resulting proposition is a suitable name for the given column. If there are no "F"s in the main column, then we take "$p_1 \vee \sim p_1$" as the conjunctive form of the given proposition.

   Question: Devise a procedure which, when applied to the conjunctive normal form of a given proposition, will produce the truth-value cases in which the proposition is false.

5. Tautologies and Valid Arguments

A proposition whose truth-value is "T" in each of the possible truth-value cases, is said to be a *tautology* or *logically true;* a proposition whose truth-value is "F" in each of the possible truth-value cases, is said to be *logically false*. For example, "$p \wedge q \rightarrow p \vee q$" and "$[\sim(p \vee q)] \rightarrow [(\sim p) \wedge \sim q]$" are both tautologies, whereas "$p \wedge \sim p$" is logically false.

The notion of a tautology is important, because it is involved in the concept of a valid argument. An argument is a list of propositions, one of which is called the *conclusion* of the argument, the others being called the *assumptions* of the argument. An argument is said to be *valid* if and only if the conclusion is true in each truth-value case in which each assumption is true. For example, consider the following argument: "If a man is married, he has troubles. This man has no troubles. Therefore, this man is not married." We show the argument is valid. First, we express the argument symbolically.

Let m = this man is married, and let t = this man has troubles. Then the assumptions of the argument are: $m \rightarrow t$, $\sim t$; and the conclusion is $\sim m$. We construct a truth-table (Table 1-9) which displays the truth-values of the

TABLE 1-9

m	t	$m \rightarrow t$	$\sim t$	$\sim m$
T	T	T	F	F
T	F	F	T	F
F	T	T	F	T
F	F	T	T	T

assumptions and the conclusion, in each of the four truth-value cases. There is only one truth-value case in which both assumptions are true: the fourth case. Since the conclusion is also true in this case, we conclude that the argument is valid.

The connection between tautologies and arguments, is displayed by the

THEOREM: The argument with assumptions $p_1, p_2, \ldots, p_n$ and conclusion q, is valid iff the proposition "$(p_1 \wedge p_2 \wedge \ldots \wedge p_n) \rightarrow q$" is a tautology. This theorem is easily proven by considering a truth-table.

The basic rules of logical inference are easily established when interpreted as an argument. For example, consider the rule of inference known as

MODUS PONENS: If p and $p \rightarrow q$, then q.

Constructing a truth-table, we easily see that this argument is valid.

EXERCISES

Show that the following are tautologies:

1. $[\sim(\sim p)] \leftrightarrow p$
2. $[\sim(p \vee q)] \leftrightarrow [(\sim p) \wedge \sim q]$
3. $[\sim(p \wedge q)] \leftrightarrow [(\sim p) \vee \sim q]$
4. $[(p \wedge q) \vee (p \wedge r)] \leftrightarrow [p \wedge (q \vee r)]$
5. $(p \rightarrow q) \rightarrow [(r \vee p) \rightarrow (r \vee q)]$
6. $(p \rightarrow q) \leftrightarrow [(\sim q) \rightarrow \sim p]$
7. $[p \wedge (q \vee \sim q)] \leftrightarrow p$
8. $[p \vee (q \wedge \sim q)] \leftrightarrow p$
9. $p \rightarrow p$
10. $[\sim(p \vee q)] \rightarrow \sim p$
11. $(p \rightarrow q) \vee (p \rightarrow \sim q)$
12. $(p \vee q) \vee (p \rightarrow q)$
13. $(p \rightarrow q) \vee (q \rightarrow r)$
14. $p \vee (p \rightarrow q)$
15. $[(p \rightarrow q) \rightarrow p] \rightarrow p$
16. $(p \wedge q) \vee (p \rightarrow \sim q)$
17. $[(p \rightarrow q) \rightarrow q] \rightarrow (p \vee q)$
18. $[\sim(p \rightarrow q)] \leftrightarrow (p \wedge \sim q)$.

Determine which of the following propositions are tautologies:

19. $p \rightarrow (p \wedge q)$
20. $p \rightarrow (p \vee q)$
21. $p \rightarrow [(\sim p) \vee q]$
22. $(p \wedge q) \rightarrow p$
23. $(p \wedge q) \rightarrow (p \wedge r)$
24. $(p \wedge q) \rightarrow (p \vee r)$
25. $[(p \vee q) \wedge (p \vee \sim q)] \leftrightarrow p$
26. $[(p \vee q) \wedge (p \vee \sim q)] \leftrightarrow q$
27. $(p \rightarrow q) \vee (q \rightarrow p)$
28. $(p \wedge \sim q) \vee (q \wedge \sim p)$
29. $(p \vee \sim q) \wedge (q \vee \sim p)$
30. $[p \wedge (q \rightarrow p)] \rightarrow p$
31. $[p \wedge (p \rightarrow q)] \rightarrow q$
32. $[p \wedge (p \rightarrow q)] \leftrightarrow q$
33. $(p \rightarrow q) \rightarrow [(\sim q) \rightarrow \sim p]$
34. $(p \rightarrow q) \leftrightarrow (q \rightarrow p)$.

Which of the following arguments are valid?

35. If today is Friday, then yesterday was Thursday; yesterday was Thursday; therefore, today is Friday.
36. Only if I save money will I finish university. I do not save money. Hence, I will not finish university.
37. If food is expensive then health suffers. Canadians excel in athletics only if health is excellent. Therefore, Canadians excel in athletics or food is expensive.

38. Music and art are not being encouraged. They must be encouraged if they are to flourish. Consequently, music and art will not flourish.

39. If Smith is a property owner, then he may vote in municipal elections. Smith votes in municipal elections. Therefore, Smith is a property owner.

40. The train is late if it snows. It is not snowing. Thus, the train is not late.

41. Today we had a war scare, because the stock market dropped sharply, and the stock market drops sharply whenever there is a war scare.

42. If the movie is made in England, then it is worth seeing. The movie is expensive or it is not worth seeing. But the movie is not expensive. Therefore, it is not made in England.

43. If I do not study I will sleep. If I am worried I will not sleep. Therefore, If I am worried I will study.

44. A democracy can survive only if the electorate is well-informed or no candidate for public office is dishonest. The electorate is well-informed only if education is free. If all candidates for public office are honest, then God exists. Therefore, a democracy can survive only if education is free or God exists.

45. I have a headache if I study logic. I take an aspirin whenever I have a headache. If I take an aspirin, I drink water. Therefore, I drink water whenever I study logic.

46. Show that "$p \to q$; therefore, $(\sim q) \to \sim p$" is a valid argument.

47. Let p and q be any propositions, not necessarily independent. Show that $p = q$ iff the proposition "$p \leftrightarrow q$" is a tautology.

6. The Algebra of Propositions

It is clear that any component of a proposition can be replaced by an equal proposition without affecting the truth-table of the given proposition. This is the basis of an extremely effective method of simplifying propositions. To simplify a proposition one must find another proposition having a simpler form (i.e., involving fewer connectives than the given proposition), yet equal to it. For example, consider the propositions "$p \vee (q \wedge \sim p)$" and "$p \vee q$". It is easy to see that $p \vee (q \wedge \sim p) = p \vee q$ by constructing a truth-table; furthermore, "$p \vee q$" is simpler than "$p \vee (q \wedge \sim p)$"—count the connectives in each proposition. The question is: Given "$p \vee (q \wedge \sim p)$", how do we find a simpler proposition equal to it?

The object of this section is to build up a technique that will enable us to construct from a given proposition another proposition equal to it and simpler in form, provided there is one. This is accomplished by replacing a proposition that appears in the given proposition by an equal proposition; by doing the same to the resulting proposition; and by continuing this process until a proposition of sufficiently simple form is obtained.

Clearly, to carry out this method we must possess an adequate stock of pairs of equal propositions. It turns out that the following nineteen pairs of equal propositions, do the job. To emphasize the importance of the following statements, we shall call them laws.

If p, q, and r are any propositions, then:

Law 1: $\sim(\sim p) = p$

Law 2: $p \vee p = p$

Law 3: $p \wedge p = p$

Law 4: $p \vee q = q \vee p$

Law 5: $p \wedge q = q \wedge p$

Law 6: $p \vee (q \vee r) = (p \vee q) \vee r$

Law 7: $p \wedge (q \wedge r) = (p \wedge q) \wedge r$

Law 8: $p \vee (q \wedge r) = (p \vee q) \wedge (p \vee r)$

Law 9: $p \wedge (q \vee r) = (p \wedge q) \vee (p \wedge r)$

Law 10: $\sim(p \vee q) = (\sim p) \wedge (\sim q)$

Law 11: $\sim(p \wedge q) = (\sim p) \vee (\sim q)$

Law 12: $p \rightarrow q = (\sim p) \vee q$

Law 13: $p \leftrightarrow q = (p \wedge q) \vee [(\sim p) \wedge (\sim q)]$

Law 14: $\sim t = f$

Law 15: $\sim f = t$

Law 16: $p \vee t = t$

Law 17: $p \wedge t = p$

Law 18: $p \vee f = p$

Law 19: $p \wedge f = f$

where "t" denotes any logically true proposition and "f" denotes any logically false proposition.

Laws 4 and 5 are called the *commutative* laws for $\vee$ and $\wedge$, respectively; laws 6 and 7 are called the *associative* laws for $\vee$ and $\wedge$, respectively; laws 8 and 9 are called the *distributive* laws; laws 10 and 11 are known as the *de Morgan* laws. Laws 16, 17, 18, and 19 are rather more sophisticated statements than are the other laws. For example, law 17 states that $p \wedge q = p$ for any propositions p and q, provided that q is logically true; law 18 states that $p \vee q = p$ for any propositions p and q, provided that q is logically false.

It is a routine matter to establish these nineteen laws by constructing truth-tables—do so! Now we are entitled to use the laws. Let us simplify the proposition that appeared at the beginning of this section; "$p \vee (q \wedge \sim p)$". Now,

$$\begin{aligned} p \vee (q \wedge \sim p) &= (p \vee q) \wedge (p \vee \sim p) && \text{by Law 8} \\ &= (p \vee q) \wedge t && \text{since } p \vee \sim p \text{ is logically true} \\ &= p \vee q && \text{by Law 17} \end{aligned}$$

As another example of this technique, we simplify "$p \wedge (p \vee q)$". Now,

$$\begin{aligned} p \wedge (p \vee q) &= [p \vee (q \wedge \sim q)] \wedge (p \vee q) && \text{by Law 18} \\ &= [(p \vee q) \wedge (p \vee \sim q)] \wedge (p \vee q) && \text{by Law 8} \\ &= [(p \vee \sim q) \wedge (p \vee q)] \wedge (p \vee q) && \text{by Law 5} \\ &= (p \vee \sim q) \wedge [(p \vee q) \wedge (p \vee q)] && \text{by Law 7} \\ &= (p \vee \sim q) \wedge (p \vee q) && \text{by Law 3} \\ &= p \vee [(\sim q) \wedge q] && \text{by Law 8} \\ &= p && \text{by Law 18} \end{aligned}$$

Of course, it is easy to show that $p \wedge (p \vee q) = p$ by carrying out a truth-table analysis; the point is that the algebraic manipulations lead us to p, from the given proposition.

With practice one can speed up the process of simplifying a proposition by telescoping several steps into one. This is accomplished by performing steps mentally, where possible, and by operating on different components of a proposition in one step. A powerful weapon in this regard is the following "bracket-omitting" convention. Law 6 asserts that, for any propositions p, q, and r, $p \vee (q \vee r) = (p \vee q) \vee r$; therefore, there is no possible ambiguity in denoting either of these propositio ns by "$p \vee q \vee r$", the expression obtained from either proposition by omitting brackets. In the same way, let us agree to drop the brackets from the propositions "$p \wedge (q \wedge r)$" and "$(p \wedge q) \wedge r$", writing "$p \wedge q \wedge r$"; this is justified by law 7. Similarly, let us agree to denote the propositions "$p \vee (q \vee r \vee s)$", "$(p \vee q \vee r) \vee s$", and "$(p \vee q) \vee (r \vee s)$"

by writing "$p \vee q \vee r \vee s$". Again, the same convention applies to "$\wedge$". Another simple method of telescoping steps, is to observe that by law 17 $p \wedge t = p$; therefore, there is no point in writing down "$p \wedge t$" at a step in a simplification—simply write down p! The same observation applies to "$p \vee f$".

These ideas are used in the following example, in which we show that $a = b$, where

$$a = \{p \vee [(q \vee r) \wedge \sim(q \wedge r)]\} \wedge \sim\{p \wedge [(q \vee r) \wedge \sim(q \wedge r)]\}$$

and $$b = \{[(p \vee q) \wedge \sim(p \wedge q)] \vee r\} \wedge \sim\{[(p \vee q) \wedge \sim(p \wedge q)] \wedge r\}.$$

Now,

$$\begin{aligned} a &= \{p \vee [(q \vee r) \wedge (\sim q \vee \sim r)]\} \wedge \{\sim p \vee [(\sim q \wedge \sim r) \vee (q \wedge r)]\} \\ &= (p \vee q \vee r) \wedge (p \vee \sim q \vee \sim r) \wedge \{\sim p \vee [(\sim q \vee (q \wedge r)) \wedge (\sim r \vee (q \wedge r))]\} \\ &= (p \vee q \vee r) \wedge (p \vee \sim q \vee \sim r) \wedge \{\sim p \vee [(\sim q \vee r) \wedge (\sim r \vee q)]\} \\ &= (p \vee q \vee r) \wedge (p \vee \sim q \vee \sim r) \wedge (\sim p \vee \sim q \vee r) \wedge (\sim p \vee \sim r \vee q); \end{aligned}$$

and

$$\begin{aligned} b &= \{(p \vee q \vee r) \wedge (\sim p \vee \sim q \vee r)\} \wedge \{[(\sim p \wedge \sim q) \vee (p \wedge q)] \vee \sim r\} \\ &= (p \vee q \vee r) \wedge (\sim p \vee \sim q \vee r) \wedge \{[(\sim p \vee (p \wedge q)) \wedge (\sim q \vee (p \wedge q))] \vee \sim r\} \\ &= (p \vee q \vee r) \wedge (\sim p \vee \sim q \vee r) \wedge \{[(\sim p \vee q) \wedge (p \vee \sim q)] \vee \sim r\} \\ &= (p \vee q \vee r) \wedge (\sim p \vee \sim q \vee r) \wedge (\sim p \vee q \vee \sim r) \wedge (p \vee \sim q \vee \sim r). \end{aligned}$$

Hence, $a = b$.

EXERCISES

1. (a) Prove that any two propositions obtained by inserting brackets in $p \vee q \vee r \vee s$ are equal.
 (b) State a bracket-omitting convention for a proposition consisting of four propositions joined by three "$\vee$"s.
 (c) State and justify a bracket-omitting convention for a proposition consisting of five propositions joined by four "$\vee$"s.
 (d) State and justify a bracket-omitting convention for a proposition consisting of $n + 1$ propositions joined by n "$\vee$"s whenever n is a natural number.

2. State and justify a bracket-omitting convention for a proposition consisting of $n + 1$ propositions joined by n "$\wedge$"s whenever n is a natural number.

Simplify the following propositions:

3. $p \wedge (q \wedge \sim p)$

4. $(p \wedge q) \vee p$

5. $(p \rightarrow q) \vee \sim p$

6. $(p \rightarrow q) \vee p$

7. $(q \rightarrow p) \rightarrow p$

8. $p \rightarrow (q \rightarrow p)$

9. $(p \leftrightarrow \sim q) \vee q$

10. $p \wedge \sim (q \rightarrow p)$

11. $\{(p \wedge q) \vee [(\sim p \wedge \sim q) \vee q]\} \wedge p$

12. $[p \vee (q \wedge r)] \vee [(q \wedge \sim p) \vee p]$

13. $(\sim p \wedge \sim q \wedge r) \vee (p \wedge q \wedge r) \vee (p \wedge \sim q \wedge r)$

14. $[p \vee (q \leftrightarrow \sim p)] \rightarrow \sim q$

7. Applications to Switching Networks*

Before continuing our development of symbolic logic, we pause to consider a most unexpected and powerful application of the techniques presented in the preceding pages: the design of switching networks. Our main interest, here, is not switching networks; rather, we want to clarify our ideas about symbolic logic by considering a particular application.

A switching network consists of a number of wires capable of carrying current and a number of switches, each capable of creating a gap in a wire. The simplest example of a switching network is 
a single wire. Current applied at one end is transmitted to the other end. Not quite so trivial, is the switching network that consists of one wire and one switch 

When the switch P is closed, current can flow; opening the switch creates a gap in the wire, so current cannot flow. This simple network suggests two propositions: "switch P is closed" and "current flows". Denote the former by "p" and the latter by "c". Notice that the truth-value of c depends upon the truth-value of p. Table 1-10 makes this clear. Examining this truth-

TABLE 1-10

p	c
T	T
F	F

table, we see that $c = p$. Thus, in the case of this example, the proposition "current flows" is logically the same as the proposition "switch P is closed".

In a similar way, the switching network 

which consists of one wire and two switches, suggests three propositions: "switch P is closed", "switch Q is closed", and "current flows". Denoting these propositions by "p", "q", and "c", respectively, we readily establish that $c = p \wedge q$. In this case, the switches P and Q are said to be in series.

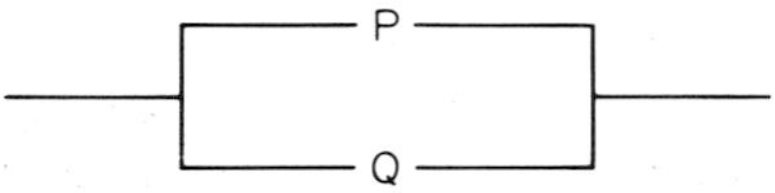

FIGURE 1-1

Next, consider a switching network with two switches in parallel (Fig. 1-1): here, current flows if and only if P is closed, or Q is closed. Thus, $c = p \vee q$.

Complicated networks can be constructed by joining together two given networks in series or in parallel. Let M and N be given switching networks: consider the switching networks I and II (Fig. 1-2), constructed as follows:

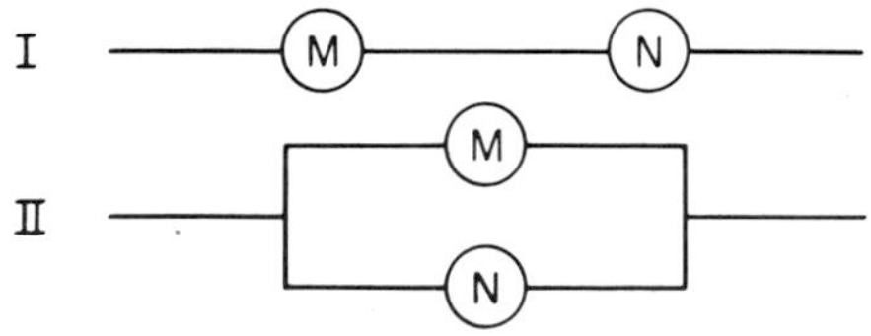

M and N are in series.

M and N are in parallel.

FIGURE 1-2

Let m = current flows through M, and let n = current flows through N. It is easily seen that the proposition "current flows through I" is given by $m \wedge n$, whereas the proposition "current flows through II" is given by $m \vee n$.

To illustrate this technique of breaking down a problem into several simpler problems, we compute "current flows" for the switching network shown in Fig. 1-3.

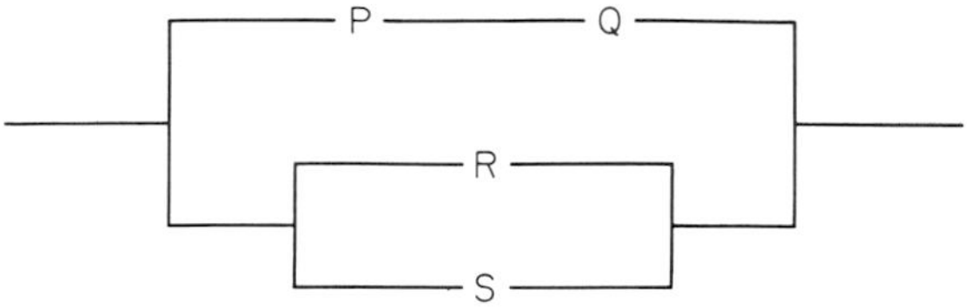

FIGURE 1-3

Figure 1-3 is an illustration of II, where M is ——— P ——— Q ——— and N is the network shown in Fig. 1-4.

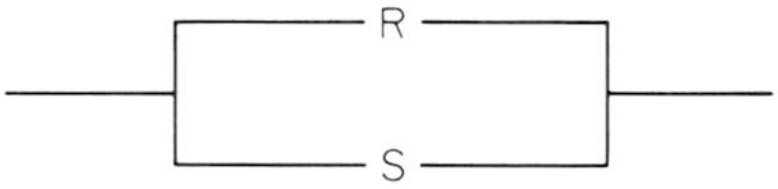

FIGURE 1-4

Thus, $m = p \wedge q$, and $n = r \vee s$; therefore, $c = (p \wedge q) \vee (r \vee s)$.

It is not always the case that the switches occuring in a network operate independently. For example, two switches may be so arranged that they close together and open together. In that case, we shall denote the switches by the same letter. We can also connect two switches so that when one is open the other is closed, and vice-versa. In this case, should the first switch be P, we shall name the other P′. Notice that if p = switch P is closed, then $\sim p$ = switch P′ is closed.

Consider the network shown in Fig. 1-5.

FIGURE 1-5

Here, $c = p \wedge (\sim p \vee q)$; simplifying, $c = (p \wedge \sim p) \vee (p \wedge q) = p \wedge q$. Thus, "current flows" is logically the same as "switch P is closed and switch Q is closed". It follows that the given switching network can be replaced by the following, simpler network: ——— P ——— Q ———
Thus, the algebra of propositions has a direct bearing on the problem of simplifying a given switching network.

So far, we have been concerned with the problem of representing the proposition "current flows" in terms of the state of the switches of a given switching network. Let us turn, now, to the preliminary question of designing a switching network so that it will possess certain stated properties. For example, consider the switching network required for a room with two doors, one light, and a switch which controls the light at each door. The desired network, then, involves two independent switches such that changing the state of either switch, changes the truth-value of "current flows". The design of the network is effected by constructing a truth-table (Table 1-11)

TABLE 1.11

p	q	c
T	T	
T	F	
F	T	
F	F	

for c, as follows: We must insert "T"s and "F"s under c, so that changing the truth-value of either p or q, changes the truth-value of c. We can accomplish this by entering a "T" under c iff an even number of "T"s are assigned to p and q. Thus, we obtain the following truth-table for c (Table 1-12).

TABLE 1.12

p	q	c
T	T	T
T	F	F
F	T	F
F	F	T

The proposition c is easily read off, in disjunctive normal form:

$$c = (p \wedge q) \vee (\sim p \wedge \sim q).$$

It is easy, now, to design the required switching network; see Fig. 1-6.

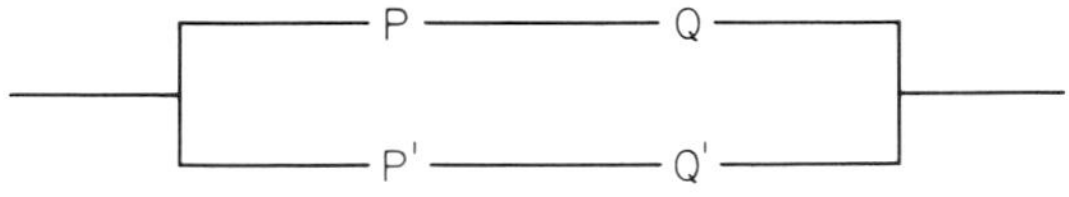

FIGURE 1-6

The idea of analyzing switching networks in the manner of this section, is due to Claude E. Shannon. The interested reader may wish to refer to Shannon's paper, "A Symbolic Analysis of Relay and Switching Circuits", *Trans. Am. Inst. Elec. Engrs.* 57 (1939).

EXERCISES

Represent the proposition "current flows" for each of the following switching networks; simplify in each case:

1.
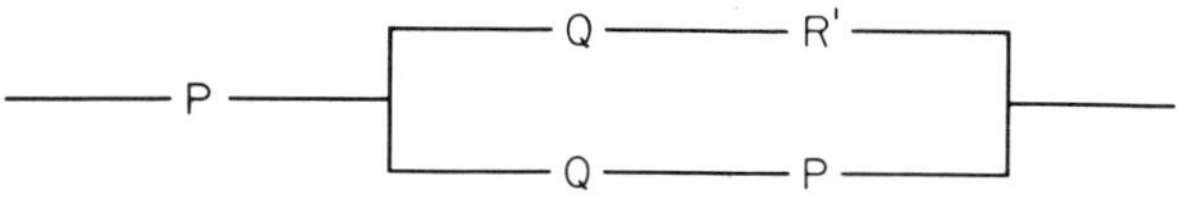

2.
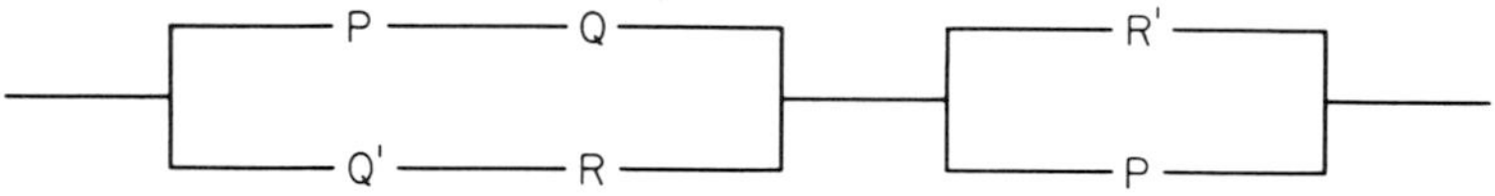

3.

4.
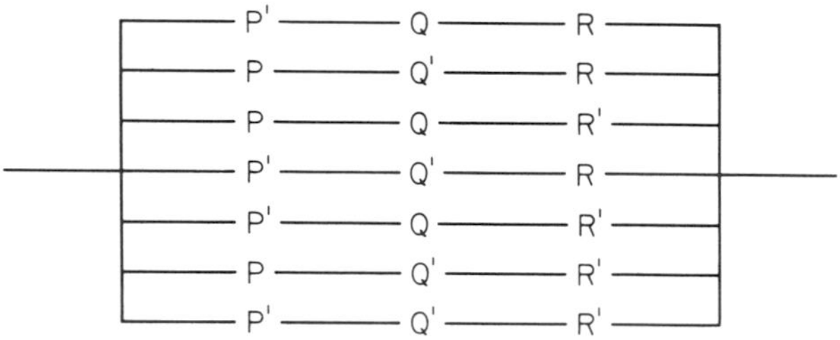

5.
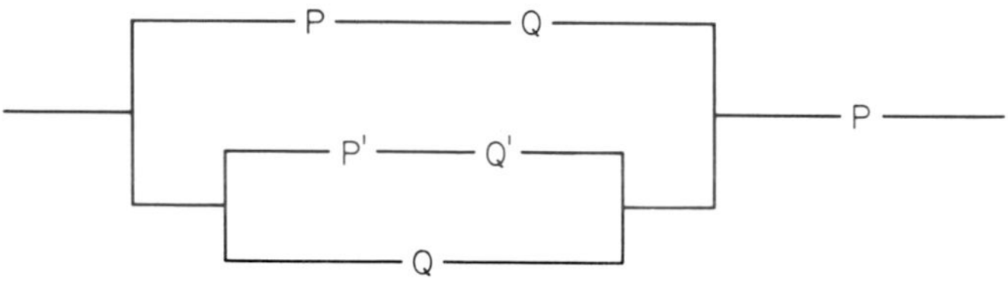

6. Design an appropriate switching network for a room with three doors, a switch at each door, and one light.

7. Design an appropriate switching network for a room with four doors, a switch at each door, and one light.

8. Each member of a committee of three votes affirmatively for a proposal by closing a switch. If the majority has voted for the proposal, a light flashes on. Design an appropriate switching network.

9. Repeat Exercise 8 for a committee of five members.

10. Repeat Exercise 8 for a committee of four members; in case of a tie, the proposal is defeated if the chairman has voted against it and is approved if the chairman has voted for the proposal.

11. A committee has four members, A, B, C, and D. A has two votes, whereas each of the others has one vote. Each member votes. Design an appropriate switching network, so that each member votes affirmatively by closing a switch, and a light indicates that the proposal has been approved.

8. The Universal Quantifier

Returning to the analysis of language, consider the following argument: "All students are clever; clever people are sure to succeed: hence, all students are sure to succeed". Examining this argument, we note that it involves three independent propositions: "all students are clever", "clever people are sure to succeed", and "all students are sure to succeed". It is apparent that the conclusion does not involve, directly, the propositions appearing in the assumptions. Thus, even though the argument appeals strongly to our intuitive logical sense—in fact, we are sure the argument is valid—we must agree that in terms of the symbolic logic so far developed, there is absolutely no logical connection between the assumptions and the conclusion. In other words, our logic does not succeed in breaking down the propositions involved in the argument to the point that the logical dependence of the conclusion upon the assumptions is made clear. We must conclude that our analysis of language—our search for the logical connectives and the basic components making up a given proposition—is not yet complete.

Studying the proposition "all students are clever", we observe that this statement can be rendered by "if a person is a student, then he is clever". Noting that "he" refers back to "a person", let us replace both by a single letter, say "x". We obtain: "if x is a student, then x is clever". Notice that this is a *propositional form* rather than a proposition. Clearly, "if x is a student, then x is clever" does not possess a truth-value; hence, it is not a proposition. On the other hand, the expression "if x is a student, then x is clever" is capable of generating propositions; i.e., the propositions obtained by substituting a person's name for the "x" which appears in the propositional form. But the statement "all students are clever" is true, provided that each proposition generated by the propositional form "if x is a student, then x is clever", is a *true* proposition. More directly, our proposition "all students are clever" is given by "*for each* x, if x is a student then x is clever". To facilitate matters, we introduce a symbol, called the *universal quantifier*, to stand for "for each"—namely, "$\forall$", an upside-down "A". So we obtain: "$\forall x$[if x is a student, then x is clever]". The scope of the universal quantifier has been indicated by the use of brackets.

Next, we want to represent symbolically the phrases "x is a student" and "x is clever". Let "S" denote the collection of all students, let "C" denote the collection of all clever people, and let "$\in$" stand for the phrase "is a member of". Then "$x \in S$" stands for "x is a member of the collection of all students"; clearly, then, "$x \in S$" means "x is a student". Similarly, "$x \in C$" stands for "x is clever". Thus, the proposition "all students are clever" is represented symbolically by "$\forall x[x \in S \rightarrow x \in C]$". It must be emphasized that the proposition "$\forall x[x \in S \rightarrow x \in C]$" is true iff the propositional form "$x \in S \rightarrow x \in C$" generates only true propositions.

We have succeeded in breaking down the proposition "all students are clever" into its basic components, through the introduction of the universal quantifier "$\forall$". It is worthwhile to state, in general terms, the definition of this important connective.

DEFINITION: Let $P(x)$ be any propositional form; then the proposition "$\forall x[P(x)]$" is true iff each proposition obtained from $P(x)$ by substituting an object for "x" is true.

In order to symbolize the remaining propositions appearing in the above argument, let "R" denote the collection of all people who are sure to succeed. Then "clever people are sure to succeed" is symbolized by "$\forall x[x \in C \rightarrow x \in R]$"; and "all students are sure to succeed" is represented by "$\forall x[x \in S \rightarrow x \in R]$". Thus, the above argument is symbolized as follows:

Assumptions: $\forall x[x \in S \rightarrow x \in C]$, $\forall x[x \in C \rightarrow x \in R]$
Conclusion: $\forall x[x \in S \rightarrow x \in R]$

Before analyzing this argument, we note that the independent propositions involved in the argument are the propositions obtained from the propositional forms $x \in S$, $x \in C$, and $x \in R$ by replacing "x" with a person's name.

To show that this is a valid argument, we must demonstrate that the conclusion is true under each combination of truth-values of the independent propositions, which makes both assumptions true. Of course, we cannot construct a truth-table to show that this is so, because there are too many independent propositions: for example, "Jones $\in S$", "Brown $\in R$", "Smith $\in C$" are each independent propositions, and in each truth-value case are assigned truth-values "T" or "F". Nor can we utilize an algebraic approach, since we have not yet discussed the properties of the universal quantifier.

What are we to do? Well, we cannot carry out a truth-table analysis in its entirety but we can construct a portion of the truth-table. In short, we shall use the *method* of the truth-table analysis to reach a decision about the validity of the given argument. Imagine that we have assigned truth-values to the independent propositions, so that both assumptions are true, yet the conclusion is false. However, assuming that "$\forall x[x \in S \rightarrow x \in R]$" is false under our assignment of truth-values, means that there is a person, say Mr. Brown, to whom truth-values have been assigned so that the proposition "Mr. Brown $\in S \rightarrow$ Mr. Brown $\in R$" is false. Therefore, the truth-value of "Mr. Brown $\in S$" is T, and the truth-value of "Mr. Brown $\in R$" is F. Since the proposition "$\forall x[x \in S \rightarrow x \in C]$" is true in this truth-value case, we know that the proposition obtained from the propositional form "$x \in S \rightarrow x \in C$" by substituting "Mr. Brown,, for "x" is true. Thus, the proposition "Mr. Brown $\in S \rightarrow$ Mr. Brown $\in C$" is true, and it follows that the truth-value of "Mr. Brown $\in C$" is T. Since the proposition "$\forall x[x \in C \rightarrow x \in R]$" is true in this truth-value case, we see that the proposition "Mr. Brown $\in C \rightarrow$ Mr. Brown $\in R$" is also true in this truth-value case; therefore, the truth-value of "Mr. Brown $\in R$" is T. But this is impossible, since we have already seen that the truth-value of "Mr. Brown $\in R$" is F. We conclude that it is impossible to construct a truth-value case under which both assumptions are true and the conclusion is false. Thus, the given argument is valid.

We now state the fundamental property of the universal quantifier.

THEOREM: Let $P(x)$ be any propositional form, and let a be any object; then the proposition "$\forall x[P(x)] \rightarrow P(a)$" is a tautology.

Proof: Consider any truth-value case under which the truth-value of "$\forall x[P(x)]$" is *T*; it is easily seen that the truth-value of the proposition "$P(a)$" is also T.

In this section we have investigated the meaning of the word "all"; our analysis revealed the existence of two fundamental notions: the universal quantifier and the propositional form, which together break down a proposition of the type handled here and reveal its basic components. We are able in this way to use a truth-table analysis in investigating the validity of a given argument.

EXERCISES

Let "C" denote the class of all Canadians, and let "H" denote the class of all honest people; express the following propositions in words, as briefly as possible, and state its truth-value (it is understood that the objects considered are people):

1. $\forall x[x \in C]$
2. $\forall y[y \in H]$
3. $\forall z[\sim (z \in H)]$
4. $\sim \{\forall z[\sim (z \in H)]\}$
5. $\forall t[t \in C \rightarrow t \in H]$
6. $\forall u[u \in H \rightarrow u \in C]$
7. $\forall v[v \in C \rightarrow v \in H] \wedge \forall w[w \in H \rightarrow w \in C]$
8. $\forall x[x \in C \leftrightarrow x \in H]$
9. Show that the following arguments are valid:
   (a) All men are mortal; Socrates is a man. Hence, Socrates is mortal.
   (b) All students are scholars; all scholars are gentlemen. Therefore, all students are gentlemen.
10. Let $P(y)$ be any propositional form, and let a and b be objects. Show that the proposition "$\forall y[P(y)] \rightarrow [P(a) \wedge P(b)]$" is a tautology.
11. Let $P(x)$ and $Q(x)$ be any propositional forms. Show that the proposition "$\forall x[P(x) \wedge Q(x)] \rightarrow \{\forall x[P(x)] \wedge \forall x[Q(x)]\}$" is a tautology.
12. Let $P(x)$ and $Q(x)$ be any propositional forms. Show that the proposition "$\{\forall x[P(x)] \wedge \forall x[Q(x)]\} \rightarrow \forall y[P(y) \wedge Q(y)]$" is a tautology.
13. Let $P(y)$ and $Q(y)$ be any propositional forms. Show that the proposition "$\forall y[P(y) \rightarrow Q(y)] \rightarrow \{\forall y[P(y)] \rightarrow \forall y[Q(y)]\}$" is a tautology.
14. Let $P(z)$ and $Q(z)$ be any propositional forms. Show that the proposition "$\{\forall z[P(z)] \rightarrow \forall z[Q(z)]\} \rightarrow \forall z[P(z) \rightarrow Q(z)]$" is *not* a tautology.
15. Distinguish, in your own words, between a proposition and a propositional form.
16. Show that a proposition can generate a propositional form.
17. Is there an essential difference between the propositional forms $P(x)$ and $P(y)$?

9. The Existential Quantifier

Consider the proposition: "Some students are clever". Unfortunately, the word "some" is vague; in mathematics, however, it is customary to interpret "some" as meaning "one or more". Let "S" denote the collection of all students, and let "C" denote the collection of all clever persons. Then the proposition "some students are clever" is true, provided that the propositional form "$x \in S \wedge x \in C$" generates one or more true propositions. It is clear that we are involved with a quantifier. Let us introduce a symbol, called the *existential quantifier*, to stand for the phrase "there is at least one"—namely, "$\exists$", a reverse "E". So we obtain: "$\exists x[x \in S \wedge x \in C]$", which is read as "there is at least one 'x' such that $x \in S \wedge x \in C$". Clearly, "$\exists x[x \in S \wedge x \in C]$" symbolizes the proposition "some students are clever". Notice that we have succeeded in displaying the basic components of the proposition "some students are clever".

DEFINITION: Let $P(x)$ be any propositional form; then the proposition "$\exists x[P(x)]$" is true iff at least one true proposition is obtained from $P(x)$ by substituting an object for "x".

It turns out that the universal and existential quantifiers are closely related.

THEOREM: Let $P(x)$ be any propositional form; then $\sim \forall x[P(x)] = \exists x[\sim P(x)]$.

Proof: We must show that the propositions "$\sim \forall x[P(x)]$" and "$\exists x[\sim P(x)]$" are logically the same; i.e., that they possess the same truth-values in each truth-value case. Suppose that "$\sim \forall x[P(x)]$" is true in a given truth-value case. Then "$\forall x[P(x)]$" is false in that truth-value case; hence, at least one of the propositions generated by $P(x)$ is false, and so at least one of the propositions generated by $\sim P(x)$ is true. Therefore, "$\exists x[\sim P(x)]$" is true. Next, suppose that "$\sim \forall x[P(x)]$" is false in a given truth-value case. Then "$\forall x[P(x)]$" is true in that truth-value case; hence, each proposition generated by $P(x)$ is true, and so each proposition generated by $\sim P(x)$ is false. Therefore, "$\exists x[\sim P(x)]$" is false. This establishes our theorem.

The following corollaries are easily proven.

COROLLARY: $\sim \forall x[\sim P(x)] = \exists x[P(x)]$.

COROLLARY: $\sim \exists x[\sim P(x)] = \forall x[P(x)]$.

COROLLARY: $\sim \exists x[P(x)] = \forall x[\sim P(x)]$.

To illustrate the value of our quantifiers, let us consider the following argument: "Some professors are humorous; all humorous persons are well-liked; therefore, some professors are well-liked".

To analyze the argument, let "P" denote the collection of all professors, let "H" denote the collection of all humorous persons, and let "L" denote the collection of all well-liked persons. The argument takes the following symbolic form:

Assumptions: $\exists x[x \in P \wedge x \in H]$, $\forall y[y \in H \to y \in L]$
Conclusion: $\exists z[z \in P \wedge z \in L]$

We note that the independent propositions involved in this argument are the propositions generated by the propositional forms $x \in P$, $x \in H$, and $x \in L$.

To demonstrate that this argument is valid, we must show that the conclusion is true in each truth-value case under which both assumptions are true. Again, we shall prove this by applying the truth-table method, although we shall not actually construct a truth-table. Consider any truth-value case under which both assumptions are true. In particular, "$\exists x[x \in P \wedge x \in H]$" is true; therefore, there is a person, Mr. Brown say, such that the truth-value of "Mr. Brown $\in P \wedge$ Mr. Brown $\in H$" is T. This means that the truth-value of "Mr. Brown $\in P$" is T, and the truth-value of "Mr. Brown $\in H$" is T. Since "$\forall y[y \in H \to y \in L]$" is true, in this truth-value case, it follows that the truth-value of "Mr. Brown $\in H \to$ Mr. Brown $\in L$" is T; therefore, the truth-value of "Mr. Brown $\in L$" is T. We conclude that the truth-value of "Mr. Brown $\in P \wedge$ Mr. Brown $\in L$" is T. Thus, "$\exists z[z \in P \wedge z \in L]$" is true in the given truth-value case. This demonstrates that the argument is valid.

As an illustration of an invalid argument, consider the following argument: "All students are clever; some clever people are geniuses; therefore, some students are geniuses".

This argument is symbolized by letting "G" denote the collection of all geniuses, and by introducing "S" and "C" as before. We obtain:

Assumptions: $\forall x[x \in S \to x \in C]$, $\exists x[x \in C \wedge x \in G]$
Conclusion: $\exists x[x \in S \wedge x \in G]$

To show that the argument is invalid, we must construct a truth-value case under which both assumptions are true and the conclusion is false. This is easy. Let "Mr. Brown $\in C$" be true, and let "Mr. Brown $\in G$" be true. This makes the second assumption true. Also, let "Mr. Brown $\in S$" be false; in fact, assign truth-values so that each proposition generated by "$x \in S$" is false, and each proposition generated by "$x \in C$" and "$x \in G$" is true. We have now spelled out a truth-value case under which both assumptions are true, yet the conclusion is false. This means that the argument is invalid.

We now consider a theorem about the existential quantifier.

THEOREM: Let $P(x)$ and $Q(x)$ be any propositional forms; then the proposition "$\exists x[P(x) \wedge Q(x)] \to (\exists x[P(x)] \wedge \exists x[Q(x)])$" is a tautology.

Proof: Consider any truth-value case under which "$\exists x[P(x) \wedge Q(x)]$" is true; it follows that "$\exists x[P(x)]$" and "$\exists x[Q(x)]$" are both true in this truth-value case. This establishes the theorem.

The proofs of this section and of Section 8 have deliberately stressed the truth-table method. There are easier ways of persuading oneself that a given argument of the sort considered here is either valid or invalid. For example, there is a pictorial technique involving Venn diagrams that is quite easy to apply. However, methods of this type are limited to the very simple kind of argument or theorem considered here, involving only propositions with one quantifier. On the other hand, the truth-table method will handle the more complicated arguments that occur in mathematics—arguments in which the assumptions and conclusion may involve several quantifiers, not just one. Since it is much easier to understand and master a method when it is applied to simple examples, rather than to complicated examples, here is the proper place to study the technique of analyzing quantifier-type arguments.

One more point is worth clarifying here. The discussions of the universal and the existential quantifiers have tacitly assumed a collection of objects involved in the process of generating propositions from the given propositional forms. Whenever a quantifier is used, there must be a definite collection of objects to which the quantifier refers in this sense. In a mathematical investigation, however, there is usually one collection of objects, given in advance, to which each quantifier refers.

EXERCISES

Test the validity of the following arguments:

1. Television programs are designed for the masses; nothing designed for the masses can be of high quality; therefore, no television program is of high quality.

2. No teacher has a sense of humor; some clever people do not have a sense of humor; hence, some teachers are clever.

3. Some mammals live in the water. All things that live in the water are fish. Therefore, some mammals are fish.

4. Some cars are vehicles. Some buses are cars. No vehicles are buses. Therefore, some cars are not vehicles.

5. All professors are wealthy, pleasant, or handsome. All wealthy people are intelligent or handsome. All handsome people are intelligent and pleasant. Some pleasant people are intelligent. Therefore, some professors are intelligent.

6. Babies are illogical. Nobody is despised who can manage a crocodile. Illogical persons are despised. Therefore, some babies can manage crocodiles.

7. Everyone who is sane can do logic. No lunatics are fit to serve on a jury. None of your friends can do logic. Therefore, none of your friends is fit to serve on a jury.

8. Some professors are fools. No fools are learned. Hence, no professors are learned.

9. Let $P(y)$ and $Q(y)$ be any propositional forms; show that the proposition "$(\exists x[P(x)] \wedge \exists y[Q(y)]) \rightarrow \exists z[P(z) \wedge Q(z)]$" is *not* a tautology.

10. Let $P(x)$ and $Q(x)$ be any propositional forms; show that the proposition "$\exists x[P(x) \vee Q(x)] \rightarrow (\exists x[P(x)] \vee \exists x[Q(x)])$" is a tautology.

11. Suppose that for a particular discussion the quantifiers refer to objects a or b. Let $P(x)$ be any propositional form; show that $\forall x[P(x)] = P(a) \wedge P(b)$, whereas $\exists x[P(x)] = P(a) \vee P(b)$.

12. Suppose that for a particular discussion the quantifiers refer to objects $a_1, a_2, \ldots, a_n$. Let $P(t)$ be any propositional form; show that

$$\forall t[P(t)] = P(a_1) \wedge P(a_2) \wedge \cdots \wedge P(a_n),$$

whereas
$$\exists t[P(t)] = P(a_1) \vee P(a_2) \vee \cdots \vee P(a_n).$$

13. Mathematics commonly makes use of quantifiers other than the universal and existential quantifiers. For example, "$\exists !$" denotes "there is a unique," so that "$\exists ! x[P(x)]$" is true iff exactly one of the propositions generated by $P(x)$ is true. Show that "$\exists !$" can be expressed in terms of the universal and existential quantifiers.

10. Propositions Involving Several Quantifiers

In Chapter 3, where we come to grips with the axiomatic method, we shall work with propositions which involve more than one quantifier. Indeed, in mathematics this is the rule rather than the exception. Our purpose, here, is to develop a technique for working out the truth-value of such a proposition.

Consider, for example, the proposition: "Given any number, say x, there is a number, say y, such that $x + y = 0$". Expressed symbolically, this becomes: $\forall x[\exists y[x + y = 0]]$. The main connective here is "$\forall x$"; therefore, the given proposition is true iff the propositional form "$\exists y[x + y = 0]$" generates only true propositions. For example, substituting 3 for "x", we obtain the proposition "$\exists y[3 + y = 0]$". Is this proposition true? Well, "$\exists y[3 + y = 0]$" is true iff the propositional form "$3 + y = 0$" generates at least one true proposition. Substituting -3 for "y", we obtain the proposition "$3 + (-3) = 0$", which is true. Similarly, each of the propositions generated by "$\exists y[x + y = 0]$" can be shown to be true. Thus,

$$\text{“}\forall x[\exists y[x + y = 0]]\text{”}$$

is true.

Consider the proposition: "There is a number, say x, such that $x \cdot y = 0$ whenever y is a number". This proposition is symbolized by $\exists x[\forall y[x \cdot y = 0]]$. The main connective here is "$\exists x$"; therefore, the given proposition is true iff the propositional form "$\forall y[x \cdot y = 0]$" generates at least one true proposition. Substituting 0 for "x", we obtain the proposition" $\forall y[0 \cdot y = 0]$". But the propositional form "$0 \cdot y = 0$" generates only true propositions; therefore, "$\forall y[0 \cdot y = 0]$" is true; hence, "$\exists x[\forall y[x \cdot y = 0]]$" is true.

As an example of a false proposition, consider the statement: "There is a number, say y, such that $x + y = 0$ whenever x is a number". This proposition is symbolized by $\exists y[\forall x[x + y = 0]]$; note that it can be obtained from the first example given above, by merely reversing the order of the quantifiers. We wish to prove that the given proposition is false. Suppose it is true; then the propositional form "$\forall x[x + y = 0]$" generates at least one true proposition. Let a be a number such that the result of substituting a for "y" is a true proposition. Then "$\forall x[x + a = 0]$" is true. This means that the propositional form "$x + a = 0$" generates only true propositions. In particular, by substituting $1 + (-a)$ for "x", we obtain the proposition "$[1 + (-a)] + a = 0$", which clearly is false. We conclude that the given proposition is false.

Whenever a symbol, say "x", is immediately preceded in a given proposition by a quantifier, we shall say that "x" is a *place-holder*. The function of a quantified symbol is to indicate not only that the following proposition is true of *all* objects (in the case of the *universal* quantifier) or of *some* objects (in the case of the *existential* quantifier), but also to indicate that certain places throughout the proposition are to be filled with the *same* name, so that the symbol marks the places in which the name of a single object is to be inserted.

The preceding examples are intended to display the technique involved in computing the truth-value of a proposition containing several quantifiers. Summarizing this technique, the question of the truth-value of such a proposition is reduced to the question of the truth-values of a host of propositions, each obtained from the given proposition by deleting one quantifier and replacing the corresponding place-holder with the name of a definite object. By applying this process as many times as there are quantifiers in the given proposition, we see that the truth-value of the given proposition depends upon the truth-values of a large number of propositions which involve no quantifiers; hence, these truth-values are readily determined. The technique, then, is to strip away quantifiers one at a time.

Once again, we introduce a bracket-omitting convention. Since we read from left to right, we shall denote the proposition "$\forall x[\exists y[P(x, y)]]$" by writing "$\forall x \exists y[P(x, y)]$", and we shall denote the proposition "$\exists x[\forall y[P(x, y)]]$" by writing "$\exists x \forall y[P(x, y)]$". In general, we shall say that the quantifier at the left of a block of quantifiers, is the main connective of the proposition.
For example, "$\forall x \forall y \forall z[x + (y + z) = (x + y) + z]$" denotes

$$\text{“}\forall x[\forall y[\forall z[x + (y + z) = (x + y) + z]]]\text{”}.$$

We shall make frequent use of this convention in Chapter 3.
We shall now establish one property of our quantifiers.

THEOREM: Let $P(x, y)$ be any propositional form involving two place-holders; then the proposition "$\exists x \forall y[P(x, y)] \rightarrow \forall y \exists x[P(x, y)]$" is a tautology.

Proof: Consider any truth-value case under which "$\exists x \forall y[P(x, y)]$" is true. It follows that there is an object, say a, such that the proposition "$\forall y[P(a, y)]$" is true. Hence, the propositional form $P(a, y)$ generates only true propositions. This means that the proposition "$P(a, b)$" is true whenever b is an object. But the proposition "$\forall y \exists x[P(x, y)]$" is true iff the propositional form $\exists x[P(x, y)]$ generates only true propositions. Let b be any object; we shall show that the proposition "$\exists x[P(x, b)]$" is true. Substituting a for "x" in the propositional form $P(x, b)$, we obtain "$P(a, b)$"—a true proposition. Therefore, the proposition "$\exists x[P(x, b)]$" is true whenever b is an object. This establishes our theorem.

EXERCISES

Express the following propositions symbolically, and compute the truth-value of each proposition:

1. Any number equals itself.
2. If one number equals a second number, then the second number equals the first number.
3. If one number equals a second number, and that number equals a third number, then the first number equals the third number, also.

4. We can find two numbers that are not equal.
5. Given any number, there is another number which equals it.
6. There is a number such that it, multiplied by itself, is itself.
7. There is a number which, when added to itself, results in the same number.
8. Any two numbers are either equal or different.
9. The sum of two numbers is independent of the order in which they are added.
10. a is a brother of b whenever b is a brother of a.
11. Brothers have the same parents.
12. a is a parent of b whenever b is a child of a.
13. a is the father of b whenever b is the child of a.
14. a is the father of b whenever b is the father of a.

Compute the truth-values of the following propositions:

15. $\forall x \forall y[x \cdot y = y \cdot x]$
16. $\forall x \forall y[x < y]$
17. $\forall x \exists y[x < y]$
18. $\forall x \forall y[x < y \rightarrow 5 + x < 5 + y]$
19. $\exists x \forall y[x < y \vee x = y]$
20. $\forall x \forall y \forall z[x \cdot (y \cdot z) = (x \cdot y) \cdot z]$
21. $\forall x \forall y \forall z[x \cdot (y+z) = x \cdot y + x \cdot z]$
22. $\forall x \forall y[x = y \veebar x < y \veebar y < x]$
23. $\exists x[x \cdot x = 2]$
24. $\forall x[x \cdot x = 2]$
25. $\forall x[x \cdot x = 2] \rightarrow \exists x[x \cdot x = 2]$
26. $\forall x[x \cdot x = 2] \rightarrow \exists y[y \cdot y = 2]$
27. Let $P(x, y)$ be any propositional form involving two place-holders. Prove that the proposition "$\forall x \forall y[P(x, y)] \leftrightarrow \forall y \forall x[P(x, y)]$" is a tautology.
28. Let $P(x, y)$ be any propositional form involving two place-holders. Prove that the proposition "$\exists x \exists y[P(x, y)] \leftrightarrow \exists y \exists x[P(x, y)]$" is a tautology.
29. Let $P(x, y)$ be any propositional form involving two place-holders. Prove that the proposition "$\forall x \exists y[P(x, y] \rightarrow \exists y \forall x[P(x, y)]$" is *not* a tautology.

2

Set theory

1. Sets

Aristotle said that Man is the *rational* animal and there is no doubt that in the golden age of Greece this comment was appropriate. In the light of several thousand years of recorded history, however, it is doubtful that Aristotle's aphorism retains its force. Nevertheless, there is one aspect of Man's make-up that has endured the test of time; Man is the *classifying* animal! The desire to put together, either physically (as a small child does) or conceptually (as an adult does), all objects that have something in common is inborn in Man. Each society, no matter how primitive or advanced, separates people into classes. In a well-developed society we may have such classes as "Rich", "Poor", "Worker", "Employer"; whereas even the most primitive society recognizes such classes as "Man", "Woman", "Adult", "Child". It is not altogether unexpected, then, that the classifying urge should find expression in mathematics. In fact, we shall see that the notion of "Class" or "Set" is one of the fundamental concepts of mathematics.

The notion of a set, which has always been implicit in mathematics, was first explicitly introduced and developed by the brilliant, but unfortunate, mathematician G. Cantor, late in the nineteenth century. By a set, Cantor meant any collection of definite, well-distinguished objects—either of perception or of thought. Thus, a member of a set is either a physical object (for example, this piece of chalk), or is a mental object—an object that has no physical existence in the world about us, but rather exists in the mind of Man (for example, the number three). By a specific set, we mean a specific collection of objects. Thus, a set is determined once we know of each object whether or not that object is a member of the set. In other words, a set is defined iff we can assert of each object either that the object is a member of the set or that the object is not a member of the set.

Generally, sets are denoted by capital letters, and the members of sets by small letters. Thus, "$x \in A$" expresses the statement: "the object x is a member of the set A". Since a set is merely a collection of objects, it is clear that two sets are the same iff they possess precisely the same members. Thus, the set whose members are 5 and 6 *is* the set whose members are 6 and 5. Also, the set whose only member is the integer 2, *is* the set of all positive, even primes.

For the purposes of a particular mathematical investigation, it is customary to designate in advance the objects under discussion. The set of all such objects is called the *universal* set and is denoted by "I". Needless to say, the universal set of one mathematical investigation may not be the universal set of a second mathematical investigation.

We turn now to the problem of *naming* sets. It is much easier to talk about a specific set if we have an efficient method of naming or denoting a set. There are two widely-used methods of naming a set: one method is to list the members of the set; the other method is to state a property that is possessed by each member of the set and is not possessed by any other object. For example, consider the set S such that $2 \in S$, $3 \in S$, and $5 \in S$, where no other object is a member of S. Listing the members of S, we obtain: 2, 3, 5. As it stands, this will hardly do as a name of S; i.e., we don't want to write "$S = 2, 3, 5$". For this reason, we insert braces, "{" and "}", around the list, so obtaining the expression "{2, 3, 5}", which we take to be a name of S. Thus, we are entitled to write "$S = \{2, 3, 5\}$". A definite code is being used: the braces "{" and "}" stand for "the set"; we then interpose "whose members are"; finally, we read off the objects listed. This code is displayed as follows:

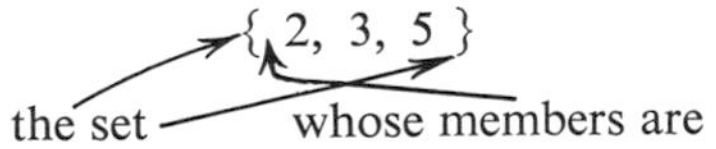

There is nothing mysterious here. The mathematical expression "{2, 3, 5}", when decoded, yields "the set whose members are 2, 3, and 5". Clearly, then, "{2, 3, 5}" is a name of S.

We turn now to the second method of naming a set. The idea is to present a property which characterizes the members of the set. For example, the collection of all positive primes is a set, since it is clear of any object whether it is a positive prime. We shall denote this set by writing:

"$\{x \mid x$ is a positive prime$\}$"

Again, a definite code is being used here: the two braces stand for "the set"; we then interpose "of all objects, say"; the "|" stands for "such that";

finally, we read off the stated condition. This code is displayed as follows:

$$\{\, x \mid x \text{ is a positive prime} \,\}$$

the set — of all objects, say — such that

Thus, the mathematical expression "$\{x \mid x$ is a positive prime$\}$", when decoded, yields "the set of all objects, say x, such that x is a positive prime". Clearly, "$\{x \mid x$ is a positive prime$\}$" is a name of the set of all positive primes. To illustrate this notation further, let "P" denote the set of all positive primes; then $\{x \mid x \in P \wedge x < 6\}$ is the set of all positive primes less than 6. Hence, $\{x \mid x \in P \wedge x < 6\} = \{2, 3, 5\}$. In general, let $P(y)$ be any propositional form, and consider the set of all objects, say t, such that the proposition "$P(t)$" is true. This set is denoted by writing "$\{y \mid P(y)\}$".

We have said that the fundamental property of a set is that we can assert of each object whether or not it is a member of the set. Consider the set constructed by asserting of each object that it is *not* a member of the set; this set has no members, and so is called the *empty* set. It is easy to construct names of the empty set using the two methods given above. Listing the members of the empty set, we obtain "$\{\ \}$", which clearly denotes the set that has no members. Observing that each object has the property that it is equal to itself, we see that we can characterize the empty set as the set of all objects, say x, such that x differs from x; thus, we obtain the name "$\{x \mid x \neq x\}$". It is customary, also, to denote the empty set by writing "$\emptyset$"; thus

$$\emptyset = \{\ \} = \{x \mid x \neq x\}$$

One more convention. Since non-membership in a set is equally important as membership in a set, we shall denote the phrase "is *not* a member of" by writing "$\bar{\in}$". Thus, "$a \mathrel{\bar{\in}} A$" stands for "a is not a member of A".

EXERCISES

Let "P" denote the set of all positive primes, let "I" denote the set of all integers, and let "C" denote the set of all non-prime integers. Show that:

1. $\{a \mid a \in P \wedge a \in I\} = P$
2. $\{b \mid b \in P \vee b \in I\} = I$
3. $\{c \mid c \in C \wedge 3 < c \wedge c < 10\} = \{4, 6, 8, 9\}$
4. $\{d \mid d \in P \wedge 5 < d \wedge d < 10\} = \{7\}$
5. $\{e \mid -e \in P \wedge -10 < e \wedge e < -2\} = \{-3, -5, -7\}$

6. $\{f \mid f \in P \lor -f \in P \lor f \in C\} = I$

7. $\{g \mid g \mathrel{\bar{\in}} P \land -g \mathrel{\bar{\in}} P\} = C$

8. $\{h \mid h \in P \land h \mathrel{\bar{\in}} C\} = P$

9. $\{i \mid (i \in C \rightarrow i \in P) \land i \in I\} = \{j \mid j \in P \lor -j \in P\}$

10. $\{k \mid (-k \in P \rightarrow k \in P) \land k \in I\} = \{l \mid l \in P \lor l \in C\}$

11. $\{m \mid (m \in P \rightarrow m \in C) \land m \in I\} = \{n \mid -n \in P \lor n \in C\}$

12. $\{o \mid o \in P \land \exists p[p \in I \land p + p = o]\} = \{2\}$

13. Characterize $\{q \mid \exists r[r + r = q \land r \in I]\}$

14. Characterize $\{s \mid \exists t[t + t = s + 1 \land t \in I]\}$

15. Characterize $\{u \mid u \in P \land \exists v[v + v = u + 1 \land v \in I]\}$

16. Characterize $\{w \mid (w \in P \lor -w \in P) \land \exists x[x \in I \land x + x = w + 1]\}$

17. Characterize $\{y \mid (y \in P \lor -y \in P) \land \exists z[z \in I \land z + z = y]\}$

18. Characterize $\{a \mid a \in I \land \forall b[b \in I \rightarrow a \cdot b = 0]\}$

19. Characterize $\{c \mid c \in I \land \forall d[d \in I \rightarrow c \cdot d = d]\}$

20. Characterize $\{e \mid e \in I \land \forall f[f \in I \rightarrow e + f = f]\}$

Let "S" denote the set of all students at the University, "M" the set of all male students, "C" the set of all co-eds, and "K" the set of all co-eds who have never been kissed. Show that:

21. $\{g \mid g \in M \lor g \in C\} = S$

22. $\{h \mid h \in C \lor h \in K\} = C$

23. $\{i \mid i \in C \land i \in K\} = K$

24. $\{j \mid j \in S \land (j \in S \rightarrow j \in C)\} = C$

25. $\{k \mid k \in M \land k \in C\} = \emptyset$

26. Characterize $\{l \mid l \in C \land l \mathrel{\bar{\in}} K\}$.

27. Which of the following statements is true: "$x = \{x\}$", "$x \in \{x\}$", "$\{x\} \in x$"?

28. Show that $\{2, 3, 5\} = \{z \mid z = 2 \lor z = 3 \lor z = 5\}$.

29. Show that $\{x \mid x \in \emptyset \rightarrow x = 2\} = \{y \mid y = y\}$.

2. Russell's Paradox

In Section 1, we considered a method of naming a given set by presenting a property that characterizes the members of the set. The order here is important. First, we have a set; next, we construct a name for that set. We must be careful not to reverse the procedure; as we shall see, it can be dangerous to construct a name first, and then to consider the set named!

The situation has been clarified by the famous philosopher and logician Bertrand Russell. Let us consider his famous paradox. Russell observed that if S is a set, then either $S \in S$ or $S \bar{\in} S$, since a given object either is a member of a given set or is not a member of that set. Generally, a set is not a member of itself; therefore, let us consider the set of all sets that are not members of themselves: $\{x \mid x \text{ is a set, and } x \bar{\in} x\}$, which we shall denote by "R". Since R is an object, either $R \in R$ or $R \bar{\in} R$. Consider both possibilities: (1) Assume that $R \in R$. Then, R is a set and $R \bar{\in} R$ by the definition of R. (2) Assume that $R \bar{\in} R$. Then, $R \in R$ by the definition of R, since we are assuming that R is a set.

Examining this argument in the light of our fundamental requirement that a set is a definite collection of objects (so that we can assert of any object whether or not it is a member of the set), we see that Russell's argument demonstrates that R is not a set. Russell has found an object—R itself—which eludes the defining property of R. We conclude that R is not a set.

To repeat, the reason that R is not a set is that the presented definition of R is unsatisfactory: there is one object, R itself, about which we can neither assert that it is a member of the collection, nor that it is not a member of the collection.

The lesson contained in Russell's Paradox, then, is this: Take care, when defining a set by the "characteristic property" method, that there actually is a set behind the name.

To illustrate, consider "$\{x \mid x \text{ is a set}\}$" in words, "the set of all sets". Is there such an animal? Applying Russell's result, we shall see that "$\{x \mid x \text{ is a set}\}$" is a meaningless name. Assume, for the moment, that "$\{x \mid x \text{ is a set}\}$" is a name of a set, say S. Now, consider an object A such that $A \in S$; we can examine A to see whether $A \bar{\in} A$. In other words, we can form $\{x \mid x \in S \wedge x \bar{\in} x\}$, which we know does not exist. This contradiction forces us to conclude that the assumption of the argument, is false. Thus, S does not exist. There is no such thing, then, as the set of *all* sets.

3. Operations on Sets

Given two sets, say A and B, composed of certain members of the universal set I, it may happen that each member of A is also a member of B;

i.e., $\forall x[x \in A \rightarrow x \in B]$. We say, then, that A is a *subset* of B and write "$A \subset B$"; we say that A is a *proper* subset of B iff $A \subset B$ and $A \neq B$.

Again, let A and B be subsets of I; it is very natural to merge these two sets together to form a larger (possibly) set, called the *union* of A and B, and denoted by writing "$A \cup B$" (read "A union B").

DEFINITION: $A \cup B$ is $\{x \mid x \in A \vee x \in B\}$.

For example, $\{1, 5, 2\} \cup \{3, 1, 4, 7\} = \{1, 2, 3, 4, 5, 7\}$.

Also, it is natural to inquire if A and B have any common members; we shall call the set of objects common to A and B, the *intersection* of A and B, and shall denote this set by writing "$A \cap B$" (read "A intersect B").

DEFINITION: $A \cap B$ is $\{y \mid y \in A \wedge y \in B\}$.

For example, $\{1, 5, 2\} \cap \{3, 1, 4, 7\} = \{1\}$.

Suppose that two given sets are *disjoint*; i.e., have no member in common; in this case, it follows from the definition that their intersection is the empty set $\emptyset$.

Given a set A, let us consider the set of all objects in I, the universal set, which are not members of A. We call this set the *complement* of A and denote it by writing "A'" or "$\in A$".

DEFINITION: A' is $\{z \mid z \in I \wedge z \bar{\in} A\}$.

For example, if $I = \{1, 2, 3, 4, 5, 6, 7, 8, 9\}$, then $\{1, 2, 3, 4, 5\}' = \{6, 7, 8, 9\}$.

We wish to establish some of the important properties of the operations "$\cup$", "$\cap$", and "$'$", but first we need a practical criterion for demonstrating that two given sets are in fact the same.

FUNDAMENTAL CRITERION: $A = B$ iff $A \subset B \wedge B \subset A$.

Proof: First, we note that two sets are the same iff they have exactly the same members. Since there is an "iff" in the theorem, there will be two parts to the proof.

1. Suppose that $A = B$. Then A and B have exactly the same members. Hence, $\forall x[x \in A \rightarrow x \in B]$ and $\forall y[y \in B \rightarrow y \in A]$; i.e., $A \subset B$ and $B \subset A$.

2. Suppose that $A \subset B$ and $B \subset A$. If $A \neq B$, then either $\exists x[x \in A \wedge x \bar{\in} B]$ or $\exists y[y \in B \wedge y \bar{\in} A]$, or both. If the former, then A is not a subset of B; if the latter, then B is not a subset of A. Hence, $A = B$. This establishes our fundamental criterion.

We now make use of the preceding result, to establish certain fundamental properties of the operations "$\cup$", "$\cap$", and "$'$".

THEOREM 1: $A \cup B = B \cap A$ whenever A and B are sets.

Proof: We shall show that $A \cup B \subset B \cup A$ and $B \cup A \subset A \cup B$. Suppose that $x \in A \cup B$; then $x \in A \vee x \in B$. Thus $x \in B \vee x \in A$; hence $x \in B \cup A$. This establishes that $A \cup B \subset B \cup A$.

Now suppose that $y \in B \cup A$; then $y \in B \vee y \in A$. Thus $y \in A \vee y \in B$; hence $y \in A \cup B$. This establishes that $B \cup A \subset A \cup B$, and so Theorem 1 is demonstrated.

THEOREM 2: $A \cup (B \cap C) = (A \cup B) \cap (A \cup C)$ whenever A, B, and C are sets.

Proof: Suppose that $x \in A \cup (B \cap C)$; then $x \in A \vee x \in B \cap C$, and so $x \in A \vee (x \in B \wedge x \in C)$. Hence $(x \in A \vee x \in B) \wedge (x \in A \vee x \in C)$; thus $x \in A \cup B \wedge x \in A \cup C$. Therefore, $x \in (A \cup B) \cap (A \cup C)$. Hence, $A \cup (B \cap C) \subset (A \cup B) \cap (A \cup C)$. Now suppose that $y \in (A \cup B) \cap (A \cup C)$; then $y \in A \cup B \wedge y \in A \cup C$, so $(y \in A \vee y \in B) \wedge (y \in A \vee y \in C)$. Thus $y \in A \vee (y \in B \wedge y \in C)$; i.e., $y \in A \vee y \in B \cap C$. Thus $y \in A \cup (B \cap C)$. Hence, $(A \cup B) \cap (A \cup C) \subset A \cup (B \cap C)$. This establishes Theorem 2.

THEOREM 3: $(A \cup B)' = A' \cap B'$ whenever A and B are sets.

Proof: Suppose that $x \in (A \cup B)'$; then $x \bar{\in} A \cup B$; i.e., $\sim(x \in A \vee x \in B)$. Hence, $\sim(x \in A) \wedge \sim(x \in B)$; therefore $x \in A' \wedge x \in B'$. Thus $x \in A' \cap B'$. Hence, $(A \cup B)' \subset A' \cap B'$. Now suppose that $y \in A' \cap B'$; then $y \in A' \wedge y \in B'$; i.e., $\sim(y \in A) \wedge \sim(y \in B)$. Hence, $\sim(y \in A \vee y \in B)$; i.e., $y \bar{\in} A \cup B$. Therefore $y \in (A \cup B)'$. Thus, $A' \cap B' \subset (A \cup B)'$. This establishes Theorem 3.

THEOREM 4: $A \cap I = A$ whenever A is a set.

Proof: Suppose that $x \in A \cap I$; then $x \in A$. Therefore, $A \cap I \subset A$. Now suppose that $y \in A$; then $y \in A \wedge y \in I$, since I is the universal set. Hence, $y \in A \cap I$. Therefore, $A \subset A \cap I$. This establishes Theorem 4.

EXERCISES

Assuming that the universal set I is the set of all integers, show that:

1. $\{8, 6, 7\} \cup \{5, 1, 7, 8\} = \{8, 6, 7, 5, 1\}$
2. $\{8, 6, 7\} \cap \{5, 1, 7, 8\} = \{7, 8\}$
3. $\{8, 6, 7\} \cap \{5, 1, 7, 8\}' = \{6\}$
4. $\{8, 6, 7\}' \cap \{5, 1, 7, 8\} = \{5, 1\}$

5. $\{8, 6, 7\}' \cap \{5, 1, 7, 8\}' = \{8, 6, 7, 5, 1\}'$
6. $\{x \mid \exists y(y \in I \wedge y + y = x)\}$ is the set of all even integers
7. $\{x \mid \exists y(y \in I \wedge y + y = x + 1)\}$ is the set of all odd integers
8. $\{x \mid \exists y(y \in I \wedge y + y = x)\}' = \{x \mid \exists y(y \in I \wedge y + y = x + 1)\}$
9. $\{x \mid \exists y(y \in I \wedge y + y = x)\} \cup \{x \mid \exists y(y \in I \wedge y + y = x + 1)\} = I$
10. $\{y \mid \exists x(x \in I \wedge x + x = y)\} \cap \{y \mid \exists x(x \in I \wedge x + x = y + 1)\} = \emptyset$

Let A, B, and C be any subsets of I, the universal set; show that

11. $A \cap B = B \cap A$
12. $A \cup (B \cup C) = (A \cup B) \cup C$
13. $A \cap (B \cap C) = (A \cap B) \cap C$
14. $A \cap (B \cup C) = (A \cap B) \cup (A \cap C)$
15. $(A \cap B)' = A' \cup B'$
16. $A \cup I = I$
17. $A \cup \emptyset = A$
18. $A \cap \emptyset = \emptyset$
19. $(A')' = A$
20. $A \subset B \wedge B \subset C \rightarrow A \subset C$
21. $A \subset B \rightarrow C \cup A \subset C \cup B$
22. Suppose that A is a proper subset of B; is it necessarily true that $C \cup A$ is a proper subset of $C \cup B$?
23. Show that $A \subset B \rightarrow B' \subset A'$ whenever A and B are subsets of I
24. Given that $A - B = \{x \mid x \in A \wedge x \bar{\in} B\}$, show that

$$(A - B) - C = (A - C) - B$$

and that

$$A - (B - C) = A \cap (B' \cup C).$$

4. The Algebra of Sets

In Section 3 we considered the problem of showing that two sets are the same and developed a basic technique to handle the problem. However, this technique does become tedious should the expressions involved be at all complicated. What we propose is this: We shall develop an algebra of sets, differing somewhat from ordinary algebra, to assist us in simplifying a given expression. Thus, after establishing certain laws by means of the basic technique, we shall use these laws to simplify expressions. The following basic laws are easily established.

1. $(A')' = A$
2. $A \cup B = B \cup A$
3. $A \cap B = B \cap A$
4. $A \cup (B \cup C) = (A \cup B) \cup C$
5. $A \cap (B \cap C) = (A \cap B) \cap C$
6. $A \cup (B \cap C) = (A \cup B) \cap (A \cup C)$
7. $A \cap (B \cup C) = (A \cap B) \cup (A \cap C)$
8. $(A \cup B)' = A' \cap B'$
9. $(A \cap B)' = A' \cup B'$
10. $I' = \emptyset$
11. $\emptyset' = I$
12. $A \cup \emptyset = A$
13. $A \cup I = I$
14. $A \cap I = A$
15. $A \cap \emptyset = \emptyset$
16. $A \cup A' = I$
17. $A \cap A' = \emptyset$

Let us show, using the algebra of sets, that $A \cup (B \cap A') = A \cup B$. Now

$$\begin{aligned} A \cup (B \cap A') &= (A \cup B) \cap (A \cup A') && \text{by Law 6} \\ &= (A \cup B) \cap I && \text{by Law 16} \\ &= A \cup B && \text{by Law 14} \end{aligned}$$

As another example, we show that $[(B \cap C) \cup A] \cap [(B \cap C) \cup B) = B \cap (C \cup A)$. Now

$$\begin{aligned} [(B \cap C) \cup A] \cap [(B \cap C) \cup B] &= (B \cap C) \cup (A \cap B) && \text{by Law 6} \\ &= (B \cap C) \cup (B \cap A) && \text{by Law 3} \\ &= B \cap (C \cup A) && \text{by Law 7} \end{aligned}$$

EXERCISES

Given that A, B, and C are subsets of I, use the algebra of sets to prove the following statements:

1. $(A \cup B')' = A' \cap B$
2. $[A \cup (B \cap C)]' = A' \cap (B' \cup C')$

3. $[(A \cup B)' \cup C]' = (A \cup B) \cap C'$

4. $[(A \cup B)' \cup A]' = B \cap A'$

5. $(A \cap B \cap C) \cup (A' \cup B' \cup C') = I$

6. $A \cup B \cup (A' \cap B') = I$

7. $A \cup A = A$

8. $A \cap A = A$

9. $A \cup (B \cap A) = A$

10. $A \cap (B \cup A) = A$

5. Ordered n^{tuples}

It is clear that the set-concept carries with it no notion of *order* among its members; an object either is a member of a given set or is not a member of the given set—nothing more is said or implied. In short, a set is completely democratic; no member is considered to be superior to another member. In particular, the order in which the members of a set are listed is completely immaterial. Certainly when listing the members of a set, we must of necessity first denote one member of the set, then another, and so on. However, the resulting order is entirely accidental and is not intended to be meaningful.

In analyzing the concepts of mathematics, it turns out that the notion of an ordered n^{tuple}, where n is a natural number, helps to clarify the situation. By an ordered n^{tuple} we mean, intuitively, a set with at most n members on which has been imposed an order, so that we regard one member of the set as the *first* member, some member as the *second* member, and in general whenever k is a natural number such that $k \leq n$, there is a member of the set which we regard as the kth member.

In other words, let n be any natural number and consider $a_1, a_2, \ldots, a_n$ where these are not necessarily distinct. We agree to label a_1 "1st", a_2 "2nd", and so on, and a_n "nth". In essence, we have n positions, each of which must be filled. The resulting object is called an ordered n^{tuple} and is denoted by writing "$(a_1, a_2, \ldots, a_n)$" where a_1 is in the 1st position, a_2 is in the 2nd position, . . . , and a_n is in the nth position. In general, given $k \leq n$, the object occupying the kth position is called the *kth term* of the ordered n^{tuple}.

DEFINITION: Let n be any natural number, and let $a_1, a_2, \ldots, a_n$ be any objects. Then "$(a_1, a_2, \ldots, a_n)$" denotes the ordered n^{tuple} with 1st term a_1, 2nd term a_2, . . . , and nth term a_n.

For example, "(5, 7)" denotes the ordered 2^{tuple} with 1st term 5, and 2nd term 7. Also, "(5, 7, 2)" denotes the ordered 3^{tuple} with 1st term 5, 2nd term 7, and 3rd term 2.

Notice our code: *braces* indicate a set, whereas *parentheses* indicate an ordered n^{tuple}. Furthermore, two ordered n^{tuples}, say $(a_1, a_2, \ldots, a_n)$ and $(b_1, b_2, \ldots, b_n)$, are the same iff $a_1 = b_1$, $a_2 = b_2, \ldots, a_n = b_n$.

Recalling the simplified treatment of geometry resulting from the introduction of co-ordinates, we see that ordered 2^{tuples} are of great value in mathematics. An ordered 2^{tuple} is also called an *ordered pair*. Similarly, an ordered 3^{tuple} is also called an *ordered triple*.

We are now in a position to introduce a vitally important operation on two sets. Let A and B be any non-empty sets (not necessarily distinct); the set of all ordered pairs with 1st term in A, and 2nd term in B, is of enormous value in constructing mathematical objects, as we shall presently see. This set is called the Cartesian product of A and B, and is denoted by writing "$A \times B$".

DEFINITION: $A \times B$ is $\{x \mid \exists a \exists b[x = (a, b) \wedge a \in A \wedge b \in B]\}$.

Notice that two quantifiers are involved in this characterization of $A \times B$. It is possible to eliminate these quantifiers (and so simplify our definition) by using a slightly more elaborate code in naming sets. We shall indicate the fact that members of our set are ordered pairs by inserting an ordered pair to the left of "$|$", in place of the "x" that appears in the definition; this means that the propositional form to the right of "$|$" will involve two placeholders. Thus, "$\{(a, b) \mid a \in A \wedge b \in B\}$" denotes the set of all ordered pairs, say (a, b), such that $a \in A \wedge b \in B$. Hence, $A \times B = \{(a, b) \mid a \in A \wedge b \in B\}$.

If A and B are both finite sets, it is easy to see that the number of members of $A \times B$ is precisely the product of the number of members of A with the number of members of B. For example,

$$\{1, 2, 3\} \times \{2, 5\} = \{(1, 2), (1, 5), (2, 2), (2, 5), (3, 2), (3, 5)\}$$

Generalizing the idea of the product of two sets, we define the product of non-empty sets A, B, and C as follows:

DEFINITION: $A \times B \times C$ is $\{(a, b, c) \mid a \in A \wedge b \in B \wedge c \in C\}$.

In general, given that $A_1, A_2, \ldots, A_n$ are non-empty sets, their product is defined as follows:

DEFINITION: $A_1 \times A_2 \times \cdots \times A_n$ is

$$\{(a_1, a_2, \ldots, a_n) \mid a_1 \in A_1 \wedge a_2 \in A_2 \wedge \cdots \wedge a_n \in A_n\}.$$

The primary purpose of this section has been to introduce the notion of an ordered pair. The idea is to link together objects a and b in such a manner that we recognize one of the given objects as being "1st" and the other as being "2nd". Since we read from left to right, we have agreed to denote the ordered pair with 1st term a and 2nd term b by writing "(a, b)". Thus, the object to the left of the comma is regarded as being 1st, while the object to the right of the comma, is regarded as being 2nd.

It is possible to achieve this same goal, using only sets! Since we wish to link objects a and b, why do we not consider the set with members a and b, namely $\{a, b\}$? Observe that $\{a, b\} = \{b, a\}$, so we cannot distinguish which object is 1st and which object is 2nd. How about $\{a, \{b\}\}$? The members of this set are a and $\{b\}$; we can regard a as 1st, and b as 2nd. Unfortunately, this code is ambiguous: consider $\{\{1\}, \{2\}\}$; this set denotes either the ordered pair $(\{1\}, 2)$, or the ordered pair $(\{2\}, 1)$. Finally, we try $\{\{a\}, \{a, b\}\}$—the set whose members are $\{a\}$ and $\{a, b\}$. Clearly, the objects a and b have been linked; furthermore, one of the members of our set $\{\{a\}, \{a, b\}\}$, is a subset of the other (clearly, $\{a\} \subset \{a, b\}$). We shall say, then, that a is the 1st term of our ordered pair, while the remaining object, b, is the 2nd term of our ordered pair. Thus, by the ordered pair with 1st term a and 2nd term b, we mean the set $\{\{a\}, \{a, b\}\}$. Notice that $\{\{a\}, \{a, b\}\} = \{\{c\}, \{c, d\}\}$ iff $a = c$ and $b = d$.

This means that "(a, b)" is a name of the set $\{\{a\}, \{a, b\}\}$. Thus, the notion of an ordered pair has been expressed in terms of sets. Furthermore, it is easily seen that the concept of an ordered n^{tuple} can be reduced to the notion of an ordered pair.

First, we show that an ordered $k + 1^{\text{tuple}}$, where $k > 1$, can be expressed in terms of an ordered k^{tuple} and an ordered pair: this is so because

$$((a_1, a_2, \ldots, a_k), a_{k+1}) = ((b_1, b_2, \ldots, b_k), b_{k+1})$$

iff

$$(a_1, a_2, \ldots, a_k) = (b_1, b_2, \ldots, b_k) \quad \text{and} \quad a_{k+1} = b_{k+1};$$

but

$$(a_1, a_2, \ldots, a_k) = (b_1, b_2, \ldots, b_k)$$

iff

$$a_1 = b_1 \wedge a_2 = b_2 \wedge \cdots \wedge a_k = b_k.$$

Hence, we may regard the ordered pair with 1st term $(a_1, a_2, \ldots, a_k)$ and 2nd term a_{k+1} as representing the ordered $k + 1^{\text{tuple}}$ $(a_1, a_2, \ldots, a_k, a_{k+1})$ whenever $k > 1$.

It is an easy exercise in mathematical induction to demonstrate that the preceding observation leads to this result: The concept of an ordered n^{tuple} can be expressed in terms of an ordered pair whenever $n > 1$.

EXERCISES

1. In your own words, distinguish between a set with n members, and an ordered n^{tuple}.
2. Compute $\{2, 5\} \times \{1, 2, 3\}$.
3. Compute $\{a\} \times \{b\}$.
4. Compute $\{a\} \times \{a\}$.
5. Compute $\{a, b, c\} \times \{d\}$.
6. Compute $\{a, b, c\} \times \{a\}$.
7. Are $A \times B$ and $B \times A$ necessarily the same?
8. Show that $A = B$ if $A \times B = B \times A$.
9. Show that $A = B$ iff $A \times B = B \times A$.
10. Describe $A \times B \cup B \times A$ in words.
11. Describe $A \times B \cup B \times A \cup A \times A \cup B \times B$ in words.
12. Write down the set whose name is "(5, 7)".
13. Write down the set whose name is "(a, a)".
14. Write down the set whose name is "(2, 2)".
15. Show that $(a, b, c) = \{\{(a, b)\}, \{(a, b), c\}\}$.
16. Show that $(2, 2, 3) = \{\{\{\{2\}\}\}, \{\{\{2\}\}, 3\}\}$.
17. Show that $A \times B \times C = [A \times B] \times C$.
18. By definition "(a)" denotes the ordered 1^{tuple} whose 1st term is a; show that $(a) = \{a\}$.

6. Mappings

We have seen that the notion of an ordered pair enables us to link together, in a particular order, objects a and b. This concept permits us to *associate* an object, say b, with a given object, say a: we need only form the ordered pair (a, b). Thus, in mathematics, we associate two objects by actually linking them together in an ordered pair.

Let A and B be any non-empty sets; a subset of $A \times B$, say M, is said to be a *mapping of A into B* iff each member of A is a 1st term of exactly one ordered pair in M. Moreover, we shall say that the mapping M *associates* with a given member of A, say a, the member of B paired with a. To be precise, if $(a, b) \in M$ we shall say that b is associated with a, under the mapping M; b is also called the *image* of a under the mapping.

Notice that our notion of a mapping of A into B expresses mathematically the intuitive idea of associating a member of B with each member of A. Figure 2-1 may clarify the situation:

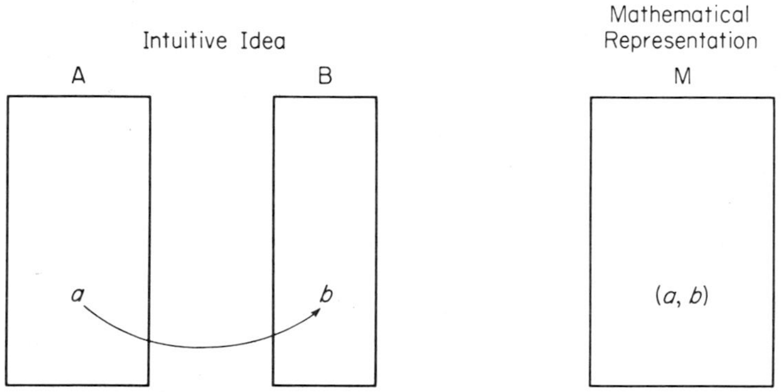

FIGURE 2-1

Under the intuitive idea, b is associated with a: this is represented by the mathematical assertion $(a, b) \in M$. In short, the set M characterizes the intuitive idea of associating a member of B with each member of A.

This important idea deserves some illustration. Suppose that "A" denotes the set of all licenced automobiles and "L" the set of all licence-plates. Then, by pairing its own licence-plate with each member of A, we obtain a subset of $A \times L$ which, in fact, is a mapping of A into L. Suppose that "S" denotes the set of all university students, and "C" the set of all universities. Then the subset of $S \times C$, obtained by pairing with each student the university he attends, is a mapping of S into C. Let "H" denote the set of all husbands, and let "W" denote the set of all wives. Then the subset of $H \times W$, obtained by pairing husband and wife, is a mapping of H into W.

As an example of a type differing from those above, let "C" denote the set of all cities in the United States, and let "P" denote the set of all persons resident in these cities. Then the subset of $C \times P$ formed by pairing each city with its mayor is a mapping of C into P. The point brought out in this example is this: A mapping of a set A into a set B does not necessarily have the property that *each* member of B occurs as a 2nd term of some ordered pair in the mapping. However, if M is a mapping of A into B such that each member of B is a 2nd term of at least one member of M, then we shall say that M is a mapping of A *onto* B. Furthermore, if a mapping of A onto B has the property that each member of B is a 2nd term of *exactly* one ordered pair in the mapping, then we shall say that this subset of $A \times B$ is a *one-one* mapping of A onto B. For example, assuming monogamy, the mapping of H into W described above is a mapping of H *onto* W and is, in fact, a *one-one* mapping of H onto W. On the other hand, the mapping of C into P is not a mapping of C onto P. Again, $\{(1, 2), (2, 4), (3, 6)\}$ is a one-one mapping of $\{1, 2, 3\}$ onto $\{2, 4, 6\}$, as is $\{(1, 4), (2, 6), (3, 2)\}$.

Note that a one-one mapping of A onto B pairs each member of A with a member of B in such a manner that no member of B is left out and no member of B is used twice. This expresses the idea that A and B are equinumerous; that is, have the same number of members. At the turn of the century Russell showed that this idea of "same number of members" is fundamental to the notion of number itself.

A word about notation. Suppose that M is a mapping of A into B and that $a \in A$; let us agree to denote the image of a under M by writing "$M(a)$". In other words, "$M(a)$" denotes the member of B paired with a by the mapping M. Thus, if $(a, b) \in M$, then "$M(a)$" and "b" are names of the same object; hence, we write "$M(a) = b$". For example, let $M = \{(1, 2), (2, 4), (3, 6)\}$; then $M(1) = 2$, $M(2) = 4$, and $M(3) = 6$. It is worth observing that a natural language possesses a corresponding "naming" device; we shall look into this in the next section.

EXERCISES

1. (a) State a method of associating a point with a circle that produces a mapping of the set of all circles of the plane *onto* the set of all points of the plane.
   (b) Construct a mapping of the set of all points of the plane *into* the set of all circles of the plane.
   (c) Is there a mapping of the set of all points of the plane *onto* the set of all circles of the plane?
2. If $A = \{2, 3, 4\}$ and $B = \{4, 5, 6\}$, which of the following sets are mappings of A into B, mappings of A onto B, one-one mappings of A onto B, or mappings of B into A?
   (a) $\{2, 6), (3, 6), (4, 6)\}$
   (b) $\{(2, 6), (3, 6)\}$
   (c) $\{(2, 6), (3, 4), (4, 4)\}$
   (d) $\{(4, 4), (6, 2), (5, 3)\}$
   (e) $\{(4, 5), (2, 6), (3, 4)\}$
   (f) $\{(4, 4), (2, 6), (2, 5)\}$
   (g) $\{(3, 6), (4, 4), (2, 2)\}$
   (h) $\{(2, 5), (3, 4), (4, 2)\}$

3. Suppose that a certain mapping of A into B is also a mapping of B into A:
   (a) Show that $A = B$.
   (b) Show that the mapping is not necessarily one-one.

4. Is a mapping of A into B necessarily not a mapping of A onto B?

5. Given that B is a subset of C, show that each mapping of A into B is also a mapping of A into C. Show that each mapping of A onto B is also a mapping of A into C.

7. Operators

Another basic concept of mathematics is the idea of an operator on a set. This is the mathematical version of a device found in any developed language, a device which permits the naming of a person without stating the person's name. For example, in a monogomous country a person is named by the phrase "the wife of . . ." where an appropriate name has been inserted in place of . . . . For example, "the wife of Mr. Brown" denotes a definite person—namely, Mrs. Brown. Of course, a name has been used, but not the name of the person being named. Another example of this device of language is the phrase "the author of". Again, this phrase has the function of transforming the following name into a person's name. Thus, "the author of" transforms the name "The Republic" into the name "Plato". So, when you read "the author of The Republic", you think "Plato".

Let us inquire into the mathematical version of this device of language. First, for example, consider the phrase "the square of"; if a is an integer, then "the square of a" denotes an integer, usually different from a. In particular, "the square of 3" is a name of the integer 9. Here, the phrase "the square of" plays a role analogous to that played by "the wife of" or "the author of" in the examples above. Clearly, we are concerned with associating a member of a set with a member of a set, but this is nothing more than a mapping of the first set into the second set. In the case of the mathematical example, the two sets involved are the same—the integers. This special kind of mapping, in which the two sets are the same, is of extreme importance in mathematics and is called a "unary operator". Thus, if A is any non-empty set, then by a *unary operator on A* we shall mean any mapping of A into A. For example, let "I" denote the set of integers, then $\{(a, b) \mid a \in I \wedge b = a^2\}$ is a unary operator on I.

A somewhat more complicated type of operator is illustrated by the process of addition. Consider two integers, say 5 and 7, and the word "add"; immediately, a certain integer pops into mind: the integer 12. Again, we are involved with a mapping—a mapping of $I \times I$ into I; since the given integers constitute an ordered pair and the instruction "add" associates an integer with that ordered pair. To be specific, we are involved with the mapping

$$\{((a, b), c) \mid a \in I \wedge b \in I \wedge c = a + b\}.$$

Now consider a definition: we shall call any mapping of $A \times A$ into A, a *binary operator on A*. In the same way, we shall call any mapping of $A \times A \times A$ into A, a *ternary operator on A*. In general, we shall call any mapping of $A \times A \times \cdots \times A$ (n A's) into A, an n^{ary} *operator on A*. Unary and binary operators are widespread throughout mathematics.

Let's see some more examples of operators. Clearly, $\{(n, b) \mid n \in N \wedge b = n!\}$ is a unary operator on N, the set of all natural numbers. Also, $\{(a, b) \mid a \in I \wedge b = -a\}$ is a unary operator on I. Multiplication is an important example of a binary operator; clearly, $\{((a, b), c) \mid a \in N \wedge b \in N \wedge c = a \cdot b\}$ is a binary operator on N.

A binary operator on A is a mapping of $A \times A$ into A and so is a set of ordered pairs. However, the 1st terms are themselves ordered pairs; therefore, each member of a given binary operator is an ordered triple—for example, note that $((5, 7), 12) = (5, 7, 12)$. Thus, our analysis of ordered n^{tuples} (see Section 5) has resulted in an automatic "bracket-omitting" convention. In this way, a binary operator on A is denoted by a set of ordered triples of members of A.

Here are two more conventions. If "U" is the name of a unary operator on A, then we shall denote the 2nd term of an ordered pair in U by writing down the first term, preceded by "U". Thus, if $(a, b) \in U$, then b is denoted by "Ua". Since "b" and "Ua" are names of the same object, we write $b = Ua$. Furthermore, if "B" is the name of a binary operator on A, then we shall denote the 3rd term of any ordered triple in B, by writing down the first two terms of the triple with "B" inserted between. Thus, if $(a, b, c) \in B$, then c is denoted by writing "aBb". Hence, $c = aBb$.

These conventions provide us with a simple and effective method of naming unary and binary operators. Apply the convention in reverse! In this way, we obtain "$\boldsymbol{-}$" as a name for the unary operator on I,

$$\{(a, b) \mid a \in I \wedge b = -a\};$$

that is, $\boldsymbol{-} = \{(a, b)\} \mid a \in I \wedge b = -a\}$. Similarly, we obtain "$\boldsymbol{+}$" as a name for the binary operator on N,

$$\{(a, b, c) \mid a \in N \wedge b \in N \wedge c = a + b\};$$

thus,

$$\boldsymbol{+} = \{(a, b, c) \mid a \in N \wedge b \in N \wedge c = a + b\}.$$

EXERCISES

1. (a) Is "division" a binary operator on the real numbers?
   (b) Find the largest subset of the real numbers on which "division" is a binary operator.
2. If $A = \{2, 3, 4\}$, which of the following sets are unary operators on A, and which are binary operators on A:
   (a) $\{(2, 2), (3, 3), (4, 4)\}$
   (b) $\{(2, 4), (4, 2), (3, 2)\}$
   (c) $\{(3, 5), (3, 4), (4, 4)\}$
   (d) $\{(2, 4), (3, 4)\}$
   (e) $\{(2, 4), (3, 4), (4, 5)\}$
   (f) $\{(2, 3), (3, 4), (4, 5)\}$
   (g) $\{(2, 2, 4), (3, 2, 4), (4, 2, 4)\}$
   (h) $\{(2, 3), (3, 4), (4, 2)\}$
   (i) $\{(2, 2, 2), (2, 3, 3), (2, 4, 4), (3, 2, 2), (3, 3, 3), (3, 4, 4), (4, 2, 2), (4, 3, 3), (4, 4, 4)\}$
   (j) $\{(2, 2, 4), (2, 3, 5), (2, 4, 6), (3, 2, 5), (3, 3, 6), (3, 4, 7), (4, 2, 6), (4, 3, 7), (4, 4, 8)\}$
3. A binary operator on A, say o, is said to be *commutative* iff $\forall x \forall y[xoy = yox]$, where quantification is over A; show that $\{(a, b, c) \mid a \in I \wedge b \in I \wedge c = a - b\}$ is *not* commutative (where I is the set of all integers).
4. A binary operator on A, say o, is said to be *associative* iff
   $$\forall x \forall y \forall z[xo(yoz) = (xoy)oz],$$
   where quantification is over A; show that the binary operator of problem 3, is *not* associative.
5. (a) Suppose that "I" denotes the universal set and that "A" denotes the set of all subsets of I. Show that $\cup$ and $\cap$ are binary operators on A and that $'$ is a unary operator on A.
   (b) Show that $\cup$ is commutative and associative.
   (c) Show that $\cap$ is commutative and associative.
6. Suppose that $o = \{(a, a, b), (a, b, a), (b, a, b), (b, b, b)$. Demonstrate the following propositions:
   (a) o is a binary operator on $\{a, b\}$
   (b) $aob = a$
   (c) $boa = b$
   (d) $ao(aob) = b$
   (e) $(boa)o(bob) = b$
   (f) $bo[(aoa)ob] = b$
   (g) $ao[(aoa)ob] = a$
   (h) $[(aoa)ob]oa = b$

8. Relations

A developed number system usually involves the symbol "$<$" (read "less than"). Given that a and b are numbers, we write "$a < b$"—this is either true or false; hence, it is a proposition. Clearly, if "$a < b$" is true, then "$b < a$" is false; thus, order is essential. This means that, when we discuss "$<$", we are concerned with ordered pairs. The question remains precisely what does the symbol "$<$" denote?

In a particular number system, it is easy to characterize the ordered pairs (a, b) such that $a < b$. For example, in the system of natural numbers, we write "$a < b$" iff "$\exists k[a + k = b]$" is true in the same number system. It is possible to dismiss the symbol "$<$" by regarding it as an abbreviation: "$a < b$" denotes the proposition "$\exists k[a + k = b]$". However, it is far more useful to regard "$<$" as an object in itself—namely, a set of ordered pairs, as follows: $< = \{(a, b) \mid \exists k[a + k = b]\}$.

We wish to assign a generic name to the object we have just constructed. Consider the following definitions.

DEFINITION: $\mathbf{R}$ is called a *binary relation on A* iff $\mathbf{R} \subset A \times A$.

DEFINITION: $\mathbf{R}$ is called a *ternary relation on A* iff $\mathbf{R} \subset A \times A \times A$.

In general for any natural number n

DEFINITION: $\mathbf{R}$ is called an n^{ary} *relation on A* iff $\mathbf{R} \subset A \times A \times \ldots \times A$ (n "A"s).

In words, any subset of $A \times A$ is called a binary relation on A; any subset of $A \times A \times A$ is called a ternary relation on A; and in general whenever n is a natural number, any subset of $A \times A \times \ldots \times A$ (n "A"s) is called an n^{ary} relation on A.

To illustrate, consider the following 4^{ary} relation on the set of real numbers: $\{(a, b, c, x) \mid ax^2 + bx + c = 0\}$. For example, the ordered 4^{tuple} $(2, -5, -3, 3)$ is a member of this relation. A more interesting example of a ternary relation on the integers, is

$$\{(g, a, b) \mid g \text{ is the greatest common divisor of } a \text{ and } b\};$$

$(5, 10, 15)$ is a member of this relation.

A remark about notation. Suppose that $\mathbf{R}$ is an n^{ary} relation on A; we shall denote the proposition "$(a_1, a_2, \ldots, a_n) \in \mathbf{R}$" by writing "$R(a_1, a_2, \ldots, a_n)$". This is an "$\in$ omitting" convention. Furthermore, if $\mathbf{R}$ is a binary relation on A, we shall denote the proposition "$(a, b) \in \mathbf{R}$" by writing "aRb". This is an "$\in$ omitting" and "bracket omitting" convention. In particular, this convention provides us with a simple and effective method of naming certain binary relations. Apply the convention in reverse! To illustrate, consider the relation "less than"; we shall denote this relation by writing "$<$", since the proposition "$(a, b) \in <$" is denoted, under our convention, by writing "$a < b$". In this way we obtain the customary notation, but with a difference! The meaning of the symbolism has been exposed!

Of course, there are many different binary relations on a set A. In case A is a set of numbers, which of these relations should we call "less than" and denote by "$<$"? It is well known that the fundamental properties of "less than" on a set of numbers, are the following:

TRANSITIVE LAW: $\forall x \forall y \forall z[x < y \wedge y < z \rightarrow x < z]$

TRICHOTOMY LAW: $\forall x \forall y[x = y \,\underline{\vee}\, x < y \,\underline{\vee}\, y < x]$

(Recall that "$\underline{\vee}$" denotes the "exclusive or").

Any binary relation on a set A which satisfies the Transitive Law and the Trichotomy Law, is called an *order* relation on A. If A is a set of numbers, an order relation on A is sometimes called "less than" and is denoted by "$<$".

EXERCISES

1. $\{(a, b, x) \mid ax^2 + bx = 0\}$ is a ternary relation on the set of real numbers. Determine one member of this relation.
2. $\{(b, x) \mid x^2 + bx = 0\}$ is a binary relation on the set of real numbers. Determine one member of this relation.
3. $\{(a, b, x) \mid x^2 + bx = a\}$ is a ternary relation on the set of real numbers. Determine one member of this relation.
4. $\{(a, b, c) \mid c^3 + 5c^2 + ac = b\}$ is a ternary relation on the set of real numbers. Determine one member of this relation.
5. $\{(a, b, c) \mid c^2 - 3c = b\}$ is a ternary relation on the set of real numbers. Determine one member of this relation.
6. $\{(a, b, c) \mid c^3 + 7c = a\}$ is a ternary relation on the set of real numbers. Determine one member of this relation.
7. Show that $\{(2, 7), (5, 7), (2, 5)\}$ is an order relation on $\{2, 5, 7\}$.
8. Show that $\{(5, 2), (7, 2), (5, 7)\}$ is an order relation on $\{2, 5, 7\}$.
9. Show that $\{(7, 5), (7, 2), (2, 5)\}$ is an order relation on $\{2, 5, 7\}$.
10. Show that $\{(5, 7), (7, 2), (2, 5)\}$ is *not* an order relation on $\{2, 5, 7\}$.
11. Show that $\{(5, 7), (2, 7)\}$ is *not* an order relation on $\{2, 5, 7\}$.

12. Show that $\{(2, 2), (5, 5), (7, 7)\}$ is *not* an order relation on $\{2, 5, 7\}$.

13. A 1^{ary} relation on A is also called a *unary relation on A*. Characterize unary relations.

14. Let $\mathbf{R}$ be an $n + 1^{\text{ary}}$ relation on A. What properties must $\mathbf{R}$ possess in order that $\mathbf{R}$ is also an n^{ary} operator on A?

9. Equivalence Relations and Partitions

By using the language of relations, it is easy to characterize the fundamental mathematical symbol "=". Recall that we write "$a = b$" iff "a" and "b" refer to the same object. This means that "=" is the mathematical equivalent of "is". The statement "a and b refer to the same object" is expressed by writing "a is b". It follows that "=" is a binary relation on any set—namely, the relation $\{(a, b) \mid a \text{ is } b\}$. It is easily seen that this binary relation possesses the following properties:

REFLEXIVE LAW: $\forall x[x = x]$.

SYMMETRIC LAW: $\forall x \forall y[x = y \rightarrow y = x]$.

TRANSITIVE LAW: $\forall x \forall y \forall z[x = y \wedge y = z \rightarrow x = z]$.

Of course, there are binary relations other than the identity relation that possess these properties. It turns out, however, that a binary relation that is reflexive, symmetric, and transitive is closely connected to the notion of equality; for this reason, it is customary to call any binary relation on a set A which possesses the above three properties an *equivalence relation on A*. In fact, it is possible to use an equivalence relation to do the work of "equals". To be precise, a binary relation on A, say $\mathbf{R}$, is said to be an *equivalence relation on A*, iff $\mathbf{R}$ possesses the following properties:

REFLEXIVE LAW: $\forall x[xRx]$.

SYMMETRIC LAW: $\forall x \forall y[xRy \rightarrow yRx]$.

TRANSITIVE LAW: $\forall x \forall y \forall z[xRy \wedge yRz \rightarrow xRz]$.

(As an aid to associating the name of a law with the law, observe that the properties are listed in order of increasing complexity, whereas the names are listed alphabetically.)

To illustrate the idea, let "W" denote the set of all words. Ordinarily, the important thing about a word is its meaning; to a type-setter, however, the *meaning* of a word is immaterial—it is the *length* of a word that interests him. Therefore, a type-setter regards two words as equal iff they possess the same length. In this way, a type-setter is involved with the following equivalence relation on W: $\{(a, b) \mid a \in W \wedge b \in W \wedge a \text{ and } b \text{ have the same length}\}$.

To understand how an equivalence relation can be used in the place of "equals", we need the method of creating mathematical objects which is called *partitioning*. Consider, for example, how the student body at a university is divided into first-year students, second-year students, third-year students, fourth-year students, graduate students, and special students. Each student fits into exactly one classification. Thus, the set of students is broken down into six subsets; moreover, the collection of subsets has the property that each student is a member of exactly one of the subsets. We say that the set of all students at the university has been partitioned into six subsets, and we call the collection of six subsets a *partition* of the set of all students. Of course, the same set of students can be partitioned in a different manner. For example, we can partition according to sex, so obtaining two subsets; or we can partition according to age, placing together all students of the same age. Again, we can partition the student body according to faculty: Arts, Science, Engineering, Medicine, and so on.

In general, any collection of subsets of a set A is called a *partition of A* iff each member of A is a member of exactly one of the subsets. For example, $\{\{a, b\}, \{c\}, \{d\}\}$ is a partition of $\{a, b, c, d\}$. Again, let "I" denote the set of all integers, let "E" denote the set of all even integers, and let "O" denote the set of all odd integers; then $\{E, O\}$ is a partition of I.

Observe that a partition of a set is a classification of the members of the set, under which each member of the set is placed in precisely one category. Thus, we obtain a partition of the set of all students at the university by classifying according to residence groups; this means that two students are placed in the same category if they live in the same fraternity house, or the same sorority house, or the same dormitory, or the same private home, etc.

There is an intimate connection between the two concepts of an equivalence relation on A and a partition of A. Let us demonstrate the very important fact that an equivalence relation on A induces, in a natural way, a partition of A; that is, we can associate with a set A and an equivalence relation on A, say $\mathbf{R}$, a unique partition of A. The idea is to gather together in the same subset, all members of A paired in $\mathbf{R}$, so that a and b are in the same subset iff $(a, b) \in \mathbf{R}$. Thus, let $S_a = \{x \mid a\mathbf{R}x\}$ whenever $a \in A$. We shall prove the

THEOREM: $\{S_a \mid a \in A\}$ is a partition of A.

Proof: First, note that $\{S_a \mid a \in A\}$ is a collection of subsets of A. Secondly, note that $a \in S_a$ whenever $a \in A$, since $\mathbf{R}$ is reflexive. Thus, each member of A is in at least one subset. We shall show that no member of A is in two subsets. Suppose that $x \in S_a$ and $x \in S_b$; then aRx and bRx. But **R** is symmetric, therefore xRb; furthermore, **R** is transitive, therefore aRb. We shall now show that S_b is a subset of S_a. Suppose $y \in S_b$; then bRy. But aRb and **R** is transitive, therefore aRy; hence $y \in S_a$. This demonstrates that $S_b \subset S_a$. Similarly, it is easy to prove $S_a \subset S_b$. And so $S_a = S_b$. In short, the assumption that two subsets possess a common member forces us to conclude that the two subsets are in fact one. This proves the theorem.

To illustrate, suppose that $A = \{1, 2, 3, 4, 5\}$ and

$$R = \{(1, 1), (2, 2), (3, 3), (4, 4), (5, 5), (1, 2), (2, 1), (3, 4), (4, 3)\}.$$

It is easily checked that R is an equivalence relation on A. Now apply the technique described above to partition A; then $S_1 = \{1, 2\}$, $S_2 = \{1, 2\}$, $S_3 = \{3, 4\}$, $S_4 = \{3, 4\}$, and $S_5 = \{5\}$. Hence, the partition of A induced by the equivalence relation R is $\{\{1, 2\}, \{3, 4\}, \{5\}\}$. It should be observed that 5 and $\{5\}$ are quite different objects; the first is a number, while the second is a set with a single member. In the same way, the set A and the partition of A induced by the equivalence relation are quite different objects. Note also that the new mathematical object, the partition, has been constructed from the material present in A.

Finally, let us demonstrate that a partition on A induces, in a natural way, an equivalence relation on A; that is, we can associate with A and a given partition of A a unique equivalence relation on A. Consider the following binary relation on A:

$\{(a, b) \mid a \text{ and } b \text{ are members of the same subset in the given partition}\}$

which we shall denote by "**R**". Let us prove the

THEOREM: **R** is an equivalence relation on A.

Proof: We must show that **R** is reflexive, symmetric, and transitive. Clearly, **R** is reflexive, since a and a are members of the same subset in the given partition. Furthermore, **R** is symmetric, since if a and b are members of the same subset, then b and a are members of the same subset. Finally, we must show that **R** is transitive. Suppose aRb and bRc; then a and b are members of the same subset, and b and c are members of the same subset. Therefore, a, b, and c are members of the same subset; in particular, a and c are members of the same subset. Hence, aRc. This proves the theorem.

We are now in a position to understand how an equivalence relation can be used in place of "equals". Suppose that A is any non-empty set and **R** is any equivalence relation on A. We wish to justify writing "$a = b$" when all that we know about a and b is that $(a, b) \in \mathbf{R}$. Form the partition of A induced by **R**. This creates new mathematical objects, the members of the partition. Let us create names of these subsets. What do you suggest?

Suppose that we take each member of a subset as a name of that subset. This means that if a and b are in the same subset, then "a" is a name of that subset, and so is "b". Therefore, we can write "$a = b$". But a and b are in the same subset iff $(a, b) \in \mathbf{R}$; and so we are justified in writing "$a = b$" iff aRb.

EXERCISES

1. Show that $\{(4, 4), (6, 6), (8, 8), (4, 6), (6, 4)\}$ is an equivalence relation on $\{4, 6, 8\}$.
2. Show that $\{(4, 4), (6, 6), (8, 8), (4, 6)\}$ is *not* an equivalence relation on $\{4, 6, 8\}$.
3. Show that $\{(4, 4), (6, 6), (8, 8), (4, 8), (8, 4)\}$ is an equivalence relation on $\{4, 6, 8\}$.
4. Show that $\{(4, 4), (6, 6), (8, 8), (4, 8), (8, 4)\}$ is *not* an equivalence relation on $\{4, 6\}$.
5. Show that $\{(4, 4), (6, 6), (8, 8), (4, 8), (8, 4)\}$ is *not* an equivalence relation on $\{4, 6, 8, 9\}$.
6. Given that $\mathbf{R}$ is an order relation on A, prove that $\mathbf{R}$ is not an equivalence relation on A.
7. Given that $\mathbf{R}$ is an equivalence relation on A, prove that $\mathbf{R}$ is not an order relation on A.
8. Demonstrate that a binary relation on A, say $\mathbf{R}$, is an equivalence relation on A iff
$$\forall x[xRx] \wedge \forall x \forall y \forall z[xRy \wedge yRz \rightarrow zRx].$$
9. Construct the partition of $\{a, b, c, d\}$ induced by the equivalence relation $\{(a, a), (b, b), (c, c), (d, d), (a, c), (c, a), (a, d), (d, a), (c, d), (d, c)\}$.
10. Construct the partition of $\{a, b, c, d, e\}$ induced by the equivalence relation $\{(a, a), (b, b), (c, c), (d, d), (e, e), (a, e), (e, a), (c, d), (d, c)\}$.
11. Construct the equivalence relation on $\{a, b, c, d, e\}$ induced by the partition $\{\{a, b, c\}, \{d, e\}\}$.
12. Define a partition of the set of students.
13. Show that $\{\{a, b\}, \{c\}, \{d, a\}\}$ is not a partition of $\{a, b, c, d\}$.
14. Show that $\{\{a, b, c\}, \{d\}, \{e\}\}$ is not a partition of $\{a, b, c, d\}$.

15. Suppose that **R** is an equivalence relation on A and that P is the partition of A induced by **R**. Prove that the equivalence relation on A induced by P is **R**.

16. Suppose that P is a partition of A and that **R** is the equivalence relation on A induced by P. Prove that the partition of A induced by **R** is P.

10. Cardinal Numbers*

When discussing the important number system known as the *natural number system* there are two widely used approaches: the *axiomatic* approach and the *constructive* approach. The Italian mathematician G. Peano used the former approach, beginning his investigation by announcing—without proof, of course—the fundamental properties of the natural number system. These famous propositions, first enunciated in 1889, are now known as the *Peano postulates*—immortalizing their discoverer. Later, the constructive approach was popularized by Russell.

We are now in a position to study the contribution of Frege and Russell to the problem of defining or constructing the natural numbers. Let us consider their basic idea. First, recall that a natural number is certainly a mathematical object; since it is convenient to represent a mathematical object by a set, we shall try to represent each natural number by a set. For example, following Russell's approach, let us construct the natural number 2. We begin with a question. At an intuitive level, what is meant by saying that a set, say S, has *exactly* two members? Well, S has exactly two members iff there are objects, say a and b, such that $a \neq b$ and $S = \{a, b\}$. It is easy to characterize this condition formally.

DEFINITION: S has exactly two members iff

$$\exists x \exists y \forall z[x \in S \wedge y \in S \dot{\wedge} z \in S \rightarrow z = x \veebar z = y].$$

Notice that "having exactly two numbers" is a property that some sets possess, and some sets do not possess. For example, {moon, sun} has exactly two members, whereas {moon, sun, earth} does not.

The idea of Frege and Russell is this. Having defined what we mean by saying that a set has exactly two members, we can characterize "twoness", the essence of the natural number 2, by gathering together all possible instances of "twoness". In other words, let us collect together all sets with exactly two members, so constructing the set

$$\{S \mid S \text{ is a set and } S \text{ has exactly two members}\}$$

which we shall call a *bundle*, following Russell's terminology. Thus, by the natural number 2, we mean this very set—the bundle formed by gathering together the sets that have exactly two members. This means that "2" is a name of the set of all sets possessing exactly two members.

DEFINITION: $2 = \{S \mid S \text{ is a set and } S \text{ has exactly two members}\}$.

It follows that a set, say M, has exactly two members iff $M \in 2$. In the same way, "3" is a name of the bundle of all sets that have exactly three members; "4" is a name of the bundle of all sets that have exactly four members; and so on.

In this way, Russell and Frege succeeded in constructing the natural numbers in terms of sets; indeed, they found it easy to introduce the notion of adding one, the successor operator, and were able to show that the Peano Postulates hold true in their system. This meant they had succeeded in constructing the rudimentary *system* of natural numbers, which Peano had assumed to exist and had taken as the starting point in his program for developing the number systems of mathematics.

Furthermore, Frege and Russell were able to generalize their procedure in a simple and effective manner, so obtaining cardinal numbers. The idea is to introduce an equivalence relation on sets, as follows:

DEFINITION: $A \equiv B$, where A and B are sets, iff there exists a one-one mapping of A onto B.

It is easy to see that this binary relation is reflexive, symmetric, and transitive. This is left as an exercise.

Next, we consider the set of all sets equivalent to a given set. Let A be any set and consider $\{S \mid S \text{ is a set} \wedge S \equiv A\}$; we shall call this set, a cardinal number, and in particular, we shall say it is the cardinal number of A; we shall denote it by writing "$\bar{\bar{A}}$".

DEFINITION: $\bar{\bar{A}} = \{S \mid S \text{ is a set} \wedge S \equiv A\}$.

Clearly, $A \in \bar{\bar{A}}$. Also, if $B \in \bar{\bar{A}}$ then $\bar{\bar{B}} = \bar{\bar{A}}$.

Notice that 2 is a cardinal number; indeed, each natural number is a cardinal number. To see that we have generalized the notion of a natural number, we must show that there is a cardinal number that is not a natural number. Consider the set of all natural numbers, which we shall denote by "N". What about the cardinal number of N—namely, $\bar{\bar{N}}$? Let us show that $\bar{\bar{N}}$ is not a natural number, i.e., $\bar{\bar{N}} \notin N$. It is easy to prove, using the Peano Postulates, that each natural number, say $\bar{\bar{A}}$, has the property that $B = A$ whenever $B \equiv A$ and $B \subset A$. But $\bar{\bar{N}}$ does not have this property. Consider the set $\{2n \mid n \in N\}$; clearly, $\{2n \mid n \in N\} \subset N$ and $\{2n \mid n \in N\} \neq N$. Furthermore, $\{2n \mid n \in N\} \equiv N$, as is easily seen. This demonstrates that $\bar{\bar{N}}$ is not a natural number.

The cardinal number $\overline{\overline{N}}$ is of great importance. As we have observed, N has the property that it is equivalent to one of its proper subsets. Any set that has this property is said to be *infinite*; whereas a set which is not infinite, is said to be *finite*. The cardinal number of an infinite set is said to be a *transfinite* cardinal. The transfinite cardinal $\overline{\overline{N}}$ is assigned the special name "$\aleph_0$" (read "aleph zero"), where "$\aleph$" is the first letter of the Hebrew alphabet. Any set whose cardinal is $\aleph_0$, is said to be *denumerable* or *enumerable*.

THEOREM: The set of all positive, rational numbers is denumerable.

Proof: We construct a mapping μ of the positive rational numbers onto N, which has the following properties. Let a/b and c/d be any two positive, rational numbers in lowest terms where a, b, c, and d are positive integers; first, we require that $\mu(1/1) = 1$; next, we require that

$$\mu(a/b) < \mu(c/d) \quad \text{if} \quad a + b < c + d$$

and

$$\mu(a/b) < \mu(c/d) \quad \text{if} \quad a + b = c + d \wedge a < c$$

Clearly, there are many mappings possessing these properties; e.g., $\mu(1/2) = 10$. Therefore, we impose one more condition on μ:

$$\mu(c/d) = 1 + \mu(a/b) \quad \text{if} \quad \mu(a/b) < \mu(c/d) \wedge \sim \exists x[\mu(a/b) < \mu(x) < \mu(c/d)]$$

Applying our three conditions, we see that

$$\mu(1/1) = 1, \quad \mu(1/2) = 2, \quad \mu(2/1) = 3, \quad \mu(1/3) = 4, \quad \mu(3/1) = 5,$$

and so on. This means that the positive rationals can be listed as follows:

$$\frac{1}{1}; \frac{1}{2}, \frac{2}{1}; \frac{1}{3}, \frac{3}{1}; \frac{1}{4}, \frac{2}{3}, \frac{3}{2}, \frac{4}{1}; \frac{1}{5}, \frac{5}{1};$$

and so on. It is clear that each positive rational has an image in N, under μ, which can be computed by extending the above list until the given positive rational is reached. Furthermore, since our list has no end, each natural number is the image of one (and only one) positive rational number; in fact, the positive rational whose image is a given natural number, say 1,000,000, can be computed by writing out the first million entries in the above listing of the positive rationals. This demonstrates that μ is a one-one mapping of the positive rationals onto N.

COROLLARY: $N \times N \equiv N$, where N is the set of all natural numbers.

Proof: Apply the method of the preceding proof.

THEOREM: Suppose that $A \subset B$ and A is infinite; then B is infinite.

Proof: We shall construct a proper subset of B equivalent to B. Since A is infinite, there is a proper subset of A, say A_1, such that $A_1 \equiv A$. Let λ be a one-one mapping of A_1 onto A; we show that $A_1 \cup (B - A) \equiv B$.

Let
$$\mu(a) = \begin{cases} a & \text{if } a \in B - A \\ \lambda(a) & \text{if } a \in A_1. \end{cases}$$

Then μ is a one-one mapping of $A_1 \cup (B - A)$ onto B; since $A_1 \cup (B - A)$ is a proper subset of B, we have established that B is infinite.

COROLLARY: The set of all real numbers is infinite.

Proof: This set possesses a denumerable subset.

THEOREM: The set of all real numbers is *not* denumerable.

Proof: Suppose that the set of all real numbers is denumerable; then there is a one-one mapping of this set onto N, say ν. Given $i \in N$, let x be the real number such that $\nu(x) = i$. Since each real number can be represented as an infinite decimal, let $x = a_i \cdot d_{i1}d_{i2}d_{i3} \ldots d_{in} \ldots$, where each d_{ij} is a digit, while a_i is the integral part of x. Now, construct the real number

$$0 \cdot d_{11}d_{22}d_{33} \ldots d_{nn} \ldots .$$

We transform this real number as follows: Replace each d_{kk} by 5 if $d_{kk} \neq 5$; otherwise replace d_{kk} by 4. By construction, the resulting real number differs from each $a_i \cdot d_{i1}d_{i2}d_{i3} \ldots d_{in} \ldots$; thus, we have constructed a real number that has no image in N under the mapping ν. This contradiction establishes our theorem.

Let "c" denote the cardinal number of the set of all real numbers; we have shown that $\aleph_0 \neq c$. Thus, there are at least two transfinite cardinal numbers; as a matter of fact, there is an infinite number of transfinite cardinal numbers. To investigate this question, we need a method of comparing cardinal numbers. We begin by establishing the

CANTOR-BERNSTEIN THEOREM: $A \equiv B$ whenever A possesses a subset A_1 and B possesses a subset B_1, such that $A \equiv B_1$ and $B \equiv A_1$.

Proof: Let μ be a one-one mapping of A onto B_1, and let ν be a one-one mapping of B onto A_1. In general, given any set C and any mapping λ, we shall denote $\{\lambda x \mid x \in C\}$ by writing "λC". We now use the given mappings μ and ν to construct additional subsets of A and B, as follows:

$$A_1 = \nu B, \quad A_2 = \nu B_1, \quad A_3 = \nu B_2, \quad \ldots$$

$$B_1 = \mu A, \quad B_2 = \mu A_1, \quad B_3 = \mu A_2, \quad \ldots$$

In general, $A_{n+1} = \nu B_n$ and $B_{n+1} = \mu A_n$ whenever $n \in N$. Clearly, $A_{n+1} \subset A_n$ and $B_{n+1} \subset B_n$ whenever $n \in N$. Let $t \in A$. Either $\forall n(t \in A_n)$, or there is a natural number j such that $t \,\bar{\in}\, A_j$. Hence,

(1) $$A = \bigcap_{n \in N} A_n \cup (A - A_1) \cup \bigcup_{n \in N} (A_n - A_{n+1});$$

clearly,

$$\bigcap_{n \in N} A_n \quad \text{and} \quad (A - A_1) \cup \bigcup_{n \in N} (A_n - A_{n+1})$$

are disjoint. Similarly,

(2) $$B = \bigcap_{n \in N} B_n \cup (B - B_1) \cup \bigcup_{n \in N} (B_n - B_{n+1});$$

again,

$$\bigcap_{n \in N} B_n \quad \text{and} \quad (B - B_1) \cup \bigcup_{n \in N} (B_n - B_{n+1})$$

are disjoint.

Let
$$A^* = (A - A_1) \cup \bigcup_{n \in N} (A_{2n} - A_{2n+1})$$
$$A^{**} = \bigcup_{n \in N} (A_{2n-1} - A_{2n})$$
$$B^* = (B - B_1) \cup \bigcup_{n \in N} (B_{2n} - B_{2n+1})$$
$$B^{**} = \bigcup_{n \in N} (B_{2n-1} - B_{2n}).$$

Then $A = \bigcap_{n \in N} A_n \cup A^* \cup A^{**}$ and $B = \bigcap_{n \in N} B_n \cup B^* \cup B^{**}$.

But $\mu A^* = B^{**}$ and $\nu B^* = A^{**}$; therefore, $A^* \equiv B^{**}$ and $B^* \equiv A^{**}$
Finally, we shall show that

$$\bigcap_{n \in N} A_n \equiv \bigcap_{n \in N} B_n.$$

Suppose that

$$a \in \bigcap_{n \in N} A_n;$$

i.e., $\forall n(a \in A_n)$. Then $\forall n(\mu a \in B_n)$ and so

$$\mu a \in \bigcap_{n \in N} B_n.$$

In other words, with each member of

$$\bigcap_{n \in N} A_n,$$

say a, we can associate a unique member of

$$\bigcap_{n \in N} B_n$$

namely, μa. Since μ is a one-one mapping of A onto B_1, we know that no member of

$$\bigcap_{n \in N} B_n$$

is used twice as an image. Furthermore, no member of

$$\bigcap_{n \in N} B_n$$

is omitted; to see this, suppose that

$$\mu a_1 \in \bigcap_{n \in N} B_n, \quad \text{but} \quad a_1 \,\overline{\in}\, \bigcap_{n \in N} A_n$$

Then, there is a natural number j such that $a_1 \,\overline{\in}\, A_j$. Hence, $\mu a_1 \,\overline{\in}\, B_{j+1}$, and so

$$\mu a_1 \,\overline{\in}\, \bigcap_{n \in N} B_n.$$

This contradiction establishes that

$$\bigcap_{n \in N} A_n \equiv \bigcap_{n \in N} B_n.$$

In view of (1) and (2), it now follows that $A \equiv B$. In particular, we can construct a one-one mapping of A onto B, say λ, as follows:

$$\lambda a = \begin{cases} \mu a & \text{if } a \in \bigcap_{n \in N} A_n \cup A^* \\ b & \text{where } \nu b = a, \text{ if } a \in A^{**} \end{cases}$$

This establishes the Cantor-Bernstein Theorem.

Expressing this result in the language of cardinal numbers, we have the

COROLLARY: $\bar{\bar{A}} = \bar{\bar{B}}$ whenever A possesses a subset A_1 and B possesses a subset B_1, such that $\bar{\bar{A}} = \bar{\bar{B}}_1$ and $\bar{\bar{B}} = \bar{\bar{A}}_1$.

This corollary suggests a natural way of comparing cardinal numbers; that is, of introducing a "less than" relation on cardinal numbers.

DEFINITION: Let A and B be any sets; we shall say that $\bar{\bar{A}} < \bar{\bar{B}}$ iff

$$\exists B_1(B_1 \subset B \wedge A \equiv B_1) \wedge \sim \exists A_1(A_1 \subset A \wedge B \equiv A_1).$$

Clearly, $<$ is transitive, but not symmetric and not reflexive.

Let A and B be any sets; there are four possibilities.

(1) $\exists B_1(B_1 \subset B \wedge A \equiv B_1) \wedge \exists A_1(A_1 \subset A \wedge B \equiv A_1)$; then $\bar{\bar{A}} = \bar{\bar{B}}$

(2) $\exists B_1(B_1 \subset B \wedge A \equiv B_1) \wedge \sim \exists A_1(A_1 \subset A \wedge B \equiv A_1)$; then $\bar{\bar{A}} < \bar{\bar{B}}$ by definition

(3) $\sim \exists B_1(B_1 \subset B \wedge A \equiv B_1) \wedge \exists A_1(A_1 \subset A \wedge B \equiv A_1)$; then $\bar{\bar{B}} < \bar{\bar{A}}$ by definition

(4) $\sim \exists B_1(B_1 \subset B \wedge A \equiv B_1) \wedge \sim \exists A_1(A_1 \subset A \wedge B \equiv A_1)$; $\bar{\bar{A}}$ and $\bar{\bar{B}}$ are not comparable.

It turns out that under a certain hypothesis known as the Axiom of Choice (4) is impossible. We shall not prove this here; rather we shall content ourselves with stating the hypothesis involved.

THE AXIOM OF CHOICE: Let I be any non-empty set, and let S_a be a non-empty set whenever $a \in I$; then there exists a set C such that $\overline{\overline{C \cap S_a}} = 1$ whenever $a \in I$ [symbolically, $\exists C \forall a(C \text{ is a set } \wedge (a \in I \rightarrow \overline{\overline{C \cap S_a}} = 1))$].

We observed, previously, that there exist infinitely many transfinite cardinal numbers. This proposition rests upon the following theorem.

THEOREM: The cardinal number of any set is less than the cardinal number of the set of all subsets of the given set.

Proof: Let A be any set, and let $S = \{T \mid T \subset A\}$. Clearly, there is a subset of S equivalent to A, namely $\{\{a\} \mid a \in A\}$. This means that $\bar{\bar{A}} = \bar{\bar{S}}$ or else $\bar{\bar{A}} < \bar{\bar{S}}$ [see (1) and (2) above]. Suppose that $\bar{\bar{A}} = \bar{\bar{S}}$. Then there exists a one-one mapping of A onto S, say μ. Let $a \in A$; then either $a \in \mu a$ or $a \mathrel{\bar{\in}} \mu a$. (Recall that μa is a subset of A.) Consider the subset of A, say T, formed as follows: $T = \{a \mid a \in A \wedge a \mathrel{\bar{\in}} \mu a\}$. Whether or not T is empty, there is by assumption a member of A, say a_1, such that $\mu a_1 = T$. There are two cases.

Case 1: $a_1 \in T$. Then $a_1 \in \mu a_1$; hence, by the construction of T, $a_1 \mathrel{\bar{\in}} T$. This contradiction means that Case 1 is impossible.

Case 2: $a_1 \mathrel{\bar{\in}} T$. Then $a_1 \mathrel{\bar{\in}} \mu a_1$; hence, by the conrtruction of T, $a_1 \in T$. This contradiction means that Case 2 is impossible.

We conclude from this argument that a_1 does not exist. Hence, each mapping of A into S must leave out at least one member of S. Thus, there is no one-one mapping of A onto S. We have demonstrated that A is *not* equivalent to S; we conclude that $\bar{\bar{A}} < \bar{\bar{S}}$.

The following two definitions are aimed at developing a notation for the cardinal number of the set of all subsets of a given set in terms of the cardinal number of the given set.

Let A and B be any sets;

DEFINITION: $A^B = \{\mu \mid \mu \text{ is a mapping of } B \text{ into } A\}$.

Let $\bar{\bar{A}} = a$ and $\bar{\bar{B}} = b$;

DEFINITION: We shall denote the cardinal number of the set A^B by writing "a^b"; i.e., $a^b = \overline{\overline{A^B}}$.

THEOREM: Let A be any set, and let $S = \{T \mid T \subset A\}$. Then $\bar{\bar{S}} = 2^a$ where $a = \bar{\bar{A}}$.

Proof: Given a subset of A, say T, either $a \in T$ or $a \bar{\in} T$ whenever $a \in A$. Therefore, $\{T \mid T \subset A\} = \{\mu \mid \mu$ is a mapping of A into $\{0, 1\}\}$; hence,

$$\bar{\bar{S}} = 2^a.$$

It is easy, now, to see that there are infinitely many transfinite cardinal numbers. Applying the two preceding theorems, we see that $m < 2^m$ whenever m is a cardinal number. In particular, $\aleph_0 < 2^{\aleph_0}$, $2^{\aleph_0} < 2^{(2^{\aleph_0})}$, and so on. Thus, given any transfinite cardinal number, there is a larger transfinite cardinal number.

EXERCISES

1. Use quantifiers to define the notion of a set that has
   (a) exactly one member
   (b) exactly three members
   (c) exactly four members
   (d) no members

2. Prove that $\equiv$ is reflexive, symmetric, and transitive.

3. Let m' denote $\overline{\overline{M \cup \{x\}}}$, where $\bar{\bar{M}} = m$ and $x \bar{\in} M$.
   (a) Show that $1' = 2$ and $2' = 3$.
   (b) Show that the set of all finite cardinal numbers; i.e., cardinal numbers that are not transfinite, together with the unary operator $'$ and the special cardinal number 1, satisfy the Peano Postulates.

4. Addition is defined as follows: $m + n = \overline{\overline{M \cup N}}$ whenever $\bar{\bar{M}} = m$, $\bar{\bar{N}} = n$ and $M \cap N = \emptyset$.
   (a) Show that $m + n = n + m$ whenever m and n are cardinal numbers.
   (b) Show that $1 + \aleph_0 = \aleph_0$. *Hint:* Consider $\{x\} \cup N$, where $x \bar{\in} N$.
   (c) Show that $\aleph_0 + \aleph_0 = \aleph_0$. *Hint:* Consider

$$\{2n - 1 \mid n \in N\} \cup \{2n \mid n \in N\}.$$

5. Multiplication is defined as follows: $m \cdot n = \overline{\overline{M \times N}}$ whenever $\bar{\bar{M}} = m$ and $\bar{\bar{N}} = n$.
   (a) Show that $m \cdot n = n \cdot m$.
   (b) Show that $2 \cdot \aleph_0 = \aleph_0$.
   (c) Show that $\aleph_0 \cdot \aleph_0 = \aleph_0$.

6. Show that $(2^{\aleph_0})^{\aleph_0} = 2^{\aleph_0}$.

7. Show that there is no such thing as the set of *all* sets.

8. "$\leq$" is defined as follows: $m \leq n$ iff $m < n$ or $m = n$ whenever m and n are cardinal numbers.
   (a) Show that $\bar{\bar{M}} \leq \bar{\bar{N}}$ iff $\exists N_1(N_1 \subset N \wedge M \equiv N_1)$.
   (b) Show that $m = n$ iff $m \leq n$ and $n \leq m$.

9. Prove that $\aleph_0$ is the smallest transfinite cardinal number; i.e., show that M is finite whenever $\bar{\bar{M}} < \aleph_0$.

part II

The axiomatic method

3

The axiomatic method and abstract algebra

1. Algebraic Systems

One of the outstanding characteristics of mathematics—for which it receives high respect—is its clarity. This aspect of mathematics, the pursuit of clear thinking, is responsible for the development in recent years of the concept of the algebraic system. Essentially, this is a matter of setting out the *kinds* of objects that are involved in a particular mathematical investigation. For example, in the study of geometry we are concerned with a set of objects called points and with certain relations on this set. Again, in the study of a number system, we are concerned with a set of objects called numbers, two binary operators on this set, called addition and multiplication, the binary relation "less than", and possibly the special numbers 0 and 1.

We see that a mathematical investigation is concerned with a non-empty set, say A, possibly certain operators on A, possibly certain relations on A, and possibly certain special members of A. In any event, there is at least one operator or relation on A involved. Thus, the "ingredients" of a mathematical investigation are found in the following list: a set, operators or relations on the set, possibly specified members of the set. It is convenient to use an ordered n^{tuple} to display the particular ingredients required for a specific mathematical investigation. The first term of this ordered n^{tuple} is the set A referred to above; the remaining terms are the operators on A, the relations on A, and the special members of A that are involved. It is convenient to give a name to this very special type of ordered n^{tuple}; we shall call it an *algebraic system*. Furthermore, we shall call the first term of an algebraic system the *basic set* of the algebraic system; the basic set of an algebraic system is important, because it fulfills the function of a universal set for the algebraic system.

For example, the ordered pair $(S, \circ)$, where $S = \{a, b\}$ and

$$\circ = \{(a, a, b), (a, b, a), (b, a, a), (b, b, b)\}$$

is an algebraic system; the basic set of this algebraic system is $\{a, b\}$, and its second term $\circ$ is a binary operator on $\{a, b\}$. Notice that b possesses the following properties:

$$\forall x[x \circ b = x] \quad \text{and} \quad \forall x \exists y[x \circ y = b]$$

where quantification is restricted to S, the basic set of this algebraic system. If we wish to draw attention to the algebraic properties of b, we do so by constructing the algebraic system $(S, \circ, b)$; in this way, b is displayed as a component part of the algebraic system.

The preceding discussion is made precise in the following

DEFINITION: Any ordered n^{tuple} whose first term is a non-empty set, say A, and whose remaining terms are operators on A, or relations on A, or specific members of A, is called an *algebraic system*, provided that it involves at least one operator or relation on A.

In the following sections, we shall be concerned with statements of the form: "This proposition is true in this algebraic system", where the proposition mentioned involves quantifiers. We must be clear about what this means. The main consideration is that quantification is restricted to the basic set of the algebraic system mentioned. This is only natural, since the basic set plays the role of a universal set. Consider, for example, the statement: "$\forall x[x \circ b = x]$ is true in the algebraic system $(S, \circ, b)$". Recalling the technique for handling quantifiers, discussed in Section 10 of Chapter 1, we must show that the propositions $a \circ b = a$ and $b \circ b = b$ are true. But $(a, b, a) \in \circ$; hence "$a \circ b$" denotes a, and so the first proposition is true. Similarly, $(b, b, b) \in \circ$; therefore "$b \circ b$" denotes b, and so the second proposition is true. It follows from this that "$\forall x[x \circ b = x]$" is true in $(S, \circ, b)$.

We shall now prove that the proposition "$\forall x \exists y[x \circ y = b]$" is true in the algebraic system $(S, \circ, b)$. Stripping away the first quantifier, we obtain the propositions: "$\exists y[a \circ y = b]$" and "$\exists y[b \circ y = b]$". We must show that both propositions are true in $(S, \circ, b)$. But "$a \circ a = b$" is true in this algebraic system; therefore ,"$\exists y[a \circ y = b]$" is true in $(S, \circ, b)$. Again, "$b \circ b = b$" is true in this algebraic system; therefore, "$\exists y[b \circ y = b]$" is true in $(S, \circ, b)$. This demonstrates that "$\forall x \exists y[x \circ y = b]$" is true in $(S, \circ, b)$.

Here is another example of an algebraic system. Consider the ordered 4^{tuple} $(B, ?, !, 0)$, where

$$B = \{0, 1\},$$
$$? = \{(0, 0, 0), (0, 1, 1), (1, 0, 1), (1, 1, 0)\}$$
and
$$! = \{(0, 0, 0), (0, 1, 0), (1, 0, 0), (1, 1, 0)\}.$$

The first term of this ordered 4^{tuple} is a set, the second term ? is a binary operator on B, the third term is also a binary operator on B, and the fourth term is a member of B. Therefore, our ordered 4^{tuple} is an algebraic system; furthermore, the basic set of this algebraic system is $\{0, 1\}$. Now consider the proposition "$\forall x[x \mathbin{?} 0 = x]$". We shall show that this proposition is true in the algebraic system $(B, ?, !, 0)$. Stripping away the quantifier, we obtain the propositions "$0 \mathbin{?} 0 = 0$" and "$1 \mathbin{?} 0 = 1$". But $(0, 0, 0) \in ?$ and $(1, 0, 1) \in ?$; therefore both propositions are true, and it follows that "$\forall x[x \mathbin{?} 0 = x]$" is true in $(B, ?, !, 0)$.

Note that the proposition "$(1 \mathbin{!} 1) \mathbin{?} 1 = 1 \mathbin{?} 1$" is false in $(B, ?, !, 0)$, since $(1 \mathbin{!} 1) \mathbin{?} 1 = 0 \mathbin{?} 1 = 1$, whereas $1 \mathbin{?} 1 = 0$. It follows from this observation that the proposition "$\forall x[(x \mathbin{!} x) \mathbin{?} x = x \mathbin{?} x]$" is false in $(B, ?, !, 0)$. However, let us show that the proposition "$\exists x[(x \mathbin{!} x) \mathbin{?} x = x \mathbin{?} x]$" is true in this algebraic system. Deleting "$\exists x$" and replacing "x" by "0", we obtain the proposition "$(0 \mathbin{!} 0) \mathbin{?} 0 = 0 \mathbin{?} 0$", which is true, since $0 \mathbin{!} 0$ is 0. Therefore, "$\exists x[(x \mathbin{!} x) \mathbin{?} x = x \mathbin{?} x]$" is true in $(B, ?, !, 0)$.

Now consider, as another example, the ordered pair $(S, \mathbf{R})$, where $S = \{a, b, c, d\}$ and $\mathbf{R} = \{(a, b), (a, c), (a, d), (b, c), (b, d), (c, d)\}$. Since $\mathbf{R}$ is a binary relation on S, we see that $(S, \mathbf{R})$ is an algebraic system. Let us show that the proposition "$\forall x \exists y[x \mathrel{\mathrm{R}} y \vee y \mathrel{\mathrm{R}} x]$" is true in $(S, \mathbf{R})$. Stripping away the first quantifier, we obtain the propositions:

$$\text{“}\exists y[a \mathrel{\mathrm{R}} y \vee y \mathrel{\mathrm{R}} a]\text{”}, \quad \text{“}\exists y[b \mathrel{\mathrm{R}} y \vee y \mathrel{\mathrm{R}} b]\text{”},$$
$$\text{“}\exists y[c \mathrel{\mathrm{R}} y \vee y \mathrel{\mathrm{R}} c]\text{”}, \quad \text{“}\exists y[d \mathrel{\mathrm{R}} y \vee y \mathrel{\mathrm{R}} d]\text{”}.$$

But "$a \mathrel{\mathrm{R}} b$" is true; hence "$a \mathrel{\mathrm{R}} b \vee b \mathrel{\mathrm{R}} a$" is true, and thus "$\exists y[a \mathrel{\mathrm{R}} y \vee y \mathrel{\mathrm{R}} a]$" is true in $(S, \mathbf{R})$.
Also, "$b \mathrel{\mathrm{R}} d$" is true; hence "$b \mathrel{\mathrm{R}} d \vee d \mathrel{\mathrm{R}} b$" is true, and thus "$\exists y[b \mathrel{\mathrm{R}} y \vee y \mathrel{\mathrm{R}} b]$" is true in $(S, \mathbf{R})$.
Also, "$a \mathrel{\mathrm{R}} c$" is true; hence "$c \mathrel{\mathrm{R}} a \vee a \mathrel{\mathrm{R}} c$" is true, and thus "$\exists y[c \mathrel{\mathrm{R}} y \vee y \mathrel{\mathrm{R}} c]$" is true in $(S, \mathbf{R})$.
Also, "$b \mathrel{\mathrm{R}} d$" is true; hence "$d \mathrel{\mathrm{R}} b \vee b \mathrel{\mathrm{R}} d$" is true, and thus "$\exists y[d \mathrel{\mathrm{R}} y \vee y \mathrel{\mathrm{R}} d]$" is true in $(S, \mathbf{R})$. Therefore, "$\forall x \exists y[x \mathrel{\mathrm{R}} y \vee y \mathrel{\mathrm{R}} x]$" is true in $(S, \mathbf{R})$.

PROBLEM: Show that the propositions "$\forall x \forall y \forall z[x \mathrel{\mathrm{R}} y \wedge y \mathrel{\mathrm{R}} z \rightarrow x \mathrel{\mathrm{R}} z]$" and "$\forall x \forall y[x = y \veebar x \mathrel{\mathrm{R}} y \veebar y \mathrel{\mathrm{R}} x]$" are both true in $(S, \mathbf{R})$.

The concept of the algebraic system is based on the elementary concepts of set theory. In the remaining sections of this chapter, we shall see how the notion of the algebraic system is itself used as a building-block in constructing mathematical concepts.

EXERCISES

1. Show that the following propositions are true in the algebraic system $(S, \circ)$ of the text:

   (a) $\forall x \forall y[x \circ y = y \circ x]$
   (b) $\forall x \forall y[(x = y \rightarrow x \circ y = b)\ (x \neq y \rightarrow x \circ y = a)]$
   (c) $\forall y \forall z[a \circ (y \circ z) = (a \circ y) \circ z]$
   (d) $\forall y \forall z[b \circ (y \circ z) = (b \circ y) \circ z]$
   (e) $\forall x \forall y \forall z[x \circ (y \circ z) = (x \circ y) \circ z]$

2. In the algebraic system $(B, ?, !, 0)$ of the text, show that

   (a) $1 \ ? \ (1 \ ! \ 0) = 1$
   (b) $(0 \ ! \ 1) \ ? \ (1 \ ? \ 1) = (0 \ ? \ 1) \ ! \ (1 \ ! \ 1)$
   (c) $[(1 \ ? \ 0) \ ? \ 1] \ ? \ 1 = (0 \ ! \ 0) \ ? \ (0 \ ? \ 1)$
   (d) $(0 \ ! \ 1) \ ! \ (0 \ ! \ 0) \neq (1 \ ? \ 0) \ ? \ (1 \ ? \ 1)$

3. Show that the following propositions are true in the algebraic system $(B, ?, !, 0)$ of the text:

   (a) $\forall x \forall y[x \ ? \ y = y \ ? \ x]$
   (b) $\forall x \forall y[x \ ! \ y = 0]$
   (c) $\forall x \forall y \forall z[x \ ? \ (y \ ! \ z) = x]$
   (d) $\forall x \exists y[x \ ? \ y = 0]$
   (e) $\forall y \forall z[0 \ ? \ (y \ ? \ z) = (0 \ ? \ y) \ ? \ z]$
   (f) $\forall y \forall z[1 \ ? \ (y \ ? \ z) = (1 \ ? \ y) \ ? \ z]$
   (g) $\forall x \forall y \forall z[x \ ? \ (y \ ? \ z) = (x \ ? \ y) \ ? \ z]$
   (h) $\forall x \forall y \exists z[x \ ? \ z = y]$ *Hint:* Apply (d) and (g).

4. Consider the algebraic system $(\{a, b, c\}, +, \circ)$ where

   $+ = \{(a, a, b), (a, b, c), (a, c, a), (b, a, a), (b, b, c), (b, c, b), (c, a, a), (c, b, b), (c, c, c)\}$

and

$\circ = \{(a, a, a), (a, b, b), (a, c, c), (b, a, a), (b, b, b), (b, c, c), (c, a, a), (c, b, b), (c, c, c)\}.$

Calculate the following:

$$a + b, \quad a + (b + a), \quad (b + c) + (a + b),$$

$$(a + b) \circ c, \quad (a \circ c) + b, \quad a + (b \circ c), \quad [a + (b \circ c)] \circ b, \quad b \circ (c \circ b),$$

$$[(a + b) \circ (b + c)] + [(a + b) \circ (a + (b \circ c))]$$

5. In the algebraic system of Exercise 4, which of the following propositions are true?

(1) $\forall x \forall y[x \circ y = y]$

(2) $\forall x \forall y \forall z[x \circ (y + z) = (x \circ y) + (x \circ z)]$

(3) $\forall x \forall y[x + y = y + x]$

(4) $\forall x \forall y[x \circ y = y \circ x]$

(5) $\forall x \exists y[x \circ y = y \circ x]$

(6) $\forall x \exists y[x + y = y + x]$

(7) $\exists x \forall y[x + y = y + x]$

(8) $\forall x \forall y \forall z[x + (y + z) = (x + y) + z]$

(9) $\forall x \forall y \forall z[x \circ (y \circ z) = (x \circ y) \circ z]$

(10) $\forall x \forall y \forall z[x + (y \circ z) = (x + y) \circ z]$

(11) $\forall x \forall y \forall z[x \circ (y + z) = (x \circ y) + z]$

(12) $\forall x \forall y \forall z[x + (y \circ z) = (x + y) \circ (x + z)]$.

6. Which is more important, the basic set of an algebraic system or the operators and relations of the algebraic system?

2. The Axiomatic Method

Let's play a game. The game is called "Find the algebraic system", and the object of the game is to construct an algebraic system—given certain hints about the desired algebraic system. For example, let's construct an algebraic system that consists of a basic set, say S, and a binary relation on S, say $\mathbf{R}$. As additional hints, we are informed that the following propositions are true in this algebraic system:

$$\exists x \exists y[x \neq y]$$

$$\exists x \exists y \forall z[z = x \vee z = y]$$

$$\forall x \forall y[x \mathrel{R} y \longleftrightarrow x \neq y]$$

Examining the hints, we see that there are at least two members in S, since that is the meaning of the proposition $\exists x \exists y[x \neq y]$. Furthermore, we see there are at most two members in S, since that is what $\exists x \exists y \forall z[z = x \vee z = y]$ asserts. We conclude that S has exactly two members. Suppose the members of S are a and b; so $S = \{a, b\}$. Then the remaining proposition,

$$\forall x \forall y[x \, R \, y \longleftrightarrow x \neq y],$$

tells us that $\mathbf{R} = \{(a, b), (b, a)\}$. We have determined the desired algebraic system—namely, $(\{a, b\}, \{(a, b), (b, a)\})$. Of course, if c and d are any two objects, then the algebraic system $(\{c, d\}, \{(c, d), (d, c)\})$ also meets the given conditions.

Now suppose that we construct an algebraic system of the form $(S, \mathbf{R})$, where $\mathbf{R}$ is a binary relation on S, in which the following propositions are true:

$$\exists x \exists y[x \neq y]$$

$$\exists x \exists y \forall z[z = x \vee z = y]$$

$$\forall x \forall y[x \neq y \rightarrow x \, R \, y]$$

so that the third proposition given above has been altered. Again, S has exactly two members, say a and b. However, we cannot be as definite about $\mathbf{R}$ as in the preceding case. There are three possibilities: $\mathbf{R} = \{(a, b), (b, a)\}$ as before, $\mathbf{R} = \{(a, b), (b, a), (a, a)\}$, or $\mathbf{R} = \{(a, b), (b, a), (a, a), (b, b)\}$. Thus, the given hints lead us to three algebraic systems:

$$\begin{array}{ll} & (\{a, b\}, \{(a, b), (b, a)\}), \\ \text{I} & (\{a, b\}, \{(a, b), (b, a), (a, a)\}), \\ & (\{a, b\}, \{(a, b), (b, a), (a, a), (b, b)\}). \end{array}$$

Actually, there are many algebraic systems which meet the given conditions. For example, let c and d be distinct objects; then the algebraic systems

$$\begin{array}{ll} & (\{c, d\}, \{(c, d), (d, c)\}), \\ \text{II} & (\{c, d\}, \{(c, d), (d, c), (c, c)\}), \\ & (\{c, d\}, \{(c, d), (d, c), (c, c), (d, d)\}) \end{array}$$

also meet the given conditions. However, each of these algebraic systems can be constructed from the corresponding algebraic system listed in **I**, by merely replacing "a" by "c", and replacing "b" by "d", throughout the algebraic system. In this sense, the algebraic systems of **I** characterize all the algebraic systems that meet the given conditions.

The two illustrations given above show that it is sometimes possible to characterize a given collection of algebraic systems *of the same type*, first by specifying the type, and then listing certain propositions which are true in each of the algebraic systems. By the *type* of an algebraic system, we mean the general shape of the algebraic system; that is, the kinds of things that are terms of the algebraic system.

The famous philosopher and logician Bertrand Russell has said that "mathematics may be defined as the subject in which we never know what we are talking about, nor whether what we are saying is true". Of course, this is a tongue-in-cheek statement and is intended to be amusing; but still, Russell has pointed out most clearly the essentials of the axiomatic method. Since the power of mathematics lies in the generality of its results, one deliberately avoids spelling out precisely the objects and operators or relations being investigated. Rather, one describes the *type* of algebraic system being studied by stating that it involves a unary operator, or two binary operators, or a binary relation, or one special member of the basic set, as the case may be; next, one lists certain propositions that are true in the algebraic system. The propositions are called *axioms* or *postulates*. On the basis of the given information, it is sometimes possible to establish that other propositions are true in each of the algebraic systems so characterized. Such propositions are called *theorems*. Thus, we don't really know what we are talking about, nor do we know whether our theorems are really true. However, should we encounter an algebraic system of the specified type, in which each of the given postulates is true, then we can assert that each of our theorems is true in this algebraic system. In this way, the sum total of knowledge has been increased.

Notice there are two aspects to the axiomatic method. First, a family of algebraic systems is described by stating the type of algebraic system in the family, and then by listing certain propositions that are true in each algebraic system of the family. Next, it is demonstrated that certain propositions are true in each algebraic system of the family; these propositions are called theorems. In general, a theorem is established by considering any algebraic system in the family and showing, usually by stripping away quantifiers, that the given proposition is true in that algebraic system.

To illustrate the axiomatic method, let us investigate the family of algebraic systems of the type $(S, \circ)$, where $\circ$ is a binary operator on S, in which the following propositions are true:

POSTULATES: (1) $\forall x[x \circ x = x]$

(2) $\forall x \forall y \forall z[x \circ (y \circ z) = (x \circ y) \circ z]$.

For example, the algebraic systems

$$(\{1\}, \{(1, 1, 1)\}),$$
$$(\{0, 1\}, \{(0, 0, 0), (0, 1, 0), (1, 0, 1), (1, 1, 1)\})$$

and

$$(\{0, 1\}, \{(0, 0, 0), (0, 1, 1), (1, 0, 0), (1, 1, 1)\})$$

are members of this family.

Having illustrated one aspect of the axiomatic method, we now demonstrate the manner in which a theorem is established.

THEOREM: $\forall x \forall y[x \circ (x \circ y) = x \circ y]$.

Proof: We must show that the given proposition "$\forall x \forall y[x \circ (x \circ y) = x \circ y]$" is true in each algebraic system of our family. Let $(S, \circ)$ be any algebraic system of our family; we wish to show that "$\forall x \forall y[x \circ (x \circ y) = x \circ y]$" is true in $(S, \circ)$. Stripping away quantifiers, we see that the given proposition is true in $(S, \circ)$ iff $a \circ (a \circ b) = a \circ b$ whenever $a \in S$ and $b \in S$. But

$$a \circ (a \circ b) = (a \circ a) \circ b \qquad \text{by (2)}$$

$$= a \circ b \qquad \text{by (1)}$$

This establishes that "$\forall x \forall y[x \circ (x \circ y) = x \circ y]$" is true in each algebraic system of our family.

It should be clear now that though we don't know the precise objects we are talking about, we do know the type of algebraic system being discussed; and though we don't know if the theorems are true, we do know that there are true in any algebraic system of the specified type in which the postulates are true.

It is worth noting that the postulates characterizing a particular family of algebraic systems need not be propositions of the kind considered in Chapter I (which are called propositions of the *lower predicate calculus*). For example, consider the famous Peano Postulates involved in characterizing the natural number system. An algebraic system of the type $(N, ', 1)$, where $'$ is a unary operator on N, and $1 \in N$ is said to be a *Peano System* iff

(1) $\forall x[x' \neq 1]$
(2) $\forall x \forall y[x' = y' \rightarrow x = y]$
(3) $\forall S[(S \subset N \wedge 1 \in S \wedge \forall x[x \in S \rightarrow x' \in S]) \rightarrow S = N]$

Here, (1) and (2) are propositions of the lower predicate calculus, whereas (3) is not. The point is that the quantifiers of (1) and (2) refer to the basic set of the algebraic system, whereas the universal quantifier of (3), "$\forall S$", refers to subsets of the basic set. In words, (3) asserts that no proper subset of N, say S, has the property that $1 \in S \wedge \forall x[x \in S \rightarrow x' \in S]$.

In the subsequent pages of this chapter we shall consider the axiomatic method against the background of modern algebra, since this important branch of mathematics serves well to illustrate the axiomatic approach.

Here, briefly, we consider the axiomatic method as applied to geometry. The concept of a *projective plane*, for example, can be characterized as follows. By a projective plane, we mean any ordered triple, say $(\Sigma, \Lambda, \mathbf{I})$, where Σ is a non-empty set whose members are called *points* and are denoted by capital letters, Λ is a non-empty set whose members are called *lines* and are denoted by small letters, and $\mathbf{I}$ is a binary relation on $\Sigma \cup \Lambda$ called the *incidence* relation, such that

(1) $\forall P \forall l[PIl \leftrightarrow lIP]$
(2) $\forall P \forall Q \exists\,!\, l[P \neq Q \rightarrow PIl \wedge QIl]$
(3) $\forall p \forall q \exists\,!\, L[p \neq q \rightarrow pIL \wedge qIL]$
(4) there are four points such that each line is incident with at most two of the four points

Note that quantification is either over Σ (indicated by a capital letter), or is over Λ (indicated by a small letter).

Though the ordered triple $(\Sigma, \Lambda, \mathbf{I})$ is not an algebraic system, it is possible to represent $(\Sigma, \Lambda, \mathbf{I})$ by an algebraic system—namely, $(\Sigma \cup \Lambda, \mathbf{P}, \mathbf{L}, \mathbf{I})$, where $\Sigma \cup \Lambda$ is the basic set of the algebraic system, $\mathbf{P}$ and $\mathbf{L}$ are unary relations on the basic set (in fact, $\mathbf{P} = \Sigma$ and $\mathbf{L} = \Lambda$), and $\mathbf{I}$ is a binary relation on the basic set. It is easy to translate the postulates above into this language; for example, (1) becomes

$$\forall x \forall y[P(x) \wedge L(y) \rightarrow (xIy \leftrightarrow yIx)]$$

where quantification is over the basic set of the algebraic system.

Thus, our analysis of the axiomatic method in terms of algebraic systems applies also to the study of geometry.

EXERCISES

1. Consider the collection of all algebraic systems of the type $(S, ')$, where $'$ is a unary operator on S, satisfying the postulates

$$\forall x[x' \neq x], \quad \forall x[(x')' = x]$$

   (a) Show that S cannot have an odd number of members.
   (b) Construct an algebraic system in the collection.

2. Consider the collection of all algebraic systems of the type $(S, \circ)$, where $\circ$ is a binary operator on S, satisfying the postulate

$$\forall x \forall y[x \circ y = x]$$

(a) Prove that the following propositions are true in each algebraic system of the collection:

$$\forall x[x \circ x = x], \quad \forall x \forall y \forall z[x \circ (y \circ z) = (x \circ y) \circ z], \quad \forall x \forall y \exists z[x \circ y = z].$$

(b) Construct an algebraic system in the collection.

3. Consider the collection of all algebraic systems of the type $(S, \mathbf{R})$, where $\mathbf{R}$ is a binary relation on S, satisfying the postulates

$$\forall x \forall y[xRy \to x \neq y], \quad \forall x \forall y \forall z[xRy \wedge yRz \to xRz].$$

(a) Prove that the following propositions are true in each algebraic system of the collection:

$$\forall x[\sim xRx], \quad \forall x \forall y[\sim xRy \vee \sim yRx].$$

(b) Construct an algebraic system in the collection.

4. Consider the collection of all algebraic systems of the type $(S, \circ, \mathbf{R})$, where $\circ$ is a binary operator on S, and $\mathbf{R}$ is a binary relation on S, satisfying the postulates

$$\forall x \forall y[x \circ y = y \circ x], \quad \forall x[x \circ x = x], \quad \forall x \forall y[xRx \circ y].$$

(a) Prove that the following propositions are true in each algebraic system of the collection:

$$\forall x \forall y[yRx \circ y], \quad \forall x[xRx].$$

(b) Construct an algebraic system in the collection.

5. By an *affine plane*, we mean an ordered triple $(\Sigma, \Lambda, \mathbf{I})$ where Σ is a non-empty set whose members are called *points* and are denoted by capital letters, Λ is a non-empty set whose members are called *lines* and are denoted by small letters, and $\mathbf{I}$ is a binary relation on $\Sigma \cup \Lambda$ called the *incidence relation*, such that:

(1) Any two points are incident with exactly one line.
(2) Given a line and a point which are not incident, there is exactly one line incident with the given point, and parallel to the given line. Note: p and q are said to be *parallel* iff no point is incident with both p and q.
(3) There are four points such that each line is incident with at most two of the four points.

Show that the concept of an affine plane can be expressed in terms of algebraic structures, and that the postulates are propositions of the lower predicate calculus.

3. Semi-groups

The purpose of this section is to illustrate the feature of the axiomatic method as a method of characterizing a collection of algebraic systems, and at the same time to provide a more intimate acquaintance with algebraic systems themselves.

By a *semi-group* we mean any algebraic system of the type $(S, \circ)$ where $\circ$ is a binary operator on S such that $\circ$ is associative. Thus, the one postulate of a semi-group is

$$\forall x \forall y \forall z[x \circ (y \circ z) = (x \circ y) \circ z].$$

The simplest example of a semi-group is the algebraic system $(\{a\}, \{(a, a, a)\})$. This example is considered to be simple because the basic set of the algebraic system has exactly one member.

There are many examples of semi-groups, of course. The algebraic system whose first term is the set of all natural numbers and whose second term is the usual operation of addition on the natural numbers is a semi-group; by taking multiplication in place of addition, we obtain another semi-group. Similarly, $(I, +)$ and $(I, \cdot)$ are semi-groups, where "I" denotes the set of all integers.

It is desirable to develop an intuition about algebraic systems and, in particular, to regard algebraic systems as mathematical objects. In order to build up a feeling of this kind, let us now characterize all semi-groups in which the basic set has exactly two members. To this end we first consider all distinct algebraic systems $(\{a, b\}, \circ)$ where $\circ$ is a binary operator on $\{a, b\}$. It is helpful to develop an efficient method of denoting a binary operator on $\{a, b\}$; let us agree to represent the binary operator

$$\{(a, a, c), (a, b, d), (b, a, e), (b, b, f)\}$$

by the array

$$\text{“}\begin{pmatrix} c & d \\ e & f \end{pmatrix}\text{”}.$$

For example,

$$\{(a, a, b), (a, b, a), (b, a, a), (b, b, b)\}$$

will be denoted by

$$\text{“}\begin{pmatrix} b & a \\ a & b \end{pmatrix}\text{”}.$$

This agreement will enable us to avoid considerable writing.

It turns out that there are only ten distinct algebraic systems of the form $(\{a, b\}, \circ)$ where $\circ$ is a binary operator on $\{a, b\}$. The binary operators of these ten algebraic systems are as follows:

1. $\begin{pmatrix} a & a \\ a & a \end{pmatrix}$ 2. $\begin{pmatrix} a & a \\ a & b \end{pmatrix}$ 3. $\begin{pmatrix} a & a \\ b & a \end{pmatrix}$ 4. $\begin{pmatrix} a & b \\ a & a \end{pmatrix}$ 5. $\begin{pmatrix} b & a \\ a & a \end{pmatrix}$

6. $\begin{pmatrix} b & a \\ a & b \end{pmatrix}$ 7. $\begin{pmatrix} a & a \\ b & b \end{pmatrix}$ 8. $\begin{pmatrix} a & b \\ a & b \end{pmatrix}$ 9. $\begin{pmatrix} b & a \\ b & a \end{pmatrix}$ 10. $\begin{pmatrix} b & b \\ a & a \end{pmatrix}$

Having named ten binary operators on $\{a, b\}$, we have in effect named ten algebraic systems. For example, using the second binary operator listed above, we obtain the algebraic system $(\{a, b\}, \{(a, a, a), (a, b, a), (b, a, a), (b, b, b)\})$. Let us show that this algebraic system is a semi-group. Denoting the binary operator of this algebraic system by "$\circ$", we see by inspection that "$\forall x[a \circ x = a]$" is true here; also, "$\forall x[b \circ x = x]$" is true in the given algebraic system. Now consider the associative law: "$\forall x \forall y \forall z[x \circ (y \circ z) = (x \circ y) \circ z]$". Stripping away the first quantifier, we obtain the propositions "$\forall y \forall z[a \circ (y \circ z) = (a \circ y) \circ z]$" and "$\forall y \forall z[b \circ (y \circ z) = (b \circ y) \circ z]$". Referring to the first of these, we see that $a \circ (y \circ z) = a$ and $(a \circ y) \circ z = a \circ z = a$, no matter what we put in place of "y" and "z". Considering the second of these propositions, we see that $b \circ (y \circ z) = y \circ z$ and $(b \circ y) \circ z = y \circ z$, no matter what we put in place of "y" and "z". It follows that the associative law is true in this algebraic system.

Five of the algebraic systems listed above are, in fact, semi-groups; the remaining five algebraic systems are not semi-groups. The results are listed as follows:

1. Semi-group	2. Semi-group	3. No	4. No	5. No
6. Semi-group	7. Semi-group	8. Semi-group	9. No	10. No.

For example, let us demonstrate that the third algebraic system listed here—namely, $(\{a, b\}, \{(a, a, a), (a, b, a), (b, a, b), (b, b, a)\})$, is not a semi-group: by denoting the binary operator of this algebraic system by "?", we note that $b\ ?\ (b\ ?\ b) = b\ ?\ a = b$, whereas $(b\ ?\ b)\ ?\ b = a\ ?\ b = a$. It follows that the associative law is not true in this algebraic system; hence, this is not a semi-group.

We turn now to the observation that there are really only ten essentially different algebraic systems consisting of a basic set with exactly two members and a binary operator. At first sight it appears there are sixteen distinct algebraic systems possessing the stated form. For example, the algebraic system with binary operator

$$\begin{pmatrix} a & b \\ b & a \end{pmatrix}$$

appears to have been left out. But this algebraic system is essentially the same as $(\{c, d\}, \{(c, c, c), (c, d, d), (d, c, d), (d, d, c)\})$. To see this consider the sixth algebraic system in the above list—namely, $(\{a, b), \{(a, a, b), (a, b, a), (b, a, a), (b, b, b)\})$, and consider the one-one mapping of $\{a, b\}$ onto $\{c, d\}$ which associates d with a and c with b. Under this mapping, the sixth algebraic system of our list becomes $(\{d, c\}, \{(d, d, c), (d, c, d), (c, d, d), (c, c, c)\})$, the algebraic system that apparently had been omitted from the list. Following a similar procedure, it is easy to show that each of the remaining five algebraic systems which appear to have been omitted, in fact are represented on the above list.

In this section we have discussed the important notion of two algebraic systems that are essentially the same; i.e., have the property that one of the algebraic systems can be constructed from the other by applying a suitably chosen one-one mapping to the given algebraic system. The technical term used in this connection is the word "isomorphic". Let us formalize this important concept.

DEFINITION: $\mathcal{S}$ is isomorphic to $\mathcal{T}$ (in symbols, $\mathcal{S} \simeq \mathcal{T}$) iff there exists a one-one mapping of the basic set of $\mathcal{S}$ onto the basic set of $\mathcal{T}$, say μ, such that $\mu\mathcal{S} = \mathcal{T}$.

Note: Let S be the basic set of $\mathcal{S}$; then "$\mu\mathcal{S}$" denotes the algebraic system obtained from $\mathcal{S}$ by replacing each instance in $\mathcal{S}$ of a member of S, say x, by μx.

For example, let $\mu 0 = a$ and $\mu 1 = b$; then

$$\mu(\{0, 1\}, \{(0, 0, 0), (0, 1, 1), (1, 0, 1), (1, 1, 0)\}, 0) = (\{a, b\}, \{(a, a, a), (a, b, b), (b, a, b), (b, b, a)\}, a)$$

Hence,
$$(\{0, 1\}, \{(0, 0, 0), (0, 1, 1), (1, 0, 1), (1, 1, 0)\}, 0) \simeq (\{a, b\}, \{(a, a, a), (a, b, b), (b, a, b), (b, b, a)\}, a)$$

Clearly, "$\simeq$" is a binary relation on algebraic systems. It is easy to prove that "$\simeq$" is an equivalence relation on the set of all algebraic systems. For this reason, we regard isomorphic algebraic systems as equal from the algebraic point-of-view.

EXERCISES

1. Construct a semi-group whose basic set has exactly three members.
2. (a) Prove that the algebraic systems numbered 1, 6, 7, and 8 in the text are semi-groups.

(b) Prove that the algebraic systems numbered 4, 5, 9, and 10 are not semi-groups.

3. (a) List the operators of the six algebraic systems that apparently are not included in the list of the text.

   (b) Demonstrate that each of these algebraic systems, in fact, is represented on the list.

4. Show that $(I, \circ)$ is not a semi-group, where I denotes the set of all integers and $\circ = \{(a, b, c) \mid a \in I \wedge b \in I \wedge c = a - b\}$.

5. Show that $(I, ?)$ is not a semi-group, where I denotes the set of all integers, and $? = \{(a, b, c) \mid a \in I \wedge b \in I \wedge c = a \cdot (a + b)\}$.

6. Consider the algebraic system

$$(\{a, b\}, \{(a, a, b), (a, b, a), (b, a, a), (b, b, a)\}):$$

   (a) Prove that $\forall x[aox \neq x]$ where o denotes the binary operator of the given algebraic system.

   (b) Prove that $\forall x[box = a]$.

7. Consider the algebraic system $(\{a, b\}, ?)$ where

$$? = \{(a, a, b), (a, b, a), (b, a, a), (b, b, b)\}:$$

   (a) Prove that $\forall x[a \ ?\ x \neq x]$
   (b) Prove that $\forall x[b \ ?\ x = x]$
   (c) Prove that $\exists y \forall x[y \ ?\ x \neq x]$
   (d) Prove that $\exists y \forall x[y \ ?\ x = x]$
   (e) Prove that $\exists x \forall y[y \ ?\ y = x]$
   (f) Prove that $\exists x \forall y[y \ ?\ y \neq x]$
   (g) Prove that $\forall x \exists y[x \ ?\ y = y]$
   (h) Prove that $\forall x \forall y[x \ ?\ y = y \ ?\ x]$.

8. Given that the algebraic system (S, o) is a semi-group, show that it is not necessarily the case that o is a mapping of $S \times S$ onto S.

4. Groups

In this section we shall apply the axiomatic method to the study of a significant mathematical concept: the notion of a group.

Consider the algebraic system

$$(\{0, 1\}, \{(0, 0, 0), (0, 1, 1), (1, 0, 1), (1, 1, 0)\}, 0)$$

consisting of a basic set, a binary operator on the basic set, and a special member of the basic set. This is a very simple algebraic system, yet it possesses interesting properties. For example, let us show that the proposition

"$\forall x \forall y[x\ ?\ y = y\ ?\ x]$" is true in this algebraic system, where "?" denotes the binary operator of the algebraic system. Stripping away the first quantifier, we must show that the propositions "$\forall y[0\ ?\ y = y\ ?\ 0]$" and "$\forall y[1\ ?\ y = y\ ?\ 1]$" are true. Consider "$\forall y[0\ ?\ y = y\ ?\ 0]$". Eliminating the quantifier, we must show that the propositions "$0\ ?\ 0 = 0\ ?\ 0$" and "$0\ ?\ 1 = 1\ ?\ 0$" are both true. Obviously, the first proposition is true; referring to the binary operator ?, we see that $0\ ?\ 1 = 1$ and $1\ ?\ 0 = 1$. Therefore, "$\forall y[0\ ?\ y = y\ ?\ 0]$" is true in this algebraic system. Now consider "$\forall y[1\ ?\ y = y\ ?\ 1]$". Eliminating the quantifier, we obtain the propositions "$1\ ?\ 0 = 0\ ?\ 1$" and "$1\ ?\ 1 = 1\ ?\ 1$". We have already shown that the first of these is true, and the second is obviously true. This establishes the truth of "$\forall y[1\ ?\ y = y\ ?\ 1]$". Therefore, "$\forall x \forall y[x\ ?\ y = y\ ?\ x]$" is true in this algebraic system.

Now, we shall show that the proposition "$\forall x[x\ ?\ 0 = x]$" is true in $(\{0, 1\}, ?, 0)$. Eliminating the quantifier, we must prove that the propositions "$0\ ?\ 0 = 0$" and "$1\ ?\ 0 = 1$" are true in this algebraic system. Referring to ?, we see that this is so. In the same way, it is easy to prove that the proposition "$\forall x[0\ ?\ x = x]$" is true in this algebraic system.

We shall now show that ? is associative. This means that we shall prove that the proposition "$\forall x \forall y \forall z[x\ ?\ (y\ ?\ z) = (x\ ?\ y)\ ?\ z]$" is true in the given algebraic system. Stripping away the first quantifier, we obtain the propositions "$\forall y \forall z[0\ ?\ (y\ ?\ z) = (0\ ?\ y)\ ?\ z]$" and "$\forall y \forall z[1\ ?\ (y\ ?\ z) = (1\ ?\ y)\ ?\ z]$". The first of these can be simplified by applying the preceding result and reduces to "$\forall y \forall z[y\ ?\ z = y\ ?\ z]$", which is obviously true. It remains to establish the truth of "$\forall y \forall z[1\ ?\ (y\ ?\ z) = (1\ ?\ y)\ ?\ z]$". Stripping away the first quantifier, we obtain "$\forall z[1\ ?\ (0\ ?\ z) = (1\ ?\ 0)\ ?\ z]$" and "$\forall z[1\ ?\ (1\ ?\ z) = (1\ ?\ 1)\ ?\ z]$". The first of these reduces to "$\forall z[1\ ?\ z = 1\ ?\ z]$", which is true; the other reduces to "$\forall z[1\ ?\ (1\ ?\ z) = z]$", since $1\ ?\ 1 = 0$ and $\forall x[0\ ?\ x = x]$. Eliminating the quantifier, we obtain the propositions "$1\ ?\ (1\ ?\ 0) = 0$" and "$1\ ?\ (1\ ?\ 1) = 1$". Referring to ?, it is easy to see that both of these propositions are true in the given algebraic system. This demonstrates that ? is associative in the given algebraic system. In particular, this means that $(\{0, 1\}, ?)$ is a semi-group.

Finally, let us prove that the proposition "$\forall x \exists y[x\ ?\ y = 0]$" is true in $(\{0, 1\}, ?, 0)$. Stripping away the first quantifier, we obtain the propositions "$\exists y[0\ ?\ y = 0]$" and "$\exists y[1\ ?\ y = 0]$". But $0\ ?\ 0 = 0$ and $1\ ?\ 1 = 0$; therefore, both propositions are true, and hence ,"$\forall x \exists y[x\ ?\ y = 0]$" is true in the given algebraic system.

The algebraic system $(\{0, 1\}, ?, 0)$, which we have been studying, is of little significance in itself; however, it is a member of a certain important collection of algebraic systems. Consider the family of all algebraic systems of the same type as our example; i.e., consisting of a basic set, a binary operator on the basic set, and a special member of the basic set, say $(S, \circ, \emptyset)$, such that the following propositions are true in $(S, \circ, \emptyset)$:

(1) $\forall x \forall y \forall z[x \circ (y \circ z) = (x \circ y) \circ z]$
(2) $\forall x[x \circ \emptyset = x]$
(3) $\forall x \exists y[x \circ y = \emptyset]$

To recognize the importance of this collection of algebraic systems, we shall call an algebraic system a *group* iff it is a member of the collection. Thus, the algebraic system $(\{0, 1\}, \{(0, 0, 0), (0, 1, 1), (1, 0, 1), (1, 1, 0)\}, 0)$ is a group.

The Propositions (1), (2), and (3), listed above, are called the *group postulates*. Let us apply the axiomatic method to establish the truth in any group of certain other propositions. Our purpose here is to illustrate the usual technique of establishing theorems; the following proofs may appear unnecessarily long-winded, but it is for a good cause!

THEOREM 1: $\emptyset \circ \emptyset = \emptyset$.

Proof: We must show that $\emptyset \circ \emptyset = \emptyset$ whenever $(S, \circ, \emptyset)$ is a group. But then "$\forall x[x \circ \emptyset = x]$" is true in $(S, \circ, \emptyset)$; hence, by substituting $\emptyset$ for "x", we see that "$\emptyset \circ \emptyset = \emptyset$" is true about the particular group $(S, \circ, \emptyset)$. This establishes Theorem 1.

It is important to be aware of the "method" of the preceding proof; that is, we begin by considering a particular group (without specifying which group we are considering) and then establish that the given proposition is true about that group.

THEOREM 2: $\forall x \forall y[x \circ y = \emptyset \rightarrow y \circ x = \emptyset]$.

Proof: Again, we must show that the given proposition is true in $(S, \circ, \emptyset)$, given that this algebraic system is a group. Eliminating quantifiers, we must prove that the proposition "$a \circ b = \emptyset \rightarrow b \circ a = \emptyset$" is true in $(S, \circ, \emptyset)$ whenever $a \in S$ and $b \in S$. Suppose that $a \circ b = \emptyset$; we must show that $b \circ a = \emptyset$. But, by (3), there is a member of S, say c, such that $b \circ c = \emptyset$. Therefore,

$$\begin{aligned}
b \circ a &= (b \circ a) \circ \emptyset && \text{by (2)} \\
&= (b \circ a) \circ (b \circ c) && \text{since } b \circ c = \emptyset \\
&= [(b \circ a) \circ b] \circ c && \text{by (1)} \\
&= [b \circ (a \circ b)] \circ c && \text{by (1)} \\
&= (b \circ \emptyset) \circ c && \text{since } a \circ b = \emptyset \\
&= b \circ c && \text{by (2)} \\
&= \emptyset.
\end{aligned}$$

This establishes Theorem 2.

COROLLARY: $\forall x \exists y[y \circ x = \emptyset]$

Proof: Consider Theorem 2 and (3).

THEOREM 3: $\forall x \forall y \forall z[x \circ z = y \circ z \rightarrow x = y]$.

Proof: Eliminating quantifiers, we see that we must prove that

$$a \circ c = b \circ c \rightarrow a = b$$

whenever $a \in S$, $b \in S$, and $c \in S$. Suppose that $a \circ c = b \circ c$; we must prove that $a = b$. But, by (3), there is a member of S, say d, such that $c \circ d = \emptyset$. Also, $(a \circ c) \circ d = (b \circ c) \circ d$ since $a \circ c = b \circ c$. But, by (1), $(a \circ c) \circ d = a \circ (c \circ d) = a \circ \emptyset = a$, by (2); and, by (1), $(b \circ c) \circ d = b \circ (c \circ d) = b \circ \emptyset = b$, by (2). We conclude that $a = b$. This establishes Theorem 3.

THEOREM 4: $\forall x[\emptyset \circ x = x]$

Proof: We must show that $\emptyset \circ a = a$ whenever $a \in S$. By (3), d exists such that $a \circ d = \emptyset$. Hence,

$$\begin{aligned} \emptyset \circ a = (a \circ d) \circ a &= a \circ (d \circ a) && \text{by (1)} \\ &= a \circ \emptyset && \text{by Theorem 2} \\ &= a && \text{by (2)} \end{aligned}$$

This establishes Theorem 4.

THEOREM 5: $\forall x \forall y \forall z[z \circ x = z \circ y \rightarrow x = y]$.

Proof: The proof is similar to the proof of Theorem 3. Use the Corollary to Theorem 2 in place of (3) and Theorem 4 in place of (2).

EXERCISES

1. Show that $(I, +, 0)$ is a group, where "I" denotes the set of all integers.
2. Show that $(\{0, 1, 2\}, *, 0)$ is a group, where

$$* = \{(0, 0, 0), (0, 1, 1), (0, 2, 2), (1, 0, 1), (1, 1, 2), (1, 2, 0), (2, 0, 2), (2, 1, 0), (2, 2, 1)\}.$$

3. Prove that the proposition "$\forall x \forall y \forall z[x \circ y = \emptyset \wedge x \circ z = \emptyset \rightarrow y = z]$" is true in any group $(S, \circ, \emptyset)$.

4. Prove that the propositions

$$\text{“}\forall x \forall y \forall z \forall w[x \circ z = \emptyset \wedge y \circ w = \emptyset \rightarrow (x \circ z) \circ (y \circ w) = \emptyset]\text{”}$$

and

$$\text{“}\forall x \forall y \forall z \forall w[x \circ z = \emptyset \wedge y \circ w = \emptyset \rightarrow (x \circ y) \circ (w \circ z) = \emptyset]\text{”}$$

are true in any group $(S, \circ, \emptyset)$.

5. Prove that the proposition “$\forall x[\exists y(x \circ y = y) \rightarrow x = \emptyset]$” is true in any group $(S, \circ, \emptyset)$.

5. Fields

In this section we shall see how the mathematical concept of a group is used as a building-block in constructing a more complex mathematical entity.

First, consider a group, say $(S, \circ, \emptyset)$, which has the property $\forall x \forall y[x \circ y = y \circ x]$. Any such group is said to be an *abelian* group or a *commutative* group. Thus, by an abelian group we mean any algebraic system of the type $(S, \circ, \emptyset)$, where $\circ$ is a binary operator on S and $\emptyset \in S$, in which the propositions

(1) $\forall x \forall y \forall z[x \circ (y \circ z) = (x \circ y) \circ z]$
(2) $\forall x[x \circ \emptyset = x]$
(3) $\forall x \exists y[x \circ y = \emptyset]$
(4) $\forall x \forall y[x \circ y = y \circ x]$

are true.

For example, $(\{0, 1\}, \{(0, 0, 0), (0, 1, 1), (1, 0, 1), (1, 1, 0)\}, 0)$ is an abelian group. Indeed, $(I, +, 0)$ is an abelian group.

Now consider an algebraic system of a much more complicated type—namely, $(S, \circ, ?, \emptyset, 1)$, where $\circ$ and $?$ are binary operators on S, $\emptyset \in S$, $1 \in S$, in which the propositions

$$\text{“}\forall x \forall y \forall z[x \mathbin{?} (y \circ z) = (x \mathbin{?} y) \circ (x \mathbin{?} z)]\text{”}$$

$$\text{“}\forall x \forall y \forall z[(y \circ z) \mathbin{?} x = (y \mathbin{?} x) \circ (z \mathbin{?} x)]\text{”}$$

and “$\emptyset \neq 1$” are true; moreover, we insist that both $(S, \circ, \emptyset)$ and $(S - \{\emptyset\}, ?', 1)$ be abelian groups where $?'$ is obtained from $?$ by deleting each member of $?$ in which $\emptyset$ is a term. Any such algebraic system is said to be a *field*. This means that the following twelve propositions are true in any field, say $(S, \circ, ?, \emptyset, 1)$:

(1) $\forall x \forall y \forall z[x \circ (y \circ z) = (x \circ y) \circ z]$
(2) $\forall x[x \circ \emptyset = x]$
(3) $\forall x \exists y[x \circ y = \emptyset]$

(4) $\forall x \forall y[x \circ y = y \circ x]$
(5) $\forall x \forall y \forall z[x \neq \emptyset \wedge y \neq \emptyset \wedge z \neq \emptyset \rightarrow x \mathbin{?} (y \mathbin{?} z) = (x \mathbin{?} y) \mathbin{?} z]$
(6) $\forall x[x \neq \emptyset \rightarrow x \mathbin{?} 1 = x]$
(7) $\forall x \exists y[x \neq \emptyset \rightarrow x \mathbin{?} y = 1 \wedge y \neq \emptyset]$
(8) $\forall x \forall y[x \neq \emptyset \wedge y \neq \emptyset \rightarrow x \mathbin{?} y = y \mathbin{?} x]$
(9) $\forall x \forall y[x \neq \emptyset \wedge y \neq \emptyset \rightarrow x \mathbin{?} y \neq \emptyset]$
(10) $\forall x \forall y \forall z[x \mathbin{?} (y \circ z) = (x \mathbin{?} y) \circ (x \mathbin{?} z)]$
(11) $\forall x \forall y \forall z[(y \circ z) \mathbin{?} x = (y \mathbin{?} x) \circ (z \mathbin{?} x)]$
(12) $\emptyset \neq 1$

The restrictions on the quantifiers in (5), (6), and (8) serve no useful purpose, and can be eliminated by establishing

THEOREM 6: $\forall x[x \mathbin{?} \emptyset = \emptyset]$

and

THEOREM 7: $\forall x[\emptyset \mathbin{?} x = \emptyset]$

Proof of Theorem 6: By (10), $(x \mathbin{?} \emptyset) \circ (x \mathbin{?} \emptyset) = x \mathbin{?} (\emptyset \circ \emptyset) = x \mathbin{?} \emptyset$ by Theorem 1 of Section 4. By (3) there is a member of S, say a, such that $(x \mathbin{?} \emptyset) \circ a = \emptyset$; therefore

$$\emptyset = [(x \mathbin{?} \emptyset) \circ (x \mathbin{?} \emptyset)] \circ a = (x \mathbin{?} \emptyset) \circ [(x \mathbin{?} \emptyset) \circ a] = (x \mathbin{?} \emptyset) \circ \emptyset = x \mathbin{?} \emptyset.$$

This establishes Theorem 6. Theorem 7 can be established in a parallel manner.

THEOREM 8: $\forall x \forall y \forall z[x \mathbin{?} (y \mathbin{?} z) = (x \mathbin{?} y) \mathbin{?} z]$.

Proof: Suppose that $a \in S$, $b \in S$, $c \in S$, if $a \neq \emptyset$ and $b \neq \emptyset$ and $c \neq \emptyset$, then by (5), $a \mathbin{?} (b \mathbin{?} c) = (a \mathbin{?} b) \mathbin{?} c$. If any one of a, b, c is $\emptyset$, then by Theorems 6 and 7, $a \mathbin{?} (b \mathbin{?} c) = \emptyset$ and $(a \mathbin{?} b) \mathbin{?} c = \emptyset$. This establishes the theorem.

THEOREM 9: $\forall x[x \mathbin{?} 1 = x]$.

Proof: Suppose that $a \in S$; if $a \neq \emptyset$, then $a \mathbin{?} 1 = a$ by (6). If $a = \emptyset$, then by Theorem 7, $a \mathbin{?} 1 = a$. This establishes the theorem.

THEOREM 10: $\forall x \forall y[x \mathbin{?} y = y \mathbin{?} x]$.

Proof: Suppose that $a \in S$ and $b \in S$; if $a \neq \emptyset$ and $b \neq \emptyset$, then by (8), $a \mathbin{?} b = b \mathbin{?} a$. If one of a or b is $\emptyset$, then by Theorems 6 and 7, $a \mathbin{?} b = \emptyset$ and $b \mathbin{?} a = \emptyset$; hence $a \mathbin{?} b = b \mathbin{?} a$. This establishes the theorem.

THEOREM: $\forall x \forall y[x \neq \emptyset \wedge y \neq \emptyset \rightarrow x \mathbin{?} y \neq \emptyset]$ is true in any algebraic system $(S, \circ, ?, \emptyset, 1)$ satisfying the propositions (1) to (12) inclusive, with (9) deleted.

Proof: Suppose there are members of S, say a and b, such that $a \mathbin{?} b = \emptyset$ yet $a \neq \emptyset$ and $b \neq \emptyset$. By (7) there is a member of S, say c, such that $b \mathbin{?} c = 1$.

Therefore,

$$(a\ ?\ b)\ ?\ c = \emptyset\ ?\ c \qquad \text{since } a\ ?\ b = \emptyset,$$

hence

$$a\ ?\ (b\ ?\ c) = \emptyset \qquad \text{by Theorems 7 and 8,}$$

that is

$$a\ ?\ 1 = \emptyset$$

and so

$$a = \emptyset \qquad \text{by (6), since } a \neq \emptyset.$$

We have arrived at a contradiction, which means that the assumption of the proof is false. This demonstrates our theorem.

Clearly, (5) is an immediate consequence of Theorem 8, (6) is an immediate consequence of Theorem 9, and (8) is an immediate consequence of Theorem 10. Furthermore, (11) is an immediate consequence of (10) and Theorem 10. Therefore, the collection of algebraic systems characterized by Postulates (1) to (12) is precisely the collection of algebraic systems characterized by the simpler set of postulates obtained by replacing (5), (6), and (8) by Theorems 8, 9, and 10, respectively, by deleting (9) and (11), and replacing (7) by the proposition $\forall x \exists y[x \neq \emptyset \rightarrow x\ ?\ y = 1]$. The last change is justified by Theorem 6. Furthermore, it is convenient to denote the binary operators of a field by "$+$" and "$\cdot$", and to denote the additive identity by "0". We have established

THEOREM 11: The algebraic system $(S, +, \cdot, 0, 1)$ is a field, where $+$ and $\cdot$ are binary operators on S, $0 \in S$ and $1 \in S$, iff

(a) $\forall x \forall y \forall z[x + (y + z) = (x + y) + z]$
(b) $\forall x[x + 0 = x]$
(c) $\forall x \exists y[x + y = 0]$
(d) $\forall x \forall y[x + y = y + x]$
(e) $\forall x \forall y \forall z[x \cdot (y \cdot z) = (x \cdot y) \cdot z]$
(f) $\forall x[x \cdot 1 = x]$
(g) $\forall x \exists y[x \neq 0 \rightarrow x \cdot y = 1]$
(h) $\forall x \forall y[x \cdot y = y \cdot x]$
(i) $\forall x \forall y \forall z[x \cdot (y + z) = x \cdot y + x \cdot z]$
(j) $0 \neq 1$

are each true in the algebraic system.

To illustrate the ease with which the eye reacts to the symbols "$+$", "$\cdot$", and "0", we shall demonstrate one more theorem about fields.

THEOREM 12: $\forall x \forall y \forall w[y + w = 0 \rightarrow (x + w) + y = x]$ in any field.

Proof: By (a),

$$\begin{aligned} (x + w) + y = x + (w + y) &= x + (y + w) && \text{by (d)} \\ &= x + 0 && \text{by assumption} \\ &= x && \text{by (b).} \end{aligned}$$

This establishes the theorem.

We used the concept of a group to build up the concept of a field; in the same way, we shall use the concept of a field to build up an even more complex mathematical entity, an ordered field. Suppose that the algebraic system $(S, +, \cdot, 0, 1)$ is a field and that "$<$" is a binary relation on S. Then we shall say that the algebraic system $(S, +, \cdot, <, 0, 1)$ is an *ordered field* provided that the propositions

(k) $\forall x \forall y \forall z[x < y \wedge y < z \rightarrow x < z]$
(l) $\forall x[x = 0 \veebar x < 0 \veebar 0 < x]$
(m) $\forall x \forall y \forall z[x < y \rightarrow x + z < y + z]$
(n) $\forall x \forall y \forall z[x < y \wedge 0 < z \rightarrow x \cdot z < y \cdot z]$

are each true in the algebraic system.

It is quite easy to construct a simple example of a field; for example,

$$(\{0, 1\}, \{(0, 0, 0), (0, 1, 1), (1, 0, 1), (1, 1, 0)\},$$
$$\{(0, 0, 0), (0, 1, 0), (1, 0, 0), (1, 1, 1)\}, 0, 1)$$

is a field. It is not so easy to construct a simple example of an ordered field. In fact, there is no ordered field whose basic set is finite; this is a consequence of Postulates (j), (m), and (l). However, it is easy to see that the algebraic system $(R, +, \cdot, <, 0, 1)$, where "R" denotes the set of all rational numbers and $+, \cdot, <, 0, 1$ are interpreted in the usual way, is an ordered field.

We should like, now, to establish some theorems about ordered fields. We saw in the Exercises of Section 4 that if $(S, +, 0)$ is a group, and if x is any member of S, there is a unique member of S, say y, such that $x + y = 0$. Since y is determined by x, it is convenient to denote y by writing "$-x$"; in short, "$-x$" denotes the unique member of S such that $x + -x = 0$. It is easy to prove that $-(-x) = x$ and $-(x + y) = -y + -x$. We shall make use of this operator in the following theorems.

THEOREM 13: $\forall x[x < 0 \rightarrow 0 < -x]$ in any ordered field.

Proof: Assume that $x < 0$. By (l), $-x = 0$ or else $-x < 0$ or else $0 < -x$. If $-x = 0$, then $x + -x = x + 0$, and hence $x = 0$; this is impossible by (l). If $-x < 0$, then $-x + x < 0 + x$ by (m), and hence $0 < x$; this is impossible by (l). We conclude, again by (l), that $0 < -x$.

THEOREM 14: $\forall x[-x = (-1) \cdot x]$ in any ordered field.

Proof:

$x + (-1) \cdot x$	$= x \cdot 1 + x \cdot (-1)$	by (f) and (h)
	$= x \cdot (1 + -1)$	by (i)
	$= x \cdot 0$	
	$= 0$	by Theorem 6

Since the additive inverse of x is unique and is denoted by "$-x$", it follows that $-x = (-1) \cdot x$. This demonstrates the theorem.

THEOREM 15: $-1 \cdot -1 = 1$ in any ordered field.

Proof: By Theorem 14, $-1 \cdot -1 = -(-1)$, but $-(-1) = 1$.

THEOREM 16: $\forall x \forall y[-x \cdot -y = x \cdot y]$ in any ordered field.

Proof: $-x \cdot -y = -x \cdot (-1 \cdot y) = (-x \cdot -1) \cdot y = (-1 \cdot -x) \cdot y = -(-x) \cdot y = x \cdot y$.

THEOREM 17: $\forall x[x \neq 0 \rightarrow 0 < x \cdot x]$ in any ordered field.

Proof: Assume $x \neq 0$; then, by (l), either $x < 0$ or else $0 < x$. If $x < 0$, then by Theorem 13, $0 < -x$; hence, by (n), $0 \cdot -x < -x \cdot -x$. But by Theorem 7, $0 \cdot -x = 0$, and by Theorem 16, $-x \cdot -x = x \cdot x$; hence, $0 < x \cdot x$. If $0 < x$, then by (n), $0 \cdot x < x \cdot x$; and so by Theorem 7, $0 < x \cdot x$. This demonstrates the theorem.

We are now in a position to demonstrate the simply stated, but scarcely obvious

THEOREM 18: $0 < 1$ in any ordered field.

Proof: By (f), $1 \cdot 1 = 1$; by (j), $0 \neq 1$; therefore, by Theorem 17, $0 < 1 \cdot 1$; that is, $0 < 1$.

Finally, we wish to say what is meant by a *complete* ordered field. Consider any ordered field, say $(S, +, \cdot, <, 0, 1)$. Suppose that K is any nonempty subset of S and that b is a member of S, not necessarily in K, such that

$$\forall x[x \in K \rightarrow x < b \vee x = b]$$

Then we call b an *upper bound of* K. Now suppose that L is an upper bound of K such that $L < b \vee L = b$ whenever b is an upper bound of K; then we call L a *least upper bound of* K. A word of warning about language—it is customary to say "K possesses an upper bound" when we mean "an upper bound of K exists", similarly we say "K possesses a least upper bound" when we mean "a least upper bound of K exists". Do not interpret "K *possesses* an upper bound" as meaning an upper bound of K *belongs* to K.

To illustrate these concepts, consider again the system of rational numbers $(R, +, \cdot, <, 0, 1)$, which is an ordered field. The set of all negative rational numbers—namely, $\{x \mid x \in R \wedge x < 0\}$ possesses many upper bounds—in fact, each rational number not in the set is an upper bound of the set. Furthermore, 0 is a least upper bound of this set.

Now we can say what is meant by a *complete* ordered field. Let $(S, +, \cdot, <, 0, 1)$ be any ordered field; then this algebraic system is said to be a complete ordered field iff each non-empty subset of S that possesses an upper bound also possesses a least upper bound. It is easy to show that the system of rational numbers is *not* a complete ordered field; on the other hand, the system of real numbers is a complete ordered field.

EXERCISES

1. Construct a group which is not an abelian group.
2. Show that $(\{0, 1\}, +, \cdot, 0, 1)$ is a field, where
$$+ = \{(0, 0, 0), (0, 1, 1), (1, 0, 1), (1, 1, 0)\}$$
and
$$\cdot = \{(0, 0, 0), (0, 1, 0), (1, 0, 0), (1, 1, 1)\}$$
3, Prove Theorem 7.
4. Define $+$ and $\cdot$ so that $(\{0, 1, a\}, +, \cdot, 0, 1)$ is a field, where $a \neq 0$ and $a \neq 1$.
5. Prove that the Trichotomy Law $\forall x \forall y[x = y \veebar x < y \veebar y < x]$ is true in any ordered field $(S, +, \cdot, <, 0, 1)$.
6. Show that $(\{0, 1\}, +, \cdot, <, 0, 1)$ is *not* an ordered field, given that
$$+ = \{(0, 0, 0), (0, 1, 1), (1, 0, 1), (1, 1, 0)\},$$
$$\cdot = \{(0, 0, 0), (0, 1, 0), (1, 0, 0), (1, 1, 1)\}$$
and
$$< = \{(0, 1)\}.$$
7. Construct an algebraic system in which each of the postulates of an ordered field is true, with the exception of (m).
8. Present an example, at least on an intuitive level, of an algebraic system in which each of the postulates of an ordered field with the exception of (n) is true.
9. Prove that $\forall x \forall y[x < y \leftrightarrow -y < -x]$ is true in each ordered field.
10. Show that $\forall x \forall y \forall z[x < y \wedge z < 0 \rightarrow y \cdot z < x \cdot z]$ is true in each ordered field.
11. Show that $\forall x \forall y \forall z \forall w[x < y \wedge z < w \rightarrow x + z < y + w]$ is true in each ordered field.
12. Show that $\forall x \forall y \forall z \forall w[0 < x \wedge x < y \wedge 0 < z \wedge z < w \rightarrow x \cdot z < y \cdot w]$ is true in each ordered field.

13. Show that $\forall x \forall y \exists z[x + z = y]$ is true in each field.

14. Show that $\forall x \forall y \exists z[x \neq 0 \rightarrow x \cdot z = y]$ is true in each field.

15. Let $(S, +, \cdot, <, 0, 1)$ be any ordered field, and suppose K is a non-empty subset of S. Show that K does not possess *two* least upper bounds. (*Note:* this result justifies speaking of *the* least upper bound of K).

16. Suppose that $(S, +, \cdot, <, 0, 1)$ is an ordered field, K is a non-empty subset of S and $b \in S$. Then b is called a *lower bound of* K iff $\forall x[x \in K \rightarrow b < x \vee b = x]$; furthermore, G is called a *greatest lower bound of* K iff G is a lower bound of K and $b < G \vee b = G$ whenever b is a lower bound of K. Assuming that $(S, +, \cdot, <, 0, 1)$ is complete, prove that each non-empty subset of S that possesses a lower bound also possesses a greatest lower bound. *Hint:* Consider $\{x \mid -x \in K\}$.

17. Prove that the ordered field $(S, +, \cdot, <, 0, 1)$ is complete iff each non-empty subset of S that possesses a lower bound also possesses a greatest lower bound.

18. Consider the twelve postulates for a field given on page 93; prove that (11) is *not* a consequence of the remaining postulates. *Hint:* Consider the algebraic system

$$(\{0, 1\}, \{(0, 0, 0), (0, 1, 1), (1, 0, 1), (1, 1, 0)\},$$
$$\{(0, 0, 0), (0, 1, 1), (1, 0, 0), (1, 1, 1)\}, 0, 1).$$

6. Boolean Algebra

The algebraic systems investigated in Sections 3, 4, and 5 are important because of their relationship to the various number systems of mathematics. We turn now to the study of a family of algebraic systems called *Boolean algebras*, an investigation that is largely motivated by the algebra of sets. In Section 4 of Chapter 2, we saw that we could simplify the name of a set by applying a strictly algebraic procedure, using seventeen basic laws. Of course, we do not need all seventeen laws, since some of these laws can be established algebraically on the basis of the remaining laws. Furthermore, we do not need all of the operators and relations $\cup$, $\cap$, $'$, $\subset$, since some of them can be defined in terms of the others. The problem that confronts us is that we want to choose certain of the operators and relations $\cup$, $\cap$, $'$, $\subset$ and to list certain of their properties in such a manner that the remaining operators and relations can be defined in terms of the chosen ones, and their properties established.

This problem was investigated by the famous American mathematician E. V. Huntington, whose solution appeared in print in 1904. He showed that by selecting the binary operators $\cup$ and $\cap$ and the special sets $\emptyset$ and I, only seven basic laws are needed. His basic laws are the following:

Law 1: $\forall x \forall y[x \cup y = y \cup x]$

Law 2: $\forall x \forall y[x \cap y = y \cap x]$

Law 3: $\forall x[x \cup \emptyset = x]$

Law 4: $\forall x[x \cap I = x]$

Law 5: $\forall x \forall y \forall z[x \cap (y \cup z) = (x \cap y) \cup (x \cap z)]$

Law 6: $\forall x \forall y \forall z[x \cup (y \cap z) = (x \cup y) \cap (x \cup z)]$

Law 7: $\forall x \exists y[x \cup y = I \wedge x \cap y = \emptyset]$

We want to demonstrate that the unary operator $'$ and the binary relation $\subset$ can be defined in terms of $\cup$, $\cap$, $\emptyset$, and I and that each of our seventeen basic laws can be established algebraically by using Huntington's seven laws. For this purpose, it is convenient to consider any algebraic system of the type $(B, \cup, \cap, \emptyset, I)$, where B is the basic set of the algebraic system, $\cup$ and $\cap$ are each binary operators on B, $\emptyset$, and I are distinct members of B, in which Huntington's seven laws are true. Such an algebraic system is called a *Boolean algebra*. For example, the algebraic system $(\{0, 1\}, \cup, \cap, 0, 1)$ where

$$\cup = \{(0, 0, 0), (0, 1, 1), (1, 0, 1), (1, 1, 1)\}$$

and

$$\cap = \{(0, 0, 0), (0, 1, 0), (1, 0, 0), (1, 1, 1)\}$$

is a Boolean algebra. Demonstrate that Huntington's seven laws are true here! Of course, the algebraic system $(S, \cup, \cap, \emptyset, I)$ in which I is a non-empty set, S is the set of all subsets of I, $\cup$, and $\cap$ are the usual operators on sets, and $\emptyset$ is the empty set—is a Boolean algebra, as is easily checked. It is this Boolean algebra that interests us particularly; we want to show that our seventeen basic laws are true here. We accomplish this by proving that these laws are true in *any* Boolean algebra. Suppose, then, that a given algebraic system, say $(B, \cup, \cap, \emptyset, I)$, is a Boolean algebra. Let us prove

THEOREM 1: $\forall x[x \cup x = x]$.

Proof: Suppose that $a \in B$, then

$a = a \cup \emptyset$	by Law 3
$= a \cup (a \cap b)$	by Law 7, for a certain $b \in B$
$= (a \cup a) \cap (a \cup b)$	by Law 6
$= (a \cup a) \cap I$	by Law 7
$= a \cup a$	by Law 4.

THEOREM 2: $\forall x[x \cap x = x]$.

The proof parallels the proof of Theorem 1 and is left as an exercise.

THEOREM 3: $\forall x[x \cup I = I]$.

Proof: Suppose $a \in B$, then

$$\begin{aligned} I &= a \cup b && \text{by Law 7, for a certain } b \in B \\ &= a \cup (b \cap I) && \text{by Law 4} \\ &= (a \cup b) \cap (a \cup I) && \text{by Law 6} \\ &= I \cap (a \cup I) && \text{since } a \cup b = I \\ &= (I \cap a) \cup (I \cap I) && \text{by Law 5} \\ &= (I \cap a) \cup I && \text{by Theorem 2} \\ &= (a \cap I) \cup I && \text{by Law 2} \\ &= a \cup I && \text{by Law 4.} \end{aligned}$$

THEOREM 4: $\forall x[x \cap \emptyset = \emptyset]$.

The proof parallels the proof of Theorem 3 and is left as an exercise.

THEOREM 5: $\forall x \forall y[x \cup (x \cap y) = x]$.

Proof: Suppose $a \in B$ and $b \in B$, then

$$\begin{aligned} a &= a \cap I && \text{by Law 4} \\ &= a \cap (b \cup I) && \text{by Theorem 3} \\ &= a \cap (I \cup b) && \text{by Law 1} \\ &= (a \cap I) \cup (a \cap b) && \text{by Law 5} \\ &= a \cup (a \cap b) && \text{by Law 4.} \end{aligned}$$

THEOREM 6: $\forall x \forall y[x \cap (x \cup y) = x]$.

The proof parallels the proof of Theorem 5 and is left as an exercise.

THEOREM 7: $\forall x \forall y \forall z \forall w[z \cup w = I \wedge z \cap w = \emptyset \wedge z \cap x = z \cap y \wedge w \cap x = w \cap y \rightarrow x = y]$.

Proof: Suppose that a, b, c, and d are members of B such that

$$c \cup d = I, \quad c \cap d = \emptyset, \quad c \cap a = c \cap b, \quad \text{and} \quad d \cap a = d \cap b;$$

then
$$(c \cap a) \cup (d \cap a) = (c \cap b) \cup (d \cap b),$$

and so $$(c \cup d) \cap a = (c \cup d) \cap b,$$

that is $$I \cap a = I \cap b,$$

hence $$a = b.$$

THEOREM 8: $\forall x \forall y \forall z[x \cup (y \cup z) = (x \cup y) \cup z]$.

Proof: Suppose a, b, and c are any members of B. Consider the two members of B, $a \cup (b \cup c)$, and $(a \cup b) \cup c$; and suppose that e is a member of B such that $a \cup e = I$ and $a \cap e = \emptyset$. Then

$$\begin{aligned} a \cap [a \cup (b \cup c)] &= (a \cap a) \cup [a \cap (b \cup c)] && \text{by Law 5} \\ &= a \cup [a \cap (b \cup c)] && \text{by Theorem 2} \\ &= a && \text{by Theorem 5;} \end{aligned}$$

and
$$\begin{aligned} a \cap [(a \cup b) \cup c] &= [a \cap (a \cup b)] \cup (a \cap c) && \text{by Law 5} \\ &= a \cup (a \cap c) && \text{by Theorem 6} \\ &= a && \text{by Theorem 5.} \end{aligned}$$

Therefore, $$a \cap [a \cup (b \cup c)] = a \cap [(a \cup b) \cup c].$$

Also,
$$\begin{aligned} e \cap [a \cup (b \cup c)] &= (e \cap a) \cup [e \cap (b \cup c)] \\ &= \emptyset \cup [e \cap (b \cup c)] \\ &= e \cap (b \cup c), \end{aligned}$$

and
$$\begin{aligned} e \cap [(a \cup b) \cup c] &= [e \cap (a \cup b)] \cup (e \cap c) \\ &= [(e \cap a) \cup (e \cap b)] \cup (e \cap c) \\ &= [\emptyset \cup (e \cap b)] \cup (e \cap c) \\ &= (e \cap b) \cup (e \cap c) \\ &= e \cap (b \cup c) \end{aligned}$$

Therefore, $$e \cap [a \cup (b \cup c)] = e \cap [(a \cup b) \cup c].$$

Thus, by Theorem 7,

$$a \cup (b \cup c) = (a \cup b) \cup c.$$

THEOREM 9: $\forall x \forall y \forall z[x \cap (y \cap z) = (x \cap y) \cap z]$.

The proof of this theorem is parallel to that of Theorem 8. This means that you must first state and prove a theorem parallel to Theorem 7. If you understand Theorems 7 and 8, you will find this easy to do.

THEOREM 10: $\forall x \forall y \forall z[x \cup y = I \wedge x \cap y = \emptyset \wedge x \cup z = I \wedge x \cap z = \emptyset \rightarrow y = z]$.

Proof: Suppose that a, b, and c are members of B such that

$$a \cup b = I, \quad a \cap b = \emptyset, \quad a \cup c = I, \quad \text{and} \quad a \cap c = \emptyset;$$

then

$$b = (a \cup c) \cap b = (a \cap b) \cup (c \cap b) = \emptyset \cup (c \cap b) = c \cap b$$

and

$$c = (a \cup b) \cap c = (a \cap c) \cup (b \cap c) = \emptyset \cup (b \cap c) = b \cap c = c \cap b$$

hence

$$b = c.$$

In view of Theorem 10, we know that given a member of B, say a, there is exactly one member of B, say b, such that $a \cup b = I$ and $a \cap b = \emptyset$. For this reason, we introduce a unary operator on B, called $'$, as follows:

DEFINITION: $' = \{(a, b) \mid a \in B \wedge b \in B \wedge a \cup b = I \wedge a \cap b = \emptyset\}$; as usual, if $(a, b) \in {}'$, then b is denoted by "a'".

THEOREM 11: $\forall x[(x')' = x]$.

Proof: Suppose that $a \in B$; then $a \cup a' = I$ and $a \cap a' = \emptyset$. Therefore, $a' \cup a = I$ and $a' \cap a = \emptyset$, and so $(a')' = a$.

THEOREM 12: $I' = \emptyset$.

Proof: $I \cup \emptyset = I$ by Law 3, and $I \cap \emptyset = \emptyset \cap I = \emptyset$ by Law 4; therefore, $I' = \emptyset$.

THEOREM 13: $\emptyset' = I$.

Proof: $\emptyset' = (I')' = I$ by Theorem 11.

THEOREM 14: $\forall x \forall y[(x \cup y)' = x' \cap y']$.

Proof: Suppose that a and b are members of B. Then

$$(a \cup b) \cup (a' \cap b') = [(a \cup b) \cup a'] \cap [(a \cup b) \cup b'] = I \cap I = I,$$

and

$$(a \cup b) \cap (a' \cap b') = [a \cap (a' \cap b')] \cup [b \cap (a' \cap b')] = \emptyset \cup \emptyset = \emptyset.$$

Therefore, $\quad (a \cup b)' = a' \cap b'$.

THEOREM 15: $\forall x \forall y[(x \cap y)' = x' \cup y']$.

Proof: Suppose that a and b are members of B. Then

$$(a' \cup b')' = (a')' \cap (b')' = a \cap b$$

and so

$$(a \cap b)' = [(a' \cup b')']' = a' \cup b'.$$

We now introduce a binary relation on B, denoted by "$\subset$".

DEFINITION: $\subset = \{(a, b) \mid a \cup b = b\}$; as usual, the statement "$(a, b) \in \subset$" is denoted by "$a \subset b$".

The proofs of the following three theorems are straightforward.

THEOREM 16: $\forall x[x \subset x]$.

THEOREM 17: $\forall x \forall y[x \subset y \wedge y \subset x \rightarrow x = y]$.

THEOREM 18: $\forall x \forall y \forall z[x \subset y \wedge y \subset z \rightarrow x \subset z]$.

This completes our program of demonstrating that each of our seventeen basic laws can be established algebraically by using Huntington's seven laws.

EXERCISES

1. Show that $(\{0, 1\}, +, \circ, 1, 0)$ is a Boolean algebra where

$$+ = \{(0, 0, 0), (0, 1, 0), (1, 0, 0), (1, 1, 1)\}$$

and

$$\circ = \{(0, 0, 0), (0, 1, 1), (1, 0, 1), (1, 1, 1)\}$$

2. Show that the algebraic system $(\{a, b, c, d\}, +, \circ, a, b)$ is a Boolean algebra where the binary operators are defined by the tables:

$+$	a	b	c	d
a	a	b	c	d
b	b	b	b	b
c	c	b	c	b
d	d	b	b	d

$\circ$	a	b	c	d
a	a	a	a	a
b	a	b	c	d
c	a	c	c	a
d	a	d	a	d

Prove that the following propositions are true in each Boolean algebra:

3. $\forall x \forall y[x \cup (y \cap x') = x \cup y]$
4. $\forall x \forall y \forall z[(x \cap y \cap z) \cup (x' \cup y' \cup z') = I]$
5. $\forall x[\emptyset \subset x \wedge x \subset I]$

6. $\forall x \forall y \forall z[x \subset y \rightarrow z \cup x \subset z \cup y]$

7. $\forall x \forall y[x \subset y \leftrightarrow x \cap y' = \emptyset]$

8. $\forall x \forall y[x \subset y \leftrightarrow y \cup x' = I]$

9. $\forall x \forall y \forall z[x \subset y \wedge x \subset z \rightarrow x \subset y \cap z]$

10. $\forall x \forall y[x \subset y \leftrightarrow y' \subset x']$

11. $\forall x \forall y[x \subset y \leftrightarrow x \cap y = x]$

12. $\forall x \forall y \forall z[x \subset y \rightarrow z \cap x \subset z \cap y]$

13. Construct a Boolean algebra such that the basic set of the algebraic system has exactly eight members.

14. Show that there is no Boolean algebra whose basic set has exactly three members.

15. Show that $(B, ?, !, a, b)$ is a Boolean algebra whenever $(B, !, ?, b, a)$ is a Boolean algebra.

16. Suppose that I is a non-empty set with an even number of members and that I has more than three members. Show that $(B, \cup, \cap, \emptyset, I)$ is *not* a Boolean algebra, where B denotes the collection of all subsets of I that have an even number of members, $\cup$ and $\cap$ are the usual operators on sets, and $\emptyset$ is the empty set.

17. Suppose that I is a non-empty set and that B is a collection of subsets of I. Prove that $(B, \cup, \cap, \emptyset, I)$ is a Boolean algebra, where $\cup$ and $\cap$ are the usual operators on sets—provided that $\cup$ and $\cap$ are binary operators on B, $\emptyset \in B$, and $I \in B$.

18. Show that no algebraic system is both a field and a Boolean algebra.

19. (a) Show that $(B, \cup, \cap, (0, 0), (1, 1))$ is a Boolean Algebra where

$$B = \{(0, 0), (0, 1), (1, 0), (1, 1)\}, \quad (a, b) \cup (c, d) = (\max\{a, c\}, \max\{b, d\})$$

and

$$(a, b) \cap (c, d) = (a \cdot c, b \cdot d).$$

(b) Construct a Boolean Algebra whose basic set has cardinal 2^n, given $n \in N$.

20. Show that $(P, \vee, \wedge, f, t)$ is a Boolean algebra where $\{q \mid q$ is a proposition and "$q \leftrightarrow p$" is logically true$\} \in P$ for each proposition p, "$\vee$" and "$\wedge$" denote the logical connectives discussed in Chapter I, "f" denotes the equivalence class consisting of logically false propositions, and "t" denotes the equivalence class consisting of logically true propositions.

part III

Mathematical logic

4

The propositional calculus

1. Introduction

In Chapter 3 we presented the axiomatic method and its intimate involvement with mathematical objects called algebraic systems. There are two main points that must be emphasized. First, it is possible—and useful—to characterize a family of algebraic systems by listing a set of postulates. Second, once we have characterized a family of algebraic systems in this way, we want to demonstrate that certain propositions are true in each of these algebraic systems. We start with a set of propositions, called postulates; this leads us to a family of algebraic systems, called models of the postulates; next, we prove that certain propositions, called theorems, are true in each of the models. It is the final step of stating and proving theorems that is of special interest here. A proposition is shown to be a theorem in a given postulational system by demonstrating that the proposition is true in each model of the given postulate-set. This may be accomplished by any means at hand. Primarily, of course, one considers the *meaning* or content of the proposition when demonstrating that it is true in each of the models. That is mathematics. Notice that the algebraic systems involved play a key role in this procedure. In fact, in demonstrating theorems the models of the postulates are at all times uppermost in mind.

In the theory of deduction, on the other hand, we shall study a set of postulates, which characterize a family of algebraic systems, in a completely abstract and pure setting, divorced absolutely from the algebraic systems involved. The purpose of a theory of deduction is to characterize the theorems of a given postulate-set by specifying formal rules and procedures that permit us to deduce theorems from the given postulates. The formal rules and procedures are completely syntactical; they operate on the *form* of the postulates, completely ignoring the *meaning* of the postulates. In particular, algebraic systems are left out in the cold. This is the astonishing thing: it is possible to demonstrate, in effect, that a given proposition is true in each algebraic system of a family of algebraic systems without ever considering algebraic systems, or even the meaning of the particular proposition.

As might be expected, the formal rules and procedures involved in a theory of deduction, are fairly complicated. Fortunately, the theory of deduction is relatively simple in the case of a language based on the connectives $\sim$ and $\vee$. This theory, known as the *Propositional Calculus*, characterizes the conclusions, or consequences, of a given set of assumptions, and so provides us with the formal side of arguments. The question of the validity of a given argument is easy to solve by the truth-table method, and so is really trivial. Therefore, in studying the accompanying theory of deduction we are able to concentrate completely on the formal apparatus and methods of a theory of deduction, without the complications owing to the subject matter under investigation. In short, the study of the Propositional Calculus is a convenient device for making clear the nature of a theory of deduction.

In rough outline, the steps in setting up a theory of deduction are as follows. First, the objects under investigation; i.e., the expressions or propositions under study, are characterized. This is achieved by actually creating a specific formal language possessing its own alphabet and rules of grammar; in fact, the words and sentences of the formal language are effectively spelled out by suitably chosen rules of grammar. Finally, the notion of *truth* within this specialized and highly artificial language is defined by specifying just what is meant by a "proof" within the language.

To illustrate, consider the language defined as follows. The alphabet of the language possesses exactly three letters: "*a*", "*b*", and "*c*". By an "expression" in this language, we mean any finite string of letters; e.g., "*abc*", "*cb*", "*aabcc*", "*aaaaab*", "*c*". On the other hand, "*abcd*" is *not* an expression in this language. By a "word" we mean any expression beginning with "*a*", for example "*acc*" and "*ab*" are words. By a "sentence" or "proposition", we mean any finite sequence of words. For example, "*acc a abaa*" is a proposition. Finally, by a "proof", we mean any finite sequence of propositions such that the letter "*b*" appears in at least one of the propositions. For example, "*ac acc accc, aca acaa acaaa, acb accb acccb*" is a proof because it is a sequence of three propositions in which "*b*" appears. Similarly, "*abacc*" is a proof. On the other hand, "*ac b, abc*" is not a proof because "*ac b*" is not a proposition.

Note: The preceding formal language is of no interest in itself; it is intended merely to illustrate the general notion of a formal language.

2. The Language of the Propositional Calculus

Ordinarily the symbols appearing in a mathematical investigation are mere names that denote the mathematical objects involved in that particular branch of mathematics. On the other hand, in the study of a *formal system* the objects under discussion are actually constructed in terms of certain symbols, which are given in advance. In particular, the basic symbols involved in a formal system possess no denotation in the usual sense; rather, when a symbol of a formal system is written, that symbol is the object we wish to denote. In other words, each symbol of a formal system denotes itself! In order to distinguish between this kind of symbol and the usual symbol (which denotes something else), we shall use boldface type for the symbols of a formal system.

Beyond question, this approach, in which it is the symbol as an object in itself that interests us, is highly sophisticated and requires some getting used to. Furthermore, we shall consider, as an object in itself, the array of symbols obtained by writing down several symbols, one after another. For this reason, this section should be studied carefully.

As we have said, the propositional calculus is intended to formalize arguments of the kind discussed in Section 5 of Chapter 1. The language of the Propositional Calculus must be capable of representing and analyzing propositions that are free of quantifiers. The first step in introducing a new language is to announce its alphabet—the basic symbols used in constructing the language. First, we require a stock of symbols to denote independent propositions; next, we require two connectives—namely, "not" and "or"—to help us form compound propositions (one connective, Sheffer's stroke, will do, but this results in an extremely cumbersome language); finally, we require parentheses to serve as punctuation. Thus, the alphabet of the propositional calculus consists of three kinds of symbols, as follows.

The Symbols of the Propositional Calculus

(1) Propositions: **X**, **Y**, **Z**, . . . (infinitely many)
(2) Logical Connectives: **~**, **∨**
(3) Parentheses: **(** , **)**

Remember that the basic symbols of a language possess no intrinsic meaning; however, as a guide in following the discussion, we have indicated the *intended* meaning or function of the above symbols. We must emphasize one idea: at this point in the development of the propositional calculus, any two of the above symbols are equally meaningless; this is because the object denoted by any one of these symbols is itself. As we have said, this is the reason that we are using boldface type for the symbols of the propositional calculus.

We now define what is meant by an *expression* in our language.

DEFINITION: The result of writing down a finite number of our symbols, one after the other, is called an *expression*.

More precisely, each symbol of the propositional calculus is said to be an expression; furthermore, $\alpha\beta$ is an expression whenever α is an expression and β is one of our symbols. This is subject to the restriction that each expression is finite. Also, since zero is a finite number, we shall regard the result of writing down no symbols to be an expression. That is,   is an expression.

Illustrating this concept further, let us show that **) ~ Z** is an expression. Clearly, **)** is an expression, since **)** is a symbol; therefore, **) ~** is an expression, since **~** is a symbol; finally, **) ~ Z** is an expression, because **) ~** is an expression and **Z** is a symbol. Roughly speaking, then, any finite string of symbols is an expression. Here are a few examples of expressions: **X**, **Y ∨ (~ Z)**, **~ Y ∨ Z**, **X)X**, **(~ Y ∨)Z**, **XXX ~ ∨ Y**. On the other hand, none of the following is an expression:

$$\begin{matrix}\mathbf{X}\\ \mathbf{X}\end{matrix},\ \mathbf{X} \wedge Y,\ \begin{matrix}(\\ )\end{matrix},\ \tilde{\mathbf{X}},\ [\mathbf{X}],\ \mathbf{XXX}\ldots\mathbf{X}\ldots \text{(infinitely many } \mathbf{X}\text{s)},\ \mathbf{((}$$

Having defined expressions, we now select certain expressions, which we shall call *well-formed formulae* or *wff* for short. First, we say that if x is a proposition, then the expression **(**x**)** is a wff. For example, **Y** is a proposition; therefore, the expression **(Y)** is a wff. Next, we say that if A is a wff, then the expression **(~** A**)** is also a wff. For example, **(Y)** is a wff; therefore, the expression **(~ (Y))** is a wff. Finally, we say that if A and B are each wff, then the expression **(**A **∨** B**)** is a wff. These are the only wff.

For example, **(X)** and **(~ (Y))** are wff; therefore, the expression **((X) ∨ (~ (Y)))** is a wff.

Notice our use of capital letters at the beginning of the alphabet as variables for wff; these symbols are in lightface type, since they possess denotation in the usual sense of a variable. This convention has the important advantage of bringing out the distinction between the symbols of the Propositional Calculus, which are set in boldface type, and the variables that denote wff, which are set in lightface type.

Since each wff is an expression and each expression is finite, we see that

THEOREM: Each wff is finite.

We shall say that a wff is *atomic* iff neither **~** nor **∨** occurs in the wff. We shall say that a wff is *composite* iff it is not atomic. For example, the wff **(X)** is atomic, while the wff **(~ (X))** is composite. By the *length* of a composite wff, we mean the number of instances of connectives occurring in the wff. For example, the length of **(((X) ∨ (Y)) ∨ (~ (X)))** is 3.

Next, we introduce the notion of the *main* connective of a composite wff. We shall say that **~** is the main connective of the wff A iff there is a wff, say B, such that A is **(~** B**)**; furthermore, we shall say that **v** is the main connective of the wff A iff there are wff, say B and C, such that A is **(**B **v** C**)**. For example, **~** is the main connective of **(~ ((X) v (Y)))**; while **v** is the main connective of the wff **((~ (X)) v (Y))**.

THEOREM: Each composite wff possesses exactly one main connective.

Proof: Consider the definition of wff.

Later on, we shall be interested in establishing properties of wff. To this purpose, we require a general method of demonstrating that each wff possesses a stated property. This is provided by the following

FUNDAMENTAL THEOREM ABOUT WFF: Each wff has property P provided that

1. Each atomic wff has property P.
2. **(~** A**)** has property P whenever A is a wff with property P.
3. **(**A **v** B**)** has property P whenever A has property P and B has property P.

Demonstration: Let P be a property satisfying the assumptions of the theorem, but such that not all wff possess property P. Consider the set S of all wff that do not possess property P; clearly, S is non-empty and no atomic wff is a member of S. Since each composite wff has a finite length, it follows that there is a natural number, say k, such that k is the length of a member of S, whereas no wff with length less than k is a member of S. In other words, if there exists a wff that does not possess property P, then there must also exist a "shortest" wff that does not possess property P. Let A be any member of S with length k. Since A is composite, it possesses a main connective. There are two possibilities.

1. The main connective of A is **~**: then there is a wff, say B, such that A is **(~** B**)**. Hence, length of $A = 1 +$ length of B. Therefore $B \bar{\in} S$; i.e., B has property P. By assumption, then, **(~** B**)** has property P, a contradiction.
2. The main connective of A is **v**: then there are wff B and C, say, such that A is **(**B **v** C**)**. Hence, length of $A = 1 +$ length of $B +$ length of C. Therefore, $B \bar{\in} S$ and $C \bar{\in} S$; i.e., B has property P and C has property P. By assumption, then, **(**B **v** C**)** has property P, a contradiction.

We have shown that the assumption of the existence of a wff which does not have property P, is false; and so our theorem is established.

As an application of the fundamental theorem about wff, we establish the obvious

THEOREM 1: Each wff begins with **(** and ends with **)**.

Demonstration: It is enough to demonstrate that each atomic wff has the stated property, that $(\sim A)$ has the property if A has the property, and that $(A \vee B)$ has the property if A has the property and B has the property. Clearly, each atomic wff has the stated property. Clearly, $(\sim A)$ has the stated property whether or not A has the property. Clearly, $(A \vee B)$ has the property whether or not A and B possess the property.

As another illustration, we prove

THEOREM 2: A proposition occurs in each wff.

Demonstration: Certainly each atomic wff possesses the property. If a proposition, say x, occurs in a wff A, then x occurs in the wff $(\sim A)$; i.e., $(\sim A)$ has the property provided that A has the property. Again, if a proposition, say x, occurs in a wff B, then x occurs in the wff $(B \vee C)$; i.e., $(B \vee C)$ has the property provided that B has the property. Applying our fundamental theorem about wff, we have established the theorem.

We now establish an important property of wff. First, we introduce two symbols "t" and "f", which have nothing to do with the symbols of the propositional calculus; we shall interpret "t" as standing for "true" and "f" as standing for "false". By an *assignment of truth-values* to the atomic wff of the propositional calculus, we mean any mapping of the set of all atomic wff into $\{t, f\}$. We want to show that any given assignment of truth-values to the atomic wff, can be extended in a natural way; i.e., reflecting the intended meaning of the logical connectives, to a mapping of the set of all wff into $\{t, f\}$. The procedure is as follows. Let λ be any mapping of the set of all atomic wff into $\{t, f\}$; then $\lambda[A]$ is t or f, whenever A is an atomic wff. We construct a mapping μ of the set of all wff into $\{t, f\}$ by applying the following rules.

(1) if A is atomic, then $\mu[A] = \lambda[A]$

(2) if A is $(\sim B)$, then $\mu[A] = \begin{cases} \text{f if } \mu[B] = \text{t} \\ \text{t if } \mu[B] = \text{f} \end{cases}$

(3) if A is $(B \vee C)$, then $\mu[A] = \begin{cases} \text{f if } \mu[B] = \mu[C] = \text{f} \\ \text{t otherwise} \end{cases}$

We shall call $\mu[A]$, as defined here, the *truth-value* of A under the assignment λ; μ is also called a valuation.

We can now state the important property of wff that interests us: μ, as defined above, is a mapping of the set of all wff into $\{t, f\}$! To demonstrate this point, we must show that $\mu[A]$ is defined by this procedure whenever A is a wff. The property that is involved is that a wff, say A, is assigned an image in $\{t, f\}$ under the above rules. That is, the wff A possesses the property iff $\mu[A]$ has been defined. To demonstrate that each wff possesses this property, we apply our fundamental theorem about wff. Clearly, each atomic wff possesses the stated property. Certainly the wff $(\sim A)$ has the property whenever the wff A has the property. Finally, the wff $(B \vee C)$ has the property, provided that B has the property and C has the property. We conclude that each wff has the stated property.

EXERCISES

1. Which of the following are expressions:

   (a) **Z** (b) **v** (c) **)Y(** (d) **(Y)**
   (e) **{X}** (f) **X,Y** (g) **((X)** (h) **X + Y**

2. Which of the following are wff:

   (a) **X** (b) **X v Y** (c) **((X) v (Y))** (d) **(X) v (Y)**
   (e) **((X) → (Y))** (f) **((~ (X)) v (Y))** (g) **(~ (X) v (Y))** (h) **((~ (X) v (Y))**
   (i) **((X)(Y))** (j) **((X) v (X))** (k) **(~ (~ (X)))** (l) **(~)**

3. Show that the length of $(\sim A) = 1 +$ length of A, and
   length of $(A \vee B) = 1 +$ length of $A +$ length of B
   whenever A and B are composite wff.

4. Precisely what is meant by saying that a proposition *occurs* in a wff?

5. Show that an atomic wff occurs in each wff.

6. Prove there are infinitely many propositions which do not occur in a given wff.

7. Is it true that each composite wff has property P, given that
   (1) $(\sim A)$ has property P whenever A is a composite wff with property P
   (2) $(B \vee C)$ has property P whenever A and B are composite wff with property P?

8. Construct a wff A such that $\mu[A] = \mathrm{t}$ no matter how λ is chosen. Construct a wff B such that $\mu[B] = \mathrm{f}$ no matter how λ is chosen. Simplify $\mu[(\sim (A \vee B))]$ and $\mu[(\sim (\sim (A)))]$.

9. Let l be a mapping of the set of all wff into the set of real numbers, such that $l[A] = 0$ whenever A is atomic,
   $$l[(\sim B)] = 1 + l[B]$$
   whenever B is a wff, and
   $$l[(C \vee D)] = 1 + l[C] + l[D]$$

whenever C and D are wff. Describe l in colloquial language. Prove that l is characterized by these conditions.

10. Let m be a mapping of the set of all wff into the set of real numbers, such that $m[A] = 1$ whenever A is atomic, $m[(\sim B)] = m[B]$ whenever B is a wff, and

$$m[(C \vee D)] = m[C] + m[D]$$

whenever C and D are wff. Describe m in colloquial language. Prove that m is characterized by these conditions.

11. Let n be a mapping of the set of all wff into the set of real numbers, such that $n[A] = 0$ whenever A is atomic,

$$n[(\sim B)] = 1 + n[B]$$

whenever B is a wff, and

$$n[(C \vee D)] = n[C] + n[D]$$

whenever C and D are wff. Describe n in colloquial language. Prove that n is characterized by these conditions.

12. Let o be a mapping of the set of all wff into the set of real numbers, such that $o[A] = 0$ whenever A is atomic, $o[(\sim B)] = o[B]$ whenever B is a wff, and

$$o[(C \vee D)] = 1 + o[C] + o[D]$$

whenever C and D are wff. Describe o in colloquial language. Prove that o is characterized by these conditions.

13. Let p be a mapping of the set of all wff into the set of real numbers, such that $p[A] = 2$ whenever A is atomic,

$$p[(\sim B)] = 2 + p[B]$$

whenever B is a wff, and

$$p[(C \vee D)] = 2 + p[C] + p[D]$$

whenever C and D are wff. Describe p in colloquial language. Prove that p is characterized by these conditions.

14. Let q be a mapping of the set of all wff into the set of real numbers, such that $q[A] = 3$ whenever A is atomic, $q[(\sim B)] = 3 + q[B]$ whenever B is a wff, and $q[(C \vee D)] = 3 + q[C] + q[D]$ whenever C and D are wff. Describe q in colloquial language. Prove that q is characterized by these conditions.

15. Let r be a mapping of the set of all wff into the set of real numbers, such that $r[(\mathbf{X})] = 1$, $r[A] = 0$ whenever A is atomic and $A \neq (\mathbf{X})$,

$$r[(\sim B]) = r[B]$$

whenever B is a wff, and

$$r[(C \vee D)] = r[C] + r[D]$$

whenever C and D are wff. Describe r in colloquial language. Prove that r is characterized by these conditions.

3. Parentheses-omitting Conventions

Now, a remark about notation. The importance of parentheses as basic symbols of the propositional calculus may not be immediately evident.

Consider the wff $((\sim(\mathbf{X})) \vee (\mathbf{Y}))$ and $(\sim((\mathbf{X}) \vee (\mathbf{Y})))$; with all parentheses omitted the first of these becomes $\sim \mathbf{X} \vee \mathbf{Y}$ and the second becomes $\sim \mathbf{X} \vee \mathbf{Y}$ —the same expression. To see that the two given wff are essentially different, consider the assignment of truth-values under which $(\mathbf{X})$ has the truth-value t, and $(\mathbf{Y})$ has the truth-value t; then the truth-value of $((\sim(\mathbf{X})) \vee (\mathbf{Y}))$ is t, and the truth-value of $(\sim((\mathbf{X}) \vee (\mathbf{Y})))$ is f. The need for parentheses is clear. Having demonstrated the importance of parentheses, we now introduce several parentheses-omitting conventions. Let A and B be any wff; we shall denote the wff $((\sim A) \vee B)$ by writing "$(A \rightarrow B)$", we shall denote the wff $(\sim((\sim A) \vee (\sim B)))$ by writing "$(A \wedge B)$", we shall denote the wff $((A \rightarrow B) \wedge (B \rightarrow A))$ by writing "$(A \leftrightarrow B)$". We shall refer to the symbols "$\rightarrow$", "$\wedge$", and "$\leftrightarrow$" as logical connectives. Now we come to a very useful parentheses-omitting convention. The prime purpose for inserting parentheses in an expression is to indicate the main connective of the wff. In case parentheses have been omitted, we shall assume that the main connective is "$\leftrightarrow$"; if this connective does not appear in the wff, then we shall assume that the main connective is "$\rightarrow$"; if this connective also does not appear in the wff, then we shall assume that the main connective is "$\wedge$"; if this connective also does not appear, then we shall assume that the main connective is "$\vee$"; if this connective does not appear, then we shall assume that the main connective of the wff is $\sim$; finally, if $\sim$ also does not appear, then the wff is atomic. In other words, we attribute a built-in bracketing power to the logical connectives in the following order: $\sim$, $\vee$, $\wedge$, $\rightarrow$, $\leftrightarrow$ (weakest connectives are written first). As part of this convention, let x be any proposition; then we shall denote the atomic wff (x) by writing "x"; furthermore, if A is any wff standing alone, we shall delete the parentheses that begin and end A.

To illustrate these conventions, the wff $((\sim(\mathbf{X})) \vee (\mathbf{Y}))$ is denoted by the expression $\sim \mathbf{X} \vee \mathbf{Y}$, whereas the wff $(\sim((\mathbf{X}) \vee (\mathbf{Y})))$ is denoted by the expression $\sim(\mathbf{X} \vee \mathbf{Y})$. Again, applying the above conventions, we see that the main connective of the wff $\mathbf{X} \vee \sim \mathbf{Y} \rightarrow \sim(\mathbf{X} \vee \mathbf{Y})$ is "$\rightarrow$". As the preceding example shows, not all parentheses can be omitted by the above conventions.

One final parentheses-omitting convention follows. It is sometimes possible to make a single dot do the work of several pairs of parentheses. This is achieved by strengthening the bracketing power of a connective by placing a dot above it. Hence, the bracketing power of the connectives is as follows: $\sim$, $\lor$, $\land$, $\rightarrow$, $\leftrightarrow$, $\dot{\sim}$, $\dot{\lor}$, $\dot{\land}$, $\overset{\cdot}{\rightarrow}$, $\overset{\cdot}{\leftrightarrow}$, $\ddot{\sim}$, $\ddot{\lor}$, $\ddot{\land}$, $\overset{\cdot\cdot}{\rightarrow}$, $\overset{\cdot\cdot}{\leftrightarrow}$, and so on.

Applying this "dot" convention, we see that the wff

$$(\mathbf{X} \rightarrow \mathbf{Y}) \rightarrow ((\mathbf{Z} \lor \mathbf{X}) \rightarrow (\mathbf{Z} \lor \mathbf{Y}))$$

can be written as

$$\mathbf{X} \rightarrow \mathbf{Y} \overset{\cdot}{\rightarrow} \mathbf{Z} \lor \mathbf{X} \rightarrow \mathbf{Z} \lor \mathbf{Y}$$

without ambiguity.

The intention of the above conventions is not to eliminate all parentheses but merely to limit the number of parentheses that appear in a given wff, so that the eye will not become lost in a maze of parentheses. One or two pairs of parentheses may not be objectionable in a wff and may even be useful. The main objective is that the wff be readable. For this reason, we prefer to write $\mathbf{X} \lor \sim \mathbf{Y} \rightarrow \sim (\mathbf{X} \lor \mathbf{Y})$ rather than $\mathbf{X} \lor \sim \mathbf{Y} \overset{\cdot}{\rightarrow} \dot{\sim} \mathbf{X} \lor \mathbf{Y}$.

EXERCISES

Simplify the following wff:

1. $((\sim (\mathbf{X})) \lor (\sim (\mathbf{Z})))$
2. $((\mathbf{X}) \lor ((\mathbf{Y}) \lor (\sim (\mathbf{W}))))$
3. $((\sim ((\mathbf{X}) \lor (\sim \mathbf{Y}))) \lor (\mathbf{W}))$

Indicate the main connective of the following wff by inserting parentheses:

4. $\sim \mathbf{X} \rightarrow \mathbf{Y} \dot{\land} \mathbf{X} \lor \mathbf{Y}$
5. $\mathbf{X} \rightarrow \mathbf{Y} \leftrightarrow \sim \mathbf{Y} \rightarrow \sim \mathbf{X}$
6. $\mathbf{W} \land \sim \mathbf{Y}$
7. $\mathbf{X} \rightarrow \mathbf{X} \lor \mathbf{X}$
8. $\mathbf{X} \land \mathbf{Y} \dot{\lor} \mathbf{Z} \lor \mathbf{W}$
9. $\mathbf{X} \land \mathbf{Y} \rightarrow \mathbf{Z}$
10. $\mathbf{X} \dot{\land} \mathbf{Y} \rightarrow \mathbf{Z}$
11. $\mathbf{X} \overset{\cdot}{\rightarrow} \mathbf{Y} \leftrightarrow \mathbf{Z}$
12. $\mathbf{X} \rightarrow \mathbf{Y} \leftrightarrow \mathbf{Z}$

Use dots to simplify the following wff:

13. $(X \wedge Y) \vee (Y \wedge X)$

14. $(\sim X \rightarrow Y) \wedge (X \vee \sim Y)$

15. $(X \rightarrow Y) \rightarrow (Z \rightarrow W)$

16. $(X \leftrightarrow \sim Y) \vee (X \wedge Y)$

4. The Concept of a "Proof"

The word *proof* is used in a highly technical sense in a theory of deduction and denotes any finite sequence of wff satisfying certain formal requirements. In order to understand the formal requirements that appear in the definition of a proof, it is helpful to consider certain properties of μ, the valuation determined by assigning truth-values to each atomic wff. It is easy to prove that $\mu[A \vee A \rightarrow A] = \text{t}$ for any wff A, that $\mu[A \rightarrow A \vee B] = \text{t}$ for any wff A and B, that $\mu[A \vee B \rightarrow B \vee A] = \text{t}$ for any wff A and B, and that

$$\mu[A \rightarrow B \dot{\rightarrow} C \vee A \rightarrow C \vee B] = \text{t}$$

for any wff A, B, and C. Furthermore, $\mu[B] = \text{t}$ whenever $\mu[A \rightarrow B] = \text{t}$ and $\mu[A] = \text{t}$.

The whole point of introducing the concept of "proof" into the framework of the propositional calculus is to characterize the intuitive idea of a "true" statement. The wff of the propositional calculus are intended to represent statements or propositions in the usual sense; we want to select those wff that represent true propositions, intuitively speaking. By a "proof" in mathematics, we mean a sequence of propositions with one common property; i.e., each proposition is true. By a "proof" in the propositional calculus, we shall mean a sequence of wff such that each wff is true in some sense of the word. The problem reduces to knowing what we mean by a "true" wff. Actually, this is not difficult: a wff, say A, is true iff the truth-value of A is t under each possible assignment of truth-values to the atomic wff of the propositional calculus. So, the intuitive idea of a "true" wff is perfectly clear. Our job is to represent this notion within the framework of the propositional calculus, without referring to objects "t" and "f". It turns out that the notion of a "true" wff can be characterized as follows. Any wff possessing any one of the four forms

$$A \vee A \rightarrow A, \quad A \rightarrow A \vee B, \quad A \vee B \rightarrow B \vee A,$$
$$A \rightarrow B \dot{\rightarrow} C \vee A \rightarrow C \vee B$$

is said to be true; furthermore, a wff, say B, is said to be true provided there is a wff A such that A is true and $A \rightarrow B$ is true.

We shall see that it is convenient first to define what we mean by a "proof" in the propositional calculus and then to define what we mean by a "true" wff in the propositional calculus. There is one point from the preceding paragraph that may not be clear; i.e., the *form* of a wff. When we say, for example, that the wff C has the form $A \vee A \to A$, we mean that there is a wff, say A, such that C *is* $A \vee A \to A$. Thus, in the preceding paragraph, we are really referring to the following *sets* of wff:

$$\{A \vee A \to A \mid A \text{ is a wff}\}$$

$$\{A \to A \vee B \mid A \text{ and } B \text{ are wff}\},$$

$$\{A \vee B \to B \vee A \mid A \text{ and } B \text{ are wff}\}$$

and

$$\{A \to B \mathrel{\dot{\to}} C \vee A \to C \vee B \mid A, B, \text{ and } C \text{ are wff}\}$$

We are now ready to formulate the important

DEFINITION: A finite sequence of wff is called a *proof* iff each term of the sequence, say E, possesses one of the four forms

I (1) $A \vee A \to A$
  (2) $A \to A \vee B$,
  (3) $A \vee B \to B \vee A$,
  (4) $A \to B \mathrel{\dot{\to}} C \vee A \to C \vee B$

or else

II there is a wff, say D, such that the two wff D and $D \to E$ precede E in the sequence.

The four sets of wff referred to under I are known as *axiom schemes*, whereas the rule of inference II is called *Modus Ponens*.

For example, the finite sequence

$$\mathbf{X} \vee \mathbf{X} \to \mathbf{X}, \quad \mathbf{X} \vee \mathbf{X} \to \mathbf{X} \mathrel{\dot{\to}} (\mathbf{X} \vee \mathbf{X} \to \mathbf{X}) \vee \mathbf{X}, \quad (\mathbf{X} \vee \mathbf{X} \to \mathbf{X}) \vee \mathbf{X}$$

is a proof. To see this, we show that each term of the sequence meets the above requirements. Consider the first term, $\mathbf{X} \vee \mathbf{X} \to \mathbf{X}$; clearly, this wff is a member of axiom scheme (1)—here, A is $\mathbf{X}$. Now consider the second term, $\mathbf{X} \vee \mathbf{X} \to \mathbf{X} \mathrel{\dot{\to}} (\mathbf{X} \vee \mathbf{X} \to \mathbf{X}) \vee \mathbf{X}$; this wff is a member of axiom scheme (2)—here A is $\mathbf{X} \vee \mathbf{X} \to \mathbf{X}$, and B is $\mathbf{X}$. Now consider the final term, $(\mathbf{X} \vee \mathbf{X} \to \mathbf{X}) \vee \mathbf{X}$; this term is preceded in the sequence by the wff $\mathbf{X} \vee \mathbf{X} \to \mathbf{X}$ and $\mathbf{X} \vee \mathbf{X} \to \mathbf{X} \mathrel{\dot{\to}} (\mathbf{X} \vee \mathbf{X} \to \mathbf{X}) \vee \mathbf{X}$. Thus, the presence of $(\mathbf{X} \vee \mathbf{X} \to \mathbf{X}) \vee \mathbf{X}$ in the sequence, is justified by *Modus Ponens*. We have shown that each term of the above sequence satisfies I or satisfies II; we conclude that the sequence is a proof.

As another illustration, consider the finite sequence.

$$\mathbf{X \vee X \to X \dot{\to} \sim X \vee (X \vee X) \to \sim X \vee X,}$$
$$\mathbf{X \vee X \to X,}$$
$$\mathbf{\sim X \vee (X \vee X) \to \sim X \vee X,}$$
$$\mathbf{X \to X \vee X,}$$
$$\mathbf{X \to X}$$

This sequence is a proof. The first term is a member of axiom scheme (4): A is $\mathbf{X \vee X}$, B is $\mathbf{X}$, and C is $\mathbf{\sim X}$. The second term is a member of axiom scheme (1). The third term is justified by *Modus Ponens* applied to the two preceding terms. The fourth term is a member of axiom scheme (2). The last term is justified by applying *Modus Ponens* to the two preceding terms.

We must regard a proof as being an entity in itself, a mathematical object worthy of study in its own right, and possessing interesting and useful properties. To illustrate this point of view, prove the following

THEOREM: If π_1 and π_2 are proofs, then π_1, π_2 is a proof. (In other words, the finite sequence obtained from two proofs by adjoining one proof to the other proof, is also a proof.)

Having defined the notion of a proof, we now introduce the concept of a *provable* wff. It is our intention to characterize the notion of a "true" wff as discussed above. Later, we shall show that the set of all true wff and the set of all provable wff are one and the same. For the moment, consider the

DEFINITION: We shall say that a wff, say C, is *provable* iff there is a proof whose last term is C.

For example, $\mathbf{(X \vee X \to X) \vee X}$ is provable; $\mathbf{X \to X}$ is provable; indeed, $\mathbf{X \vee X \to X}$ is provable.

It is convenient to introduce the following abbreviation: we shall denote the statement "C is provable" by prefixing the symbol "$\vdash$" to C; thus "$\vdash C$" means "C is provable".

One more definition. Suppose that $\vdash C$; then there exists at least one proof whose last term is C. We shall call any such proof, *a proof of C*. For example,

$$\mathbf{X \vee X \to X \dot{\to} \sim X \vee (X \vee X) \to \sim X \vee X,}$$
$$\mathbf{X \vee X \to X,}$$
$$\mathbf{\sim X \vee (X \vee X) \to \sim X \vee X,}$$
$$\mathbf{X \to X \vee X,}$$
$$\mathbf{X \to X}$$

is a proof of $\mathbf{X \to X}$.

Analogous to the fundamental theorem about wff, we have the important

FUNDAMENTAL THEOREM ABOUT PROVABLE WFF: Each provable wff has property P provided that

1. Each member of each axiom scheme has property P
2. B has property P whenever there exists a wff, say A, such that A and $A \rightarrow B$ are both provable and both possess property P.

Demonstration: Let P be a property that satisfies the assumptions of the theorem, but such that not all provable wff possess property P. Let C be a provable wff which does not have property P. Now consider any proof of C. Clearly, each term of this sequence is provable; furthermore, since there is a term of the sequence which does not have property P, there must be a *first* such term, say E. Certainly E is not a member of an axiom scheme, since any such provable wff has property P by assumption. Therefore, E is preceded in the sequence by two wff, D and $D \rightarrow E$. By assumption, D has property P, and $D \rightarrow E$ has property P; and, of course, $\vdash D$ and $\vdash D \rightarrow E$. Hence, E has property P. This contradiction establishes the theorem.

We shall make frequent use of the preceding theorem. For the moment, we illustrate the theorem by establishing one important property of provable wff:

THEOREM: Each assignment of truth-values to the atomic wff of the propositional calculus assigns t to each provable wff.

Demonstration: We have already observed that each member of any axiom scheme has this property; furthermore, we have seen that E has the property whenever D and $D \rightarrow E$ have the property. Applying the fundamental theorem about provable wff, we conclude that each provable wff has the stated property.

The content of this theorem is that each provable wff is true; later on, we shall demonstrate that each true wff is provable.

EXERCISES

Show that the following are proofs:

1. $\mathbf{Y} \rightarrow \mathbf{Y} \vee \mathbf{Z}$, $\mathbf{Y} \vee \mathbf{Z} \rightarrow \mathbf{Z} \vee \mathbf{Y}$
2. $\mathbf{Y} \vee \mathbf{Y} \rightarrow \mathbf{Y}$
3. $\mathbf{Z} \vee \mathbf{Y} \rightarrow \mathbf{Y} \vee \mathbf{Z}$

4. $\mathbf{X \vee (Y \vee X) \rightarrow (Y \vee X) \vee X}$

5. $\mathbf{Y \rightarrow Y \vee (X \rightarrow \sim X)}$

6. $\mathbf{X \rightarrow X \vee Y \dot{\rightarrow} \sim Y \vee X \rightarrow \sim Y \vee (X \vee Y), \quad X \rightarrow X \vee Y,}$
   $\mathbf{Y \rightarrow X \dot{\rightarrow} Y \rightarrow (X \vee Y)}$

7. $\mathbf{Y \vee X \rightarrow (Y \vee X) \vee Y \dot{\rightarrow} \sim Y \vee (Y \vee X) \rightarrow \sim Y \vee ((Y \vee X) \vee Y),}$
   $\mathbf{Y \vee X \rightarrow (Y \vee X) \vee Y, \quad \sim Y \vee (Y \vee X) \rightarrow \sim Y \vee ((Y \vee X) \vee Y),}$
   $\mathbf{Y \rightarrow Y \vee X, \quad Y \rightarrow (Y \vee X) \vee Y}$

8. Let A be any wff such that $A \vee A$ is provable, and let π be a proof of $A \vee A$. Show that the sequence π, $A \vee A \rightarrow A$, A is a proof. *Hint:* consider the last term of π.

9. Let A be any provable wff, let π be any proof of A, and let B be any wff. Show that the sequence π, $A \rightarrow A \vee B$, $A \vee B$ is a proof.

10. Suppose that $\vdash A \vee B$, and let π be a proof of $A \vee B$. Show that the sequence π, $A \vee B \rightarrow B \vee A$, $B \vee A$ is a proof.

11. Suppose that $\vdash A \rightarrow B$, π is a proof of $A \rightarrow B$, and C is a wff. Show that the sequence π, $A \rightarrow B \dot{\rightarrow} C \vee A \rightarrow C \vee B$, $C \vee A \rightarrow C \vee B$ is a proof.

12. Suppose that $\vdash A \rightarrow B$, $\vdash B \rightarrow C$, π_1 is a proof of $A \rightarrow B$ and π_2 is a proof of $B \rightarrow C$. Show that the sequence π_1, π_2, $B \rightarrow C \ddot{\rightarrow} A \rightarrow B \dot{\rightarrow} A \rightarrow C$, $A \rightarrow B \dot{\rightarrow} A \rightarrow C$, $A \rightarrow C$ is a proof.

13. Suppose $\vdash A$ and $\vdash A \rightarrow B$, and suppose π_1 is a proof of A and π_2 is a proof of $A \rightarrow B$. Show that the sequence π_1, π_2, B is a proof.

14. Show that $\vdash A$ if $\vdash A \vee A$.

15. Show that $\vdash A \vee B$ if $\vdash A$, provided B is a wff.

16. Show that $\vdash B \vee A$ if $\vdash A \vee B$.

17. Show that $\vdash C \vee A \rightarrow C \vee B$ provided that $\vdash A \rightarrow B$ and C is a wff.

18. Prove that $\vdash A \rightarrow B \ddot{\rightarrow} C \rightarrow A \dot{\rightarrow} C \rightarrow B$ whenever A, B, and C are wff.

19. Show that $\vdash A \rightarrow C$ provided that $\vdash A \rightarrow B$ and $\vdash B \rightarrow C$.

20. Show that $\vdash B$ provided that $\vdash A$ and $\vdash A \rightarrow B$.

21. Show that $\vdash A \rightarrow A$ whenever A is a wff.

22. Show that $\vdash A \vee \sim A$ whenever A is a wff.

5. Components and Wff-builders

We continue our study of provable wff. To begin, we list the results of the preceding set of exercises.

THEOREM 1: $\vdash A$ if $\vdash A \vee A$.

THEOREM 2: $\vdash A \vee B$ if $\vdash A$, provided B is a wff.

THEOREM 3: $\vdash B \vee A$ if $\vdash A \vee B$.

THEOREM 4: $\vdash C \vee A \to C \vee B$ provided that $\vdash A \to B$ and C is a wff.

THEOREM 5: $\vdash A \to B \overset{\cdot\cdot}{\to} C \to A \overset{\cdot}{\to} C \to B$ whenever A, B, and C are wff.

THEOREM 6: $\vdash A \to C$ provided that $\vdash A \to B$ and $\vdash B \to C$.

THEOREM 7: $\vdash B$ provided that $\vdash A$ and $\vdash A \to B$.

THEOREM 8: $\vdash A \to A$ whenever A is a wff.

THEOREM 9: $\vdash A \vee \sim A$ whenever A is a wff.

An immediate consequence of Theorem 9 is

THEOREM 10: $\vdash \sim A \vee \sim \sim A$ whenever A is a wff.

In other words,

THEOREM 11: $\vdash A \to \sim \sim A$ whenever A is a wff.

Now we are in a position to establish

THEOREM 12: $\vdash \sim \sim A \to A$ whenever A is a wff.

Demonstration: Let A be any wff. Then $\sim A$ is a wff, and so by Theorem 11, $\vdash \sim A \to \sim \sim \sim A$; by Theorem 4, $\vdash A \vee \sim A \to A \vee \sim \sim \sim A$. By Theorems 9 and 7, $\vdash A \vee \sim \sim \sim A$; by Theorem 3, $\vdash \sim \sim \sim A \vee A$; i.e., $\vdash \sim \sim A \to A$.

THEOREM 13: $\vdash A \to B \overset{\cdot}{\to} \sim B \to \sim A$ whenever A and B are wff.

Demonstration: Let A and B be any wff. By Theorem 11, $\vdash B \to \sim \sim B$; by Theorem 4, $\vdash \sim A \vee B \to \sim A \vee \sim \sim B$. But $\vdash \sim A \vee \sim \sim B \to \sim \sim B \vee \sim A$ by (3); hence, by Theorem 6, $\vdash \sim A \vee B \to \sim \sim B \vee \sim A$; i.e., $\vdash A \to B \overset{\cdot}{\to} \sim B \to \sim A$.

COROLLARY: $\vdash \sim B \to \sim A$ if $\vdash A \to B$.

We now introduce the notion of a *component* of a wff. The idea is this: a wff, say B, is said to be a component of a wff A iff there exist expressions ϕ and θ such that the expression $\phi B \theta$ is A. Either or both of ϕ and θ may be empty expressions. For example, if B is a wff, then B is a component of B and B is a component of $\sim B$. In the former case, ϕ and θ are both empty; in the latter case, ϕ is (~ and θ is).

This concept can be defined formally as follows.

DEFINITION: If A is an atomic wff, then A is the only component of A; the components of $\sim A$ are $\sim A$ and each component of A; the components of $A \vee B$ are $A \vee B$, each component of A, and each component of B.

For example, the components of ~ ((X ∨ ~ Y) ∨ ~ (Y ∨ ~ ~ Z)) are the following wff: ~ ((X ∨ ~ Y) ∨ ~ (Y ∨ ~ ~ Z)), (X ∨ ~ Y) ∨ ~ (Y ∨ ~ ~ Z), X ∨ ~ Y, X, ~ Y, Y, ~ (Y ∨ ~ ~ Z), Y ∨ ~ ~ Z, ~ ~ Z, ~ Z, Z.

Let us establish some properties of components.

THEOREM 14: C is a component of A whenever C is a component of B and B is a component of A.

Demonstration: We shall show that each wff, say A, has the property that any component of a component of A is again a component of A. Applying the fundamental theorem about wff, we must show that each atomic wff has the property, and that $\sim A$ has the property if A has the property, and that $D \vee E$ has the property if D has the property and E has the property. Clearly, each atomic wff has the property. Now suppose that A has the property, and consider $\sim A$. Let C be any component of a component of $\sim A$; the components of $\sim A$ are $\sim A$ itself and each component of A. Hence, either C is a component of $\sim A$ or C is a component of a component of A. But A possesses the stated property; thus, either C is a component of $\sim A$, or C is a component of A. In either case, C is a component of $\sim A$. Finally, we show that $D \vee E$ has the property if both D and E possess the property. Recalling that the components of $D \vee E$ are $D \vee E$ itself, the components of D, and the components of E, we see that any component of a component of $D \vee E$ is either a component of $D \vee E$, a component of a component of D, or a component of a component of E. It now follows, as before, that any component of a component of $D \vee E$ is again a component of $D \vee E$. This establishes the theorem.

We show now that our formal definition has captured the intended idea.

THEOREM 15: Let A be any wff and let B be any component of A. Then there are expressions ϕ and θ, either or both of which may be empty, such that A is $\phi B \theta$.

Demonstration: We shall show that each wff A has the stated property. Clearly, if A is atomic and B is a component of A, then B is A, and ϕ and θ are empty, so that A is $\phi B \theta$. Suppose that C has the property, and consider the wff $\sim C$ and its components. First $\sim C$ itself; but then, as before, ϕ and θ are empty. Now let B be any component of C; since C has the stated property, there exist expressions ϕ and θ such that C is $\phi B \theta$; hence, $\sim C$ is $(\sim \phi B \theta)$. Thus, $\sim C$ possesses the property. In a similar way, we can show that $D \vee E$ has the property if both D and E possess the property. This establishes the theorem.

It remains to establish the converse of Theorem 15. This is not easy! We must first improve our knowledge of the *structure* of wff; in particular, we need to understand the role of parentheses in a wff.

DEFINITION: The *mate* of a particular left-hand parenthesis occurring in a wff is the first right-hand parenthesis to its right such that an equal number of left-hand parentheses and right-hand parentheses occur in between.

DEFINITION: The *mate* of a particular right-hand parenthesis occurring in a wff is the first left-hand parenthesis to its left such that an equal number of left-hand parentheses and right-hand parentheses occur in between.

For example, the parentheses of the following wff are mated as indicated:

$$\begin{array}{c}(((X) \vee (\sim (Y))) \vee (Z))\\ \text{abc c d e edb f fa}\end{array}$$

[the *same* letter is placed under two parentheses iff they are mated].

THEOREM 15-1: Each wff possesses an equal number of left-hand and right-hand parentheses.

Demonstration: Apply the Fundamental Theorem about Wff.

THEOREM 15-2: Counting from left to right, the number of instances of left-hand parentheses in a wff is in excess of the number of instances of right-hand parentheses in the wff, until the final right-hand parenthesis is reached.

Demonstration: Apply the Fundamental Theorem about Wff.

THEOREM 15-3: Each parenthesis occurring in a wff possesses a mate.

Demonstration: Apply the Fundamental Theorem about Wff (use Theorem 15-2).

THEOREM 15-4: No two parentheses of a wff have the same mate.

Demonstration: Apply the Fundamental Theorem about Wff (use Theorem 15-2).

THEOREM 15-5: The first and last parentheses of a wff are mated.

Demonstration: Theorem 15-3 and Theorem 15-2.

We can now establish the converse of Theorem 15.

THEOREM 15-6: Let A and B be any wff, and let ϕ and θ be any expressions such that $A = \phi B \theta$; then B is a component of A.

Demonstration: We apply the Fundamental Theorem about Wff. Clearly, if A is atomic and B is a wff such that $A = \phi B \theta$, then B is A; so, B is a component of A. Suppose that C has the property; we shall show that **(**~ C**)** has the property. Let B be a wff such that **(**~ C**)** $= \phi B\theta$. If $C = \phi_1 B\theta_1$, then B is a component of C by assumption; hence, B is a component of **(**~ C**)**. If B is not contained within C, then $B =$ **(**~ α, where α is contained within C**)**. Since B is a wff it follows from Theorem 15.5 that $\alpha = C$**)** so that $B =$ **(**~ C**)**; otherwise, the first parenthesis of B has no mate. Thus, B is a component of **(**~ C**)**. In a similar way, we can show that **(**D **∨** E**)** has the property if both D and E possess the property. This establishes the theorem.

The expressions ϕ and θ referred to in Theorems 15 and 15-6 are not necessarily wff. Consider, for example, the wff **((Y) ∨ (~ (Z)))**, which we have written out in full. The wff **(Z)** is a component of this wff; here ϕ is the expression **((Y) ∨ (~** and θ is the expression **))**, neither of which is a wff.

We turn our attention from the component of a wff to the accompanying two expressions.

DEFINITION: We say that $[\phi, \theta]$ is a *wff-builder* iff $\phi A\theta$ is a wff whenever A is a wff.

For example, we obtain a wff-builder if ϕ and θ are both empty expressions. Again, let ϕ be **(**~ and let θ be **)** and we have a wff-builder.

We establish some properties of wff-builders.

THEOREM 16: Let ϕ and θ be expressions such that $\phi A\theta$ is a wff, where A is a suitably chosen wff; then $[\phi, \theta]$ is a wff-builder.

Demonstration: The theorem asserts that if there exists one wff A such that $\phi A\theta$ is a wff, then $\phi B\theta$ is a wff whenever B is a wff. To prove this theorem it is convenient to change our point of view; clearly, our theorem states that the expression obtained from a given wff, say C, by replacing a component of C by another wff is again a wff. Let us show that each wff C possesses this property. Certainly, if C is an atomic wff, the result of substituting a wff B for a component of C is the wff B. Next, let us show that ~ D has the property whenever the wff D has the property. The components of ~ D are ~ D or components of D. Substituting B for a component of ~ D produces B in the first case, and ~ (D') in the second case, where D' is a wff, by assumption. Finally, we show that the wff E **∨** F has the property if E has the property and F has the property. Considering the components of E **∨** F, it is easy to see, as before, that the result of substituting a wff for a component of E **∨** F is again a wff. This establishes our theorem.

THEOREM 17: Suppose that $\vdash A \rightarrow B$ and $\vdash B \rightarrow A$ and $\phi A\theta$ is a wff; then $\vdash \phi A\theta \rightarrow \phi B\theta$ and $\vdash \phi B\theta \rightarrow \phi A\theta$.

Demonstration: The theorem asserts that each wff C has the following property. Suppose A is a component of C, so that C is $\phi A\theta$; then $\vdash \phi A\theta \rightarrow \phi B\theta$

and $\vdash \phi B\theta \rightarrow \phi A\theta$, provided $\vdash A \rightarrow B$ and $\vdash B \rightarrow A$. Clearly, each atomic wff has this property. Next, let us show that $\sim C$ has the property whenever the wff C has the property. One component of $\sim C$ is $\sim C$; if $\vdash \sim C \rightarrow B$ and $\vdash B \rightarrow \sim C$, then $\vdash \sim C \rightarrow B$ and $\vdash B \rightarrow \sim C$. Now let D be any other component of $\sim C$; then D is a component of C. Hence, by assumption, $\vdash \phi D\theta \rightarrow \phi B\theta$ and $\vdash \phi B\theta \rightarrow \phi D\theta$ whenever $\vdash D \rightarrow B$ and $\vdash B \rightarrow D$. It now follows from Theorem 13 and Theorem 7 that $\vdash \sim \phi B\theta \rightarrow \sim \phi D\theta$ and $\vdash \sim \phi D\theta \rightarrow \sim \phi B\theta$ provided that $\vdash D \rightarrow B$ and $\vdash B \rightarrow D$. This shows that $\sim C$ has the property whenever C has the property. Now suppose that wff E and F possess the property; we shall show that $E \vee F$ has the property. One component of $E \vee F$ is $E \vee F$; if $\vdash E \vee F \rightarrow B$ and $\vdash B \rightarrow E \vee F$, then $\vdash E \vee F \rightarrow B$ and $\vdash B \rightarrow E \vee F$. Now suppose that D is any other component of $E \vee F$; then D is a component of E, or D is a component of F. Suppose that F is $\phi D\theta$ and $\vdash D \rightarrow B$ and $\vdash B \rightarrow D$. Then, by assumption $\vdash \phi D\theta \rightarrow \phi B\theta$ and $\vdash \phi B\theta \rightarrow \phi D\theta$; hence, by Theorem 4, $\vdash E \vee \phi D\theta \rightarrow E \vee \phi B\theta$ and $\vdash E \vee \phi B\theta \rightarrow E \vee \phi D\theta$. The case in which D is a component of E is easily established in a similar way. This demonstrates our theorem.

The following is an important corollary to Theorem 17.

THEOREM 18 (THE SUBSTITUTION THEOREM): If $\vdash \phi A\theta$ and $\vdash A \rightarrow B$ and $\vdash B \rightarrow A$, then $\vdash \phi B\theta$.

Demonstration: Theorem 17 and Theorem 7.

The following definition is useful.

DEFINITION: We shall say that the wff A and B are *equivalent* iff $\vdash A \rightarrow B$ and $\vdash B \rightarrow A$. We shall denote the statement "A and B are equivalent" by writing "$A \equiv B$".

For example, $\sim \sim A \equiv A$ by Theorems 11 and 12. Again, by (3), if C and D are any wff, then $C \vee D \equiv D \vee C$. Also, by Theorem 8, if A is any wff, then $A \equiv A$.

THEOREM 19: $\equiv$ is an equivalence relation on the set of all wff.

Demonstration: We must show that $\equiv$ is reflexive, symmetric, and transistive.

1. $\equiv$ is reflexive; i.e., $A \equiv A$ whenever A is a wff. We have already shown this.
2. $\equiv$ is symmetric; i.e., $B \equiv A$ whenever $A \equiv B$. But $A \equiv B$ means that $\vdash A \rightarrow B$ and $\vdash B \rightarrow A$; therefore, $B \equiv A$.
3. $\equiv$ is transistive; i.e., $A \equiv C$ whenever $A \equiv B$ and $B \equiv C$. Suppose that $A \equiv B$ and $B \equiv C$; then $\vdash A \rightarrow B$ and $\vdash B \rightarrow A$ and $\vdash B \rightarrow C$ and $\vdash C \rightarrow B$. Hence, by Theorem 6, $\vdash A \rightarrow C$, since $\vdash A \rightarrow B$ and $\vdash B \rightarrow C$; again, by Theorem 6, $\vdash C \rightarrow A$, since $\vdash C \rightarrow B$ and $\vdash B \rightarrow A$. Therefore, $A \equiv C$.

This demonstrates Theorem 19.

We are now in a position to interpret Theorem 17 in the following way:

THEOREM 20: $\phi A\theta \equiv \phi B\theta$ provided that $A \equiv B$ and $[\phi, \theta]$ is a wff-builder.

In other words, the wff constructed from equivalent wff by applying the same wff-builder to each are equivalent. For example, $A \vee B \equiv B \vee A$; hence, $\phi A \vee B\theta \equiv \phi B \vee A\theta$ whenever $[\phi, \theta]$ is a wff-builder. Similarly, $\phi A\theta \equiv \phi \sim \sim A\theta$ whenever $[\phi, \theta]$ is a wff-builder.

THEOREM 21: $A \equiv B$ iff $\sim A \equiv \sim B$.

Demonstration: Since we have an "iff", there are two parts to the demonstration.

(1) Assume that $A \equiv B$. Then by Theorem 20 $\sim A \equiv \sim B$, since $[(\sim,)]$ is a wff-builder.

(2) Assume that $\sim A \equiv \sim B$. Then $\sim \sim A \equiv \sim \sim B$ by (1). But $A \equiv \sim \sim A$ and $B \equiv \sim \sim B$; therefore, $A \equiv B$ by Theorem 19.

This establishes the theorem.

EXERCISES

1. Show that $\vdash A \rightarrow B \dot{\rightarrow} A \vee C \rightarrow B \vee C$ whenever A, B, and C are wff.
2. Show that $\vdash \sim A \rightarrow \sim B \dot{\rightarrow} \sim \sim B \rightarrow \sim \sim A$ whenever A and B are wff.
3. Show that $\vdash \sim A \rightarrow \sim B \dot{\rightarrow} B \rightarrow A$ whenever A and B are wff.
4. Consider the formal definition of the notion of component. Is it possible that there is a wff which possesses no components?
5. List the components of **((Y) ∨ (~ (X)))**.
6. List the components of **(((Z) ∨ (~ (X))) ∨ (~ (~ (Y))))**.
7. Show that $\phi A\theta$ is a wff whenever A is a wff, given that ϕ is (, and θ is **∨ (X))**.
8. Show that $A \vee C \equiv B \vee D$ whenever $A \equiv B$ and $C \equiv D$.
9. Show that $A \wedge C \equiv B \wedge D$ whenever $A \equiv B$ and $C \equiv D$.
10. Given that $A \equiv B$, show that $\mu[A] = \mu[B]$ no matter how λ is chosen.

6. Normal Form

The symbol "∧" was introduced into the propositional calculus, ostensibly because of its abbreviating powers in connection with a parentheses-omitting convention. Here and in the following section, we shall present fundamental reasons for the desirability of "∧".

Recalling that $A \wedge B = \sim(\sim A \vee \sim B)$, we see that

$$\sim(A \wedge B) = \sim\sim(\sim A \vee \sim B)$$

Therefore, by Theorems 11 and 12, $\sim(A \wedge B) \equiv \sim A \vee \sim B$ whenever A and B are wff. Hence, $\sim(\sim A \wedge \sim B) \equiv \sim\sim A \vee \sim\sim B$ whenever A and B are wff; but $\sim\sim A \vee \sim\sim B \equiv A \vee B$, thus $\sim(\sim A \wedge \sim B) \equiv A \vee B$ whenever A and B are wff. In particular, $\sim(A \vee B) \equiv \sim A \wedge \sim B$ whenever A and B are wff.

In the above, we have used the important

(a) $\sim\sim A \equiv A$ whenever A is a wff to develop
(b) $\sim(A \vee B) \equiv \sim A \wedge \sim B$ whenever A and B are wff and
(c) $\sim(A \wedge B) \equiv \sim A \vee \sim B$ whenever A and B are wff.

Now consider the wff $((\mathbf{X} \vee \sim \mathbf{Y}) \vee (\mathbf{Z} \wedge \mathbf{W})) \wedge (\mathbf{Y} \vee \sim \mathbf{W})$, which we shall denote by "E".
Then

$$\sim E = \sim(((\mathbf{X} \vee \sim \mathbf{Y}) \vee (\mathbf{Z} \wedge \mathbf{W})) \wedge (\mathbf{Y} \vee \sim \mathbf{W}))$$

hence

$$\begin{aligned} \sim E &\equiv \sim((\mathbf{X} \vee \sim \mathbf{Y}) \vee (\mathbf{Z} \wedge \mathbf{W})) \vee \sim(\mathbf{Y} \vee \sim \mathbf{W}) && \text{by (c)} \\ &\equiv \sim(\mathbf{X} \vee \sim \mathbf{Y}) \wedge \sim(\mathbf{Z} \wedge \mathbf{W}) \dot{\vee} \sim \mathbf{Y} \wedge \sim\sim \mathbf{W} && \text{by (b)} \\ &\equiv (\sim \mathbf{X} \wedge \sim\sim \mathbf{Y}) \wedge (\sim \mathbf{Z} \vee \sim \mathbf{W}) \dot{\vee} \sim \mathbf{Y} \wedge \sim\sim \mathbf{W} && \text{by (b) and (c).} \end{aligned}$$

Let us denote $(\sim \mathbf{X} \wedge \sim\sim \mathbf{Y}) \wedge (\sim \mathbf{Z} \vee \sim \mathbf{W}) \dot{\vee} \sim \mathbf{Y} \wedge \sim\sim \mathbf{W}$ by "F". Observe that F is closely related, in form, to E. In fact, F can be obtained from E by carrying out the following transformation on E:

(i) the symbols $\wedge$ and $\vee$ are interchanged throughout E
(ii) each atomic wff in E, say x, is replaced by $\sim x$.

In Section 7 we shall formalize the above transformation, and show that our result is no mere accident. For the moment, let us consider the normal form of a wff discussed in Chapter 1. Roughly put, a wff A is in *normal* form if, after replacing each component of A of the form $\sim(\sim B \vee \sim C)$ by $B \wedge C$, we observe that the symbol $\sim$ occurs only prefixed to atomic wff. More precisely, after carrying out the transformation on A involved in replacing $\sim(\sim B \vee \sim C)$ by $B \wedge C$, the only connectives that occur in A are $\sim$, $\vee$, $\wedge$; furthermore, $\sim$ occurs only prefixed to atomic wff.

For example, the following wff are in normal form: $\sim \mathbf{X} \vee \mathbf{Y}$, $\sim \mathbf{W}$, $\sim(\sim \mathbf{X} \vee \sim \mathbf{Y}) \dot{\vee} (\mathbf{Z} \vee \sim \mathbf{Y}) \vee \sim(\sim \mathbf{W} \vee \sim\sim \mathbf{Z})$, $\sim \mathbf{Z} \vee \mathbf{W} \dot{\vee} \sim \mathbf{X} \vee (\mathbf{Y} \vee \mathbf{Z})$ On the other hand, the following wff are not in normal form: $\mathbf{X} \vee \sim\sim \mathbf{W}$, $\sim(\sim \mathbf{X} \vee \mathbf{Y})$, $\sim\sim \mathbf{X}$.

We have introduced the notion of normal form, partly to demonstrate the desirability of definitions that "ape" the construction-steps involved in forming a wff. Notice that this definition of normal form does *not* follow this pattern. As a result, we shall experience difficulty in establishing the main properties of normal form. Let us see how far we can get.

THEOREM 22: If A and B are in normal form, then $A \vee B$ is in normal form.

THEOREM 23: No wff of the form $\sim \sim A$ is in normal form.

These theorems are obvious; now consider

THEOREM 24: Let A be any wff; there exists a wff in normal form, say B, such that $A \equiv B$.

Demonstration: We apply the fundamental theorem about wff to establish that each wff possesses the stated property. If A is atomic, then A itself is in normal form. Now suppose that C is a wff with the property; we must show that $\sim C$ also has the property. By assumption, there is a wff in normal form, say B, such that $C \equiv B$; then by Theorem 21, $\sim C \equiv \sim B$.

Now we appeal to intuition. By applying (a), (b), and (c) as necessary to $\sim B$, we construct from $\sim B$ a wff in normal form, which is equivalent to $\sim B$, and so is equivalent to $\sim C$. Finally, suppose that D and E are wff which possess the property; we shall show that $D \vee E$ also has the property. By assumption, there exist wff, D_1 and E_1, in normal form such that $D \equiv D_1$ and $E \equiv E_1$. By Exercise 8 on page 127, it follows that $D \vee E \equiv D_1 \vee E_1$; but $D_1 \vee E_1$ is in normal form, by Theorem 22. This establishes Theorem 24.

Note that the demonstration of Theorem 24 relied on an appeal to intuition at a crucial point; hence, the demonstration is not rigorous. In Section 7 we shall present definitions of this and related concepts that follow the pattern of the permitted construction-steps. We shall see that such definitions are clear and unambiguous; furthermore, our fundamental theorem about wff is readily applied; thus, we obtain rigorous proofs.

EXERCISES

1. Show that

$$\sim ((\sim \mathbf{X} \vee \mathbf{Y}) \wedge (\mathbf{X} \vee \sim \mathbf{Y})) \equiv (\sim \sim \mathbf{X} \wedge \sim \mathbf{Y}) \vee (\sim \mathbf{X} \wedge \sim \sim \mathbf{Y})$$

2. Show that

$$\sim (\sim \mathbf{Y} \vee (\mathbf{Z} \wedge \sim \sim \mathbf{W})) \equiv \sim \sim \mathbf{Y} \wedge (\sim \mathbf{Z} \vee \sim \sim \sim \mathbf{W})$$

3. Show that

$$\sim ((\sim \mathbf{X} \vee \sim \sim \mathbf{Y}) \wedge \mathbf{Z} \mathbin{\dot\vee} \mathbf{X} \vee (\sim \mathbf{Y} \wedge \mathbf{Z}))$$
$$\equiv (\sim \sim \mathbf{X} \wedge \sim \sim \sim \mathbf{Y}) \vee \sim \mathbf{Z} \mathbin{\dot\wedge} \sim \mathbf{X} \wedge (\sim \sim \mathbf{Y} \vee \sim \mathbf{Z})$$

Which of the following wff are in normal form?

4. $\sim \mathbf{Y}$

5. $\sim \sim \mathbf{Y}$
6. $\mathbf{Y}$
7. $\mathbf{Y} \vee \mathbf{Z}$
8. $\sim \mathbf{Y} \vee \mathbf{Z} \dot{\vee} \sim \mathbf{X}$
9. $\sim \mathbf{Y} \vee \mathbf{Z} \dot{\vee} \sim \sim \mathbf{X}$
10. $\mathbf{X} \vee \sim (\sim \mathbf{Y} \vee \mathbf{Z})$
11. $\mathbf{X} \vee \sim (\sim \mathbf{Y} \vee \sim \sim \mathbf{Z})$
12. $\sim \mathbf{X} \vee \sim (\sim \mathbf{Y} \vee \sim \sim \mathbf{Z})$
13. $\sim (\sim \mathbf{X} \vee \sim \mathbf{Y}) \vee \sim (\sim \mathbf{W} \vee \sim \mathbf{Z})$
14. $\sim (\sim \mathbf{X} \vee \sim \mathbf{Y}) \vee \sim (\sim \mathbf{W} \vee \mathbf{Z})$
15. $\sim (\sim \mathbf{X} \vee \sim \mathbf{Y}) \vee \sim (\sim \mathbf{W} \vee \sim \mathbf{Z}) \dot{\vee} \sim (\sim \mathbf{Y} \vee \sim \sim \mathbf{Z})$
16. $\sim (\sim \mathbf{X} \vee \sim \sim (\sim \mathbf{Y} \vee \sim \mathbf{Z}))$

7. Syntactical Transforms and Duality

In order to formalize our notion of normal form, introduced in Section 6, it is helpful to consider the general concept of a *syntactical transform*. By a syntactical transform, we mean a formalized procedure that produces a wff from a given wff by considering the *form* of the given wff; thus, the given wff is transformed by rules which operate on the shape or structure of the wff. Let $\mathscr{T}$ be any syntactical transform; then $\mathscr{T}$ is a mapping of the set of all wff *into* the set of all wff. This means, following the usual code, that "$\mathscr{T}(A)$" denotes the wff constructed from A by applying the syntactical transform $\mathscr{T}$. Frequently, we shall drop the parentheses—denoting $\mathscr{T}(A)$ by writing "$\mathscr{T}A$".

Now that we know what we mean by a syntactical transform, let us consider an efficient method of presenting or defining particular syntactical transforms. To know a given syntactical transform, say $\mathscr{T}$, is to know what $\mathscr{T}$ does to each wff; in particular, we must know what $\mathscr{T}A$ is whenever A is atomic, we must know $\mathscr{T}(\sim B)$, possibly in terms of $\mathscr{T}B$. Finally we must know $\mathscr{T}(D \vee E)$, again possibly in terms of $\mathscr{T}D$ and $\mathscr{T}E$. It turns out that this information characterizes the syntactical transform; in fact, let us establish the following

THEOREM 25: $\mathscr{T}A$ is defined for each wff A, provided that

1. $\mathscr{T}B$ is defined for each atomic wff B;
2. $\mathscr{T}(\sim C)$ is defined in terms of the same transform of one or more "shorter" wff;
3. $\mathscr{T}(D \vee E)$ is defined in terms of the same transform of one or more "shorter" wff.

Demonstration: Suppose there is a wff, say A, such that $\mathscr{T}A$ is not defined; then, by 1, A is not atomic, and so A possesses a length. Considering the set of all wff with this property, we see that there exists a "shortest" wff which does not possess the property. Since this wff is not atomic, it possesses a "main" connective, either $\sim$ or $\mathbf{v}$. Clearly, $\sim$ is not the main connective of our wff, since $\mathscr{T}(\sim C)$ is defined in terms of the transform of shorter wff; by assumption, the transform of a wff shorter than our wff is defined. Thus, the main connective of our wff can only be $\mathbf{v}$; but again in view of 3, we see that this entails that the transform of our wff *is* defined. Thus, Theorem 25 is established.

In Section 6 we referred to a wff as being in normal form, provided that certain conditions were met. It turns out that this concept can be handled more easily if we think of it from the point of view of syntactical transforms. Let us associate with a given wff, say A, a wff which we shall call *the normal form of A* and denote by writing "$\mathscr{N}A$". The syntactical transform $\mathscr{N}$ is defined as follows:

DEFINITION OF $\mathscr{N}$:

(1) $$\mathscr{N}A = A \text{ if } A \text{ is atomic}$$

(2) $$\mathscr{N}(\sim A) = \begin{cases} \sim A \text{ if } A \text{ is atomic} \\ \mathscr{N}(B) \text{ if } A = \sim B \\ \mathscr{N}(\sim C) \wedge \mathscr{N}(\sim D) \text{ if } A = C \mathbf{v} D \end{cases}$$

(3) $$\mathscr{N}(C \mathbf{v} D) = \mathscr{N}C \mathbf{v} \mathscr{N}D$$

For example,

$$\begin{aligned}
&\mathscr{N}((\mathbf{X} \mathbf{v} \sim \mathbf{Y}) \mathbf{v} \sim (\sim \mathbf{W} \mathbf{v} (\mathbf{Z} \mathbf{v} \sim \mathbf{X})))\\
&\quad = \mathscr{N}(\mathbf{X} \mathbf{v} \sim \mathbf{Y}) \mathbf{v} \mathscr{N}(\sim (\sim \mathbf{W} \mathbf{v} (\mathbf{Z} \mathbf{v} \sim \mathbf{X}))) && \text{by (3)}\\
&\quad = \mathscr{N}(\mathbf{X} \mathbf{v} \sim \mathbf{Y}) \mathbf{v} (\mathscr{N}(\sim \sim \mathbf{W}) \wedge \mathscr{N}(\sim (\mathbf{Z} \mathbf{v} \sim \mathbf{X}))) && \text{by (2)}\\
&\quad = \mathscr{N}(\mathbf{X} \mathbf{v} \sim \mathbf{Y}) \mathbf{v} (\mathscr{N}\mathbf{W} \wedge (\mathscr{N}(\sim \mathbf{Z}) \wedge \mathscr{N}(\sim \sim \mathbf{X})) && \text{by (2)}\\
&\quad = \mathscr{N}(\mathbf{X} \mathbf{v} \sim \mathbf{Y}) \dot{\mathbf{v}} \mathbf{W} \wedge (\sim \mathbf{Z} \wedge \mathscr{N}\mathbf{X}) && \text{by (1) and (2)}\\
&\quad = \mathscr{N}(\mathbf{X} \mathbf{v} \sim \mathbf{Y}) \dot{\mathbf{v}} \mathbf{W} \wedge (\sim \mathbf{Z} \wedge \mathbf{X}) && \text{by (1)}\\
&\quad = \mathscr{N}\mathbf{X} \mathbf{v} \mathscr{N}(\sim \mathbf{Y}) \dot{\mathbf{v}} \mathbf{W} \wedge (\sim \mathbf{Z} \wedge \mathbf{X}) && \text{by (3)}\\
&\quad = \mathbf{X} \mathbf{v} \sim \mathbf{Y} \dot{\mathbf{v}} \mathbf{W} \wedge (\sim \mathbf{Z} \wedge \mathbf{X}) && \text{by (1) and (2)}
\end{aligned}$$

We now establish the basic properties of this syntactical transform.

THEOREM 26: $\sim \mathscr{N}B \equiv \mathscr{N}(\sim B)$ for any wff B.

Demonstration: We show that each wff B has the property that $\sim \mathscr{N}B \equiv \mathscr{N}(\sim B)$, by applying the fundamental theorem about wff. First, we show that each atomic wff possesses the stated property. Let B be atomic, then $\sim \mathscr{N}B = \sim B$ and $\mathscr{N}(\sim B) = \sim B$ by definition. Now suppose that C

is a wff with the property; we shall show that $\sim C$ also has the property; i.e., we shall show that $\mathcal{N}(\sim\sim C) \equiv \sim\mathcal{N}(\sim C)$. But $\mathcal{N}(\sim\sim C) = \mathcal{N}(C)$ by (2); and we are supposing that $\sim\mathcal{N}(C) \equiv \mathcal{N}(\sim C)$. Finally, we show that $C \vee D$ has the property whenever C has the property and D has the property. We are assuming that $\sim\mathcal{N}(C) \equiv \mathcal{N}(\sim C)$ and $\sim\mathcal{N}(D) \equiv \mathcal{N}(\sim D)$. But $\mathcal{N}(C \vee D) = \mathcal{N}(C) \vee \mathcal{N}(D)$ by (3), and so $\mathcal{N}(C \vee D) \equiv \sim\mathcal{N}(\sim C) \vee \sim\mathcal{N}(\sim D)$ by assumption. Furthermore, $\mathcal{N}(\sim(C \vee D)) = \mathcal{N}(\sim C) \wedge \mathcal{N}(\sim D)$ by (2); hence, $\sim\mathcal{N}(\sim(C \vee D)) \equiv \sim\mathcal{N}(\sim C) \vee \sim\mathcal{N}(\sim D)$. This establishes the theorem.

THEOREM 27: $A \equiv \mathcal{N}A$ for each wff A.

Demonstration: Again, we shall apply our fundamental theorem about wff. Let B be any atomic wff; then $\mathcal{N}(B) = B$ and so $\mathcal{N}(B) \equiv B$. Now suppose that C is a wff such that $\mathcal{N}(C) \equiv C$; we shall show that $\mathcal{N}(\sim C) \equiv \sim C$. By Theorem 26, $\mathcal{N}(\sim C) \equiv \sim\mathcal{N}(C)$, but $\mathcal{N}(C) \equiv C$ by assumption; hence, by Theorem 21, $\sim\mathcal{N}(C) \equiv \sim C$, and so by Theorem 19, $\mathcal{N}(\sim C) \equiv \sim C$. Finally, we show that $\mathcal{N}(C \vee D) \equiv C \vee D$ whenever $\mathcal{N}(C) \equiv C$ and $\mathcal{N}(D) \equiv D$. By (3), $\mathcal{N}(C \vee D) = \mathcal{N}C \vee \mathcal{N}D$; hence, by Exercise 8, page 127, $\mathcal{N}(C \vee D) \equiv C \vee D$. This establishes the theorem.

THEOREM 28: $\mathcal{N}(A \rightarrow B) \equiv \mathcal{N}A \rightarrow \mathcal{N}B$ whenever A and B are wff.

Demonstration:

$$\mathcal{N}(\sim A \vee B) = \mathcal{N}(\sim A) \vee \mathcal{N}B \equiv \sim\mathcal{N}A \vee \mathcal{N}B = \mathcal{N}A \rightarrow \mathcal{N}B.$$

THEOREM 29: Let A be any wff such that $\vdash A$; then $\vdash \mathcal{N}A$.

Demonstration: $\vdash A \rightarrow \mathcal{N}A$ by Theorem 27.

THEOREM 30: $\mathcal{N}A \equiv \mathcal{N}B$ whenever $A \equiv B$.

Demonstration: Since $\vdash A \rightarrow B$, it follows from Theorem 29 that $\vdash \mathcal{N}(A \rightarrow B)$, and so by Theorem 28 and Modus Ponens $\vdash \mathcal{N}A \rightarrow \mathcal{N}B$. Again, $\vdash B \rightarrow A$; so, by the same argument, $\vdash \mathcal{N}B \rightarrow \mathcal{N}A$. Thus, $\mathcal{N}A \equiv \mathcal{N}B$.

We now introduce another syntactical transform $\mathcal{M}$, designed to first transform a wff into normal form, then to interchange $\wedge$ and $\vee$ throughout, and finally to replace each instance of an atomic wff, say x, by $\sim x$, and each instance of $\sim x$ by x. $\mathcal{M}$ is defined as follows.

DEFINITION OF $\mathcal{M}$:

(1) $$\mathcal{M}A = \sim A \text{ if } A \text{ is atomic}$$

(2) $$\mathcal{M}(\sim A) = \begin{cases} A \text{ if } A \text{ is atomic} \\ \mathcal{M}(B) \text{ if } A = \sim B \\ \mathcal{M}(\sim B) \vee \mathcal{M}(\sim C) \text{ if } A = B \vee C \end{cases}$$

(3) $$\mathcal{M}(A \vee B) = \mathcal{M}A \wedge \mathcal{M}B.$$

For example,

$\mathscr{M}((\mathbf{X} \vee \sim \mathbf{Y}) \vee \sim(\sim \mathbf{Y} \vee \sim \mathbf{Z}))$

$= \mathscr{M}(\mathbf{X} \vee \sim \mathbf{Y}) \wedge \mathscr{M}(\sim(\sim \mathbf{Y} \vee \sim \mathbf{Z}))$ by (3)

$= (\mathscr{M}\mathbf{X} \wedge \mathscr{M}(\sim \mathbf{Y})) \wedge (\mathscr{M}(\sim \sim \mathbf{Y}) \vee \mathscr{M}(\sim \sim \mathbf{Z}))$ by (3) and (2)

$= (\sim \mathbf{X} \wedge \mathbf{Y}) \wedge (\mathscr{M}\mathbf{Y} \vee \mathscr{M}\mathbf{Z})$ by (1) and (2)

$= (\sim \mathbf{X} \wedge \mathbf{Y}) \wedge (\sim \mathbf{Y} \vee \sim \mathbf{Z})$ by (1).

We now establish some properties of the syntactical transform $\mathscr{M}$.

THEOREM 31: $\mathscr{M}(\sim A) \equiv \sim \mathscr{M}A$ for any wff A.

Demonstration: We show that each wff A has the property that $\mathscr{M}(\sim A) \equiv \sim \mathscr{M}A$ by applying the fundamental theorem about wff. First, we show that each atomic wff possesses the stated property. Let A be atomic; then $\mathscr{M}(\sim A) = A$, whereas $\sim \mathscr{M}A = \sim \sim A$ by definition; but $A \equiv \sim \sim A$. Now suppose that C is a wff with the property; we shall show that $\sim C$ also has the property; i.e., we shall show that $\mathscr{M}(\sim \sim C) \equiv \sim \mathscr{M}(\sim C)$. But $\mathscr{M}(\sim \sim C) = \mathscr{M}C$ by definition; and by assumption, $\mathscr{M}C \equiv \sim \mathscr{M}(\sim C)$. Finally, we show that $C \vee D$ has the property whenever C has the property and D has the property. Now

$$\mathscr{M}(\sim(C \vee D)) = \mathscr{M}(\sim C) \vee \mathscr{M}(\sim D) \equiv \sim \mathscr{M}C \vee \sim \mathscr{M}D$$

by assumption, and

$$\sim \mathscr{M}(C \vee D) = \sim(\mathscr{M}C \wedge \mathscr{M}D) \equiv \sim \mathscr{M}C \vee \sim \mathscr{M}D.$$

This establishes the theorem.

THEOREM 32: $\mathscr{M}A \equiv \sim A$ for each wff A.

Demonstration: Again, we shall apply our fundamental theorem about wff. Let A be any atomic wff. Then $\mathscr{M}A = \sim A$; thus each atomic wff has the property. Now suppose that C is a wff with the property; we show that $\sim C$ also has the property. But $\mathscr{M}(\sim C) \equiv \sim \mathscr{M}C$, by Theorem 31; and $\mathscr{M}C \equiv \sim C$ by assumption. Thus, $\mathscr{M}(\sim C) \equiv \sim \sim C$. Finally, we show that $C \vee D$ has the property whenever C has the property and D has the property. We assume, then, that $\mathscr{M}C \equiv \sim C$ and $\mathscr{M}D \equiv \sim D$; hence, $\mathscr{M}(C \vee D) = \mathscr{M}C \wedge \mathscr{M}D \equiv \sim C \wedge \sim D \equiv \sim(C \vee D)$. This establishes our theorem.

COROLLARY: $\mathscr{M}(\mathscr{M}A) \equiv A$ for each wff A.

Demonstration: $\mathscr{M}(\mathscr{M}A) \equiv \sim \mathscr{M}A \equiv \sim \sim A \equiv A$ by Theorem 32.

The following theorem is the basis of the principle of duality, which we shall consider later.

THEOREM 33: $\mathscr{M}A \equiv \mathscr{M}B$ whenever $A \equiv B$.

Demonstration: Since $A \equiv B$, it follows from Theorem 21 that $\sim A \equiv \sim B$. But $\sim A \equiv \mathscr{M}A$ and $\sim B \equiv \mathscr{M}B$; therefore, by Theorem 19, $\mathscr{M}A \equiv \mathscr{M}B$.

In connection with the principle of duality, which we shall soon meet, we require a syntactical transform, $\mathscr{R}$, which reverses the effect of $\mathscr{M}$ on atomic wff. We define $\mathscr{R}$ as follows:

DEFINITION OF $\mathscr{R}$:

(1) $$\mathscr{R}A = \sim A \text{ if } A \text{ is atomic}$$

(2) $$\mathscr{R}(\sim A) = \begin{cases} A \text{ if } A \text{ is atomic} \\ \mathscr{R}B \text{ if } A = \sim B \\ \sim \mathscr{R}A \text{ if } A = B \lor C \end{cases}$$

(3) $$\mathscr{R}(A \lor B) = \mathscr{R}A \lor \mathscr{R}B.$$

For example,

$$\begin{aligned}\mathscr{R}((\mathbf{X} \lor \sim \mathbf{Y}) \lor \sim (\sim \mathbf{W} \lor \mathbf{Z})) &= \mathscr{R}(\mathbf{X} \lor \sim \mathbf{Y}) \lor \mathscr{R}(\sim (\sim \mathbf{W} \lor \mathbf{Z})) \\ &= (\mathscr{R}\mathbf{X} \lor \mathscr{R}(\sim \mathbf{Y})) \lor \sim \mathscr{R}(\sim \mathbf{W} \lor \mathbf{Z}) \\ &= (\sim \mathbf{X} \lor \mathbf{Y}) \lor \sim (\mathscr{R}(\sim \mathbf{W}) \lor \mathscr{R}\mathbf{Z}) \\ &= (\sim \mathbf{X} \lor \mathbf{Y}) \lor \sim (\mathbf{W} \lor \sim \mathbf{Z}).\end{aligned}$$

In short, the effect of $\mathscr{R}$ on a wff is to replace each instance of an atomic wff, say x, by $\sim x$, and each instance of $\sim x$ by x. Thus, we can cancel the effect of $\mathscr{M}$ on atomic wff by applying $\mathscr{R}$ after applying $\mathscr{M}$.

We now establish some properties of the syntactical transform $\mathscr{R}$.

THEOREM 34: $\mathscr{R}(\sim A) \equiv \sim \mathscr{R}A$ for any wff A.

Demonstration: Apply the fundamental theorem about wff.

COROLLARY: $\mathscr{R}(A \rightarrow B) \equiv \mathscr{R}A \rightarrow \mathscr{R}B$ whenever A and B are wff.

Demonstration: $\mathscr{R}(A \rightarrow B) = \mathscr{R}(\sim A) \lor \mathscr{R}B \equiv \sim \mathscr{R}A \lor \mathscr{R}B$ by Theorems 34 and 20.

THEOREM 35: $\vdash \mathscr{R}A$ if $\vdash A$.

Demonstration: Apply the fundamental theorem about provable wff.

COROLLARY: $\mathscr{R}A \equiv \mathscr{R}B$ whenever $A \equiv B$.

Demonstration: Since $\vdash A \rightarrow B$, it follows from Theorem 35 that $\vdash \mathscr{R}(A \rightarrow B)$; hence applying the Corollary to Theorem 34, $\vdash \mathscr{R}A \rightarrow \mathscr{R}B$. Similarly, since, $\vdash B \rightarrow A$, we obtain $\vdash \mathscr{R}(B \rightarrow A)$ and so $\vdash \mathscr{R}B \rightarrow \mathscr{R}A$. Thus, $\mathscr{R}A \equiv \mathscr{R}B$.

At last we are in a position to introduce the *dual* of a wff. By the dual of A we mean the wff obtained from A by interchanging $\wedge$ and $\vee$ throughout A. The dual of A is denoted by "$\mathscr{D}A$" and is defined as follows.

DEFINITION OF $\mathscr{D}$:

(1) $$\mathscr{D}A = A \text{ if } A \text{ is atomic}$$

(2) $$\mathscr{D}(\sim A) = \begin{cases} \sim A \text{ if } A \text{ is atomic} \\ \mathscr{D}B \text{ if } A = \sim B \\ \mathscr{D}(\sim B) \vee \mathscr{D}(\sim C) \text{ if } A = B \vee C \end{cases}$$

(3) $$\mathscr{D}(A \vee B) = \mathscr{D}A \wedge \mathscr{D}B.$$

For example,

$$\begin{aligned} \mathscr{D}(\sim \mathbf{X} \vee (\mathbf{Y} \vee \sim (\sim \mathbf{Y} \vee \mathbf{W}))) &= \mathscr{D}(\sim \mathbf{X}) \wedge \mathscr{D}(\mathbf{Y} \vee \sim (\sim \mathbf{Y} \vee \mathbf{W})) \\ &= \sim \mathbf{X} \wedge (\mathscr{D}\mathbf{Y} \wedge \mathscr{D}(\sim (\sim \mathbf{Y} \vee \mathbf{W}))) \\ &= \sim \mathbf{X} \wedge (\mathbf{Y} \wedge (\mathscr{D}(\sim \sim \mathbf{Y}) \vee \mathscr{D}(\sim \mathbf{W}))) \\ &= \sim \mathbf{X} \wedge (\mathbf{Y} \wedge (\mathscr{D}\mathbf{Y} \vee \sim \mathbf{W})) \\ &= \sim \mathbf{X} \wedge (\mathbf{Y} \wedge (\mathbf{Y} \vee \sim \mathbf{W})) \end{aligned}$$

THEOREM 36: $\mathscr{D}(\sim A) \equiv \sim \mathscr{D}A$ for any wff A.

Demonstration: Apply the fundamental theorem about wff.

We intend to prove that $\mathscr{R}(\mathscr{M}A) \equiv \mathscr{D}A$ for each wff A; first, we prove

THEOREM 37: $\mathscr{R}(\mathscr{M}(\sim A)) \equiv \sim \mathscr{R}(\mathscr{M}A)$ for each wff A.

Demonstration: We use the results $\mathscr{M}(\sim A) \equiv \sim \mathscr{M}A$ for any wff A, $\mathscr{R}(\sim A) \equiv \sim \mathscr{R}A$ for any wff A, $\mathscr{R}A \equiv \mathscr{R}B$ whenever $A \equiv B$. Since $\mathscr{M}(\sim A) \equiv \sim \mathscr{M}A$, it follows that $\mathscr{R}(\mathscr{M}(\sim A)) \equiv \mathscr{R}(\sim \mathscr{M}A)$; but

$$\mathscr{R}(\sim \mathscr{M}A) \equiv \sim \mathscr{R}(\mathscr{M}A).$$

Therefore, by Theorem 19, $\mathscr{R}(\mathscr{M}(\sim A)) \equiv \sim \mathscr{R}(\mathscr{M}A)$.

THEOREM 38: $\mathscr{R}(\mathscr{M}(\sim A)) \equiv \mathscr{D}(\sim A)$ for each wff A.

Demonstration: Apply the fundamental theorem about wff.

THEOREM 39: $\mathscr{R}(\mathscr{M}A) \equiv \mathscr{D}A$ for each wff A.

Demonstration: $\mathscr{R}(\mathscr{M}A) = \mathscr{R}(\mathscr{M}(\sim \sim A))$, since $\mathscr{M}(\sim \sim A) = \mathscr{M}A$ by definition; therefore, $\mathscr{R}(\mathscr{M}A) \equiv \mathscr{D}(\sim \sim A)$ by Theorem 38; but $\mathscr{D}(\sim \sim A) = \mathscr{D}A$ by definition; hence, $\mathscr{R}(\mathscr{M}A) \equiv \mathscr{D}A$.

We can now state and prove the important

PRINCIPLE OF DUALITY: $\mathscr{D}A \equiv \mathscr{D}B$ whenever $A \equiv B$.

Demonstration: Assume that $A \equiv B$; then $\mathscr{M}A \equiv \mathscr{M}B$ by Theorem 33, and so $\mathscr{R}(\mathscr{M}A) \equiv \mathscr{R}(\mathscr{M}B)$ by the Corollary to Theorem 35. But $\mathscr{R}(\mathscr{M}A) \equiv \mathscr{D}A$ and $\mathscr{R}(\mathscr{M}B) \equiv \mathscr{D}B$ by Theorem 39. Hence, by Theorem 19, $\mathscr{D}A \equiv \mathscr{D}B$.

In applying the Principle of Duality, it is convenient to make use of

THEOREM 40: $\mathscr{D}(A \wedge B) = \mathscr{D}A \vee \mathscr{D}B$ for any wff A and B.

Demonstration: $A \wedge B = \sim(\sim A \vee \sim B)$, hence

$$\mathscr{D}(A \wedge B) = \mathscr{D}(\sim\sim A) \vee \mathscr{D}(\sim\sim B) = \mathscr{D}A \vee \mathscr{D}B.$$

We also require the following

THEOREM 41: $\mathscr{D}(\mathscr{D}A) \equiv A$ for each wff A.

Demonstration: The demonstration is quite elegant, so we present the details. We show, by applying our fundamental theorem about wff, that each wff A has the property that $\mathscr{D}(\mathscr{D}A) \equiv A$. Let A be any atomic wff; then $\mathscr{D}(\mathscr{D}A) = \mathscr{D}A = A$ by definition; thus, each atomic wff possesses the property. Now suppose that C is a wff with the property; we show that $\sim C$ also has the property. But

$$\mathscr{D}(\mathscr{D}(\sim C)) \equiv \mathscr{D}(\sim \mathscr{D}C) \equiv \sim \mathscr{D}(\mathscr{D}C)$$

by Theorem 36; since C has the property, $\mathscr{D}(\mathscr{D}C) \equiv C$. Hence, by Theorem 19, $\mathscr{D}(\mathscr{D}(\sim C)) \equiv \sim C$. Finally, we show that $C \vee D$ has the property whenever C has the property and D has the property. We assume, then, that $\mathscr{D}(\mathscr{D}C) \equiv C$ and $\mathscr{D}(\mathscr{D}D) \equiv D$; but $\mathscr{D}(\mathscr{D}(C \vee D)) = \mathscr{D}(\mathscr{D}C \wedge \mathscr{D}D)$ by definition, and $\mathscr{D}(\mathscr{D}C \wedge \mathscr{D}D) = \mathscr{D}(\mathscr{D}C) \vee \mathscr{D}(\mathscr{D}D)$ by Theorem 40; therefore,

$$\mathscr{D}(\mathscr{D}(C \vee D)) = \mathscr{D}(\mathscr{D}C) \vee \mathscr{D}(\mathscr{D}D) \equiv C \vee D$$

by Exercise 8, page 127. This establishes the theorem.

To illustrate the power of the principle of duality, we recall that we have established the following theorems:

(1) $A \vee A \equiv A$ whenever A is a wff
(2) $A \vee B \equiv B \vee A$ whenever A and B are wff

Applying the principle of duality to (1), we obtain $\mathscr{D}(A \vee A) \equiv \mathscr{D}A$ whenever A is a wff; i.e., $\mathscr{D}A \wedge \mathscr{D}A \equiv \mathscr{D}A$. Therefore, $\mathscr{D}(\mathscr{D}A) \wedge \mathscr{D}(\mathscr{D}A) \equiv \mathscr{D}(\mathscr{D}A)$; hence, by Theorem 41, and Theorem 20,

(1′) $A \wedge A \equiv A$ whenever A is a wff.
In the same way, it is easy to establish

(2′) $A \wedge B \equiv B \wedge A$ whenever A and B are wff.

We present one more useful theorem in this connection.

THEOREM 42: $\vdash \mathscr{D}B \to \mathscr{D}A$ if $\vdash A \to B$.

Demonstration: Assume that $\vdash A \to B$; then $\vdash \sim B \to \sim A$ by the Corollary to Theorem 13. But by Theorem 32, $\sim B \equiv \mathscr{M}B$ and $\sim A \equiv \mathscr{M}A$; thus, by Theorem 18 $\vdash \mathscr{M}B \to \mathscr{M}A$. Now apply Theorem 35 to obtain $\vdash \mathscr{R}(\mathscr{M}B \to \mathscr{M}A)$; by the Corollary to Theorem 34, $\vdash \mathscr{R}(\mathscr{M}B) \to \mathscr{R}(\mathscr{M}A)$. But

$$\mathscr{R}(\mathscr{M}B) \equiv \mathscr{D}B \quad \text{and} \quad \mathscr{R}(\mathscr{M}A) \equiv \mathscr{D}A$$

by Theorem 39. It now follows that $\vdash \mathscr{D}B \to \mathscr{D}A$. This establishes the theorem.

EXERCISES

1. Simplify $\mathscr{N}(\sim \mathbf{Y} \vee \sim \mathbf{X} \mathbin{\dot{\vee}} \sim \sim \mathbf{W} \vee \mathbf{X})$
2. Simplify $\mathscr{N}(\mathbf{Y} \wedge \sim \mathbf{X} \vee \mathbf{W})$
3. Simplify $\mathscr{N}(\sim \sim \mathbf{X} \vee \mathbf{Y} \mathbin{\dot{\vee}} \sim (\mathbf{X} \wedge \sim \mathbf{Y}))$
4. Simplify $\mathscr{N}(\sim \mathbf{X} \to \mathbf{Y} \wedge \sim \mathbf{Z})$
5. Simplify $\mathscr{N}(\mathscr{N}(\mathbf{X} \to \sim \mathbf{Y}) \wedge \sim \sim \mathbf{W})$
6. Apply the fundamental theorem about wff to show that $\mathscr{N}(\mathscr{N}A) = A$ for each wff A. Use Theorem 30.
7. Simplify $\mathscr{M}(\sim \mathbf{Y} \vee \sim \mathbf{X} \mathbin{\dot{\vee}} \sim \sim \mathbf{W} \vee \mathbf{X})$
8. Simplify $\mathscr{M}(\mathbf{X} \wedge \mathbf{Y} \mathbin{\dot{\vee}} \sim \mathbf{Z})$
9. Simplify $\mathscr{M}(\mathscr{N}(\mathbf{X} \to \sim \mathbf{Y}) \wedge \sim \sim \mathbf{W})$
10. Simplify $\mathscr{N}(\mathscr{N}(\mathbf{X} \to \sim \mathbf{Y}) \wedge \sim \sim \mathbf{W})$
11. Simplify $\mathscr{M}(\mathscr{N}(\mathbf{X} \to \mathbf{Y}))$
12. Simplify $\mathscr{N}(\mathscr{M}(\mathbf{X} \to \mathbf{Y}))$
13. Simplify $\mathscr{R}(\sim \mathbf{Y} \vee \sim \sim \mathbf{X} \mathbin{\dot{\vee}} \mathbf{W} \vee \sim \mathbf{X})$
14. Simplify $\mathscr{R}(\mathbf{W} \wedge \mathbf{X} \to \sim \mathbf{Y} \mathbin{\dot{\vee}} \mathbf{X} \wedge \mathbf{Y} \to \mathbf{Z})$
15. Simplify $\mathscr{M}(\mathscr{R}(\mathbf{W} \wedge \mathbf{X} \to \sim \mathbf{Y} \mathbin{\dot{\vee}} \mathbf{X} \wedge \mathbf{Y} \to \mathbf{Z}))$
16. Simplify $\mathscr{R}(\mathscr{M}(\mathbf{W} \wedge \mathbf{X} \to \sim \mathbf{Y} \mathbin{\dot{\vee}} \mathbf{X} \wedge \mathbf{Y} \to \mathbf{Z}))$
17. Prove that $\mathscr{M}(\sim C) \equiv C$ for each wff C.
18. Show that $\mathscr{R}(\mathscr{M}A) \equiv \mathscr{M}(\mathscr{R}A)$ for each wff A.
19. Prove Theorem 34.

20. Prove Theorem 35.

21. Simplify $\mathscr{D}(\sim\ \sim \mathbf{Y}\ \dot{\vee}\ \mathbf{W} \vee \mathbf{Z})$

22. Simplify $\mathscr{D}(\mathbf{X} \rightarrow\ \sim \mathbf{W}\ \dot{\vee}\ \sim \mathbf{X} \vee\ \sim\ \sim \mathbf{Y})$

23. Simplify $\mathscr{D}(\sim \mathbf{X} \leftrightarrow \mathbf{Y})$

24. Simplify $\mathscr{D}(\mathscr{N}(\sim \mathbf{X} \leftrightarrow \mathbf{Y}))$

25. Simplify $\mathscr{N}(\mathscr{D}(\sim \mathbf{X} \leftrightarrow \mathbf{Y}))$

26. Prove Theorem 36.

27. Prove Theorem 38.

28. Prove Theorem 39.

29. By considering the definition of $\wedge$, prove that $\sim (\sim A \wedge \sim B) \equiv A \vee B$ whenever A and B are wff.

30. Simplify $\mathscr{D}(A \rightarrow B \dot{\rightarrow} C \vee A \rightarrow C \vee B)$.

31. Prove that $\vdash \mathscr{D}(C \vee A \rightarrow C \vee B) \rightarrow \mathscr{D}(A \rightarrow B)$ whenever A, B, and C are wff.

32. Prove that $\mathscr{D}(A \rightarrow B) \equiv\ \sim \mathscr{D}A \wedge \mathscr{D}B$ whenever A and B are wff.

33. Consider the syntactical transform $\mathcal{S}$ defined as follows:
    (1) $\mathcal{S}A = A$ if A is atomic
    (2) $\mathcal{S}(\sim A) =\ \sim A$ whenever A is a wff
    (3) $\mathcal{S}(A \vee B) = A$ whenever A and B are wff
    (a) Simplify $\mathcal{S}(\sim \mathbf{X} \rightarrow \mathbf{Y}\ \dot{\vee}\ \sim\ \sim \mathbf{Y} \wedge \mathbf{Z})$
    (b) Simplify $\mathcal{S}(\mathbf{X} \wedge \mathbf{Y}\ \dot{\wedge}\ \sim \mathbf{Z})$
    (c) Prove that $\vdash \mathcal{S}A \rightarrow A$ for each wff A
    (d) Describe $\mathcal{S}$ in intuitive terms

34. Consider the syntactical transform $\mathscr{T}$ defined as follows:
    (1) $\mathscr{T}A = \mathbf{X}$ if A is atomic
    (2) $\mathscr{T}(\sim A) =\ \sim \mathscr{T}A$ whenever A is a wff
    (3) $\mathscr{T}(A \vee B) = \mathscr{T}A \vee \mathscr{T}B$ whenever A and B are wff
    (a) Simplify $\mathscr{T}(\sim \mathbf{Y} \vee \mathbf{X}\ \dot{\vee}\ \sim\ \sim \mathbf{Z})$
    (b) Simplify $\mathscr{T}(\sim \mathbf{Z} \rightarrow \mathbf{W} \vee \sim \mathbf{X})$
    (c) Prove that $\mathscr{T}(A \rightarrow B) = \mathscr{T}A \rightarrow \mathscr{T}B$ whenever A and B are wff.
    (d) Show that $\vdash \mathscr{T}A$ if $\vdash A$.
    (e) Describe $\mathscr{T}$ in intuitive terms.

35. Consider the syntactical transform $\mathscr{V}$ defined as follows:
    (1) $\mathscr{V}A = \mathbf{X}$ if A is atomic
    (2) $\mathscr{V}(\sim A) = \begin{cases} \mathbf{Y} \text{ if } A \text{ is atomic} \\ \sim \mathscr{V}A \text{ if } A \text{ is not atomic} \end{cases}$
    (3) $\mathscr{V}(A \vee B) = \mathscr{V}A \vee \mathscr{V}B$ whenever A and B are wff.
    (a) Simplify $\mathscr{V}(\sim \mathbf{X} \rightarrow \mathbf{Y} \dot{\vee} \sim \sim \mathbf{Y} \wedge \mathbf{Z})$
    (b) Simplify $\mathscr{V}(\sim \mathbf{X} \vee \sim \mathbf{Y} \wedge \mathbf{Z} \vee \sim \sim \mathbf{Y})$
    (c) Describe $\mathscr{V}$ intuitively.
    (d) Find a wff A such that $\vdash A$ but $\mathscr{V}A$ is not provable.

36. Prove that $\mathscr{N}A$ is in normal form whenever A is a wff.

37. Demonstrate Theorem 29 by applying the fundamental theorem about provable wff.

38. Demonstrate Theorem 39 by applying the fundamental theorem about wff.

8. More Provable Wff

In order to establish that each true wff is provable, we shall need much more information about provable wff.

THEOREM 43: $\vdash A \vee (B \vee C) \rightarrow (B \vee (A \vee C)) \vee A$ whenever A, B, and C are wff.

Demonstration:

$\vdash C \rightarrow C \vee A$	by (2)
$\vdash C \rightarrow A \vee C$	by Theorem 18
$\vdash B \vee C \rightarrow B \vee (A \vee C)$	by Theorem 4
$\vdash A \vee (B \vee C) \rightarrow A \vee (B \vee (A \vee C))$	by Theorem 4
$\vdash A \vee (B \vee C) \rightarrow (B \vee (A \vee C)) \vee A$	by Theorem 18

THEOREM 44: $\vdash (B \vee (A \vee C)) \vee A \rightarrow B \vee (A \vee C)$ whenever A, B, and C are wff.

Demonstration:

$\vdash A \vee C \rightarrow (A \vee C) \vee B$	by (2)
$\vdash A \vee C \rightarrow B \vee (A \vee C)$	by Theorem 18
$\vdash A \rightarrow A \vee C$	by (2)
$\vdash A \rightarrow B \vee (A \vee C)$	by Theorem 6
$\vdash (B \vee (A \vee C)) \vee A \rightarrow (B \vee (A \vee C)) \vee (B \vee (A \vee C))$	by Theorem 4
$\vdash (B \vee (A \vee C)) \vee A \rightarrow B \vee (A \vee C)$	by Theorem 18

THEOREM 45: $\vdash A \vee (B \vee C) \rightarrow B \vee (A \vee C)$ whenever A, B, and C are wff.

Demonstration: Apply Theorem 6 to Theorems 43 and 44.

THEOREM 46: $\vdash A \vee (B \vee C) \rightarrow (A \vee B) \vee C$ whenever A, B, and C are wff.

Demonstration:

$\vdash B \vee C \rightarrow C \vee B$	by (3)
$\vdash A \vee (B \vee C) \rightarrow A \vee (C \vee B)$	by Theorem 4
$\vdash A \vee (C \vee B) \rightarrow C \vee (A \vee B)$	by Theorem 45
$\vdash A \vee (B \vee C) \rightarrow C \vee (A \vee B)$	by Theorem 6
$\vdash A \vee (B \vee C) \rightarrow (A \vee B) \vee C$	by Theorem 18

THEOREM 47: $\vdash (A \vee B) \vee C \rightarrow A \vee (B \vee C)$ whenever A, B, and C are wff.

Demonstration:

$\vdash C \vee (B \vee A) \rightarrow (C \vee B) \vee A$	by Theorem 46
$\vdash C \vee (A \vee B) \rightarrow (B \vee C) \vee A$	by Theorem 18
$\vdash (A \vee B) \vee C \rightarrow A \vee (B \vee C)$	by Theorem 18

THEOREM 48: $A \vee (B \vee C) \equiv (A \vee B) \vee C$ whenever A, B, and C are wff.

Demonstration: Theorems 46 and 47.

In view of Theorem 48, we shall denote both $A \vee (B \vee C)$ and $(A \vee B) \vee C$ by "$A \vee B \vee C$", omitting parentheses.

THEOREM 49: Suppose that

$$E_1 = A \vee B \vee C \dot{\vee} D, \quad E_2 = A \vee B \dot{\vee} C \vee D, \quad E_3 = A \dot{\vee} B \vee C \vee D,$$

then $E_1 \equiv E_2$ and $E_2 \equiv E_3$.

Demonstration: $A \vee B \dot{\vee} C \vee D \equiv (A \vee B) \vee C \dot{\vee} D$ and $A \vee B \dot{\vee} C \vee D \equiv A \dot{\vee} B \vee (C \vee D)$ by Theorem 48.

In view of Theorem 49, we shall denote any one of E_1, E_2, or E_3 by "$A \vee B \vee C \vee D$", omitting parentheses.

It is easy to prove by mathematical induction

THEOREM 50: Let n be any natural number, and let $B_1, B_2, \ldots, B_n$ be any wff; then any two wff obtained by inserting parentheses in the expression "$B_1 \vee B_2 \vee \ldots \vee B_n$" are equivalent.

In view of Theorem 50, we shall denote any wff obtained by inserting parentheses in the expression $B_1 \vee B_2 \vee \ldots \vee B_n$ by "$B_1 \vee B_2 \vee \ldots \vee B_n$"

THEOREM 51: $A \wedge (B \wedge C) \equiv (A \wedge B) \wedge C$ whenever A, B, and C are wff.

Demonstration: Consider Theorem 48 and apply the principle of duality and Theorem 41.

THEOREM 52: Let n be any natural number, and let $B_1, B_2, \ldots, B_n$ be any wff; then any two wff obtained by inserting parentheses in $B_1 \wedge B_2 \wedge \ldots \wedge B_n$ are equivalent.

Demonstration: Consider Theorem 50 and apply the principle of duality and Theorem 41.

In view of Theorem 52, we shall denote any wff obtained by inserting parentheses in $B_1 \wedge B_2 \wedge \ldots \wedge B_n$, by "$B_1 \wedge B_2 \wedge \ldots \wedge B_n$".

THEOREM 53: $\vdash A \rightarrow (B \rightarrow A \wedge B)$ whenever A and B are wff.

Demonstration:

	$\vdash(\sim A \vee \sim B) \vee \sim(\sim A \vee \sim B)$	by Theorem 9
	$\vdash \sim A \vee (\sim B \vee (A \wedge B))$	by Theorem 48
that is,	$\vdash A \rightarrow (B \rightarrow A \wedge B)$	

COROLLARY: $\vdash A \wedge B$ whenever $\vdash A$ and $\vdash B$.

Demonstration: Theorems 53 and 7.

THEOREM 54: $\vdash B_1 \wedge B_2 \wedge \ldots \wedge B_n$ whenever $\vdash B_1$ and $\vdash B_2$ and ... and $\vdash B_n$.

Demonstration: By mathematical induction, using the Corollary to Theorem 53.

THEOREM 55: $\vdash A \wedge B \rightarrow A$ whenever A and B are wff.

Demonstration:

$\vdash \mathscr{D}A \rightarrow \mathscr{D}A \vee \mathscr{D}B$	by (2)
$\vdash \mathscr{D}(\mathscr{D}A \vee \mathscr{D}B) \rightarrow \mathscr{D}(\mathscr{D}A)$	by Theorem 42
$\vdash \mathscr{D}(\mathscr{D}A) \wedge \mathscr{D}(\mathscr{D}B) \rightarrow \mathscr{D}(\mathscr{D}A)$	definition of $\mathscr{D}$
$\vdash A \wedge B \rightarrow A$	by Theorems 41 and 18

THEOREM 56: $A \wedge B \equiv B \wedge A$ whenever A and B are wff.

Demonstration: By duality, applied to the theorem $A \vee B \equiv B \vee A$ whenever A and B are wff.

THEOREM 57: $\vdash A \wedge B \rightarrow B$ whenever A and B are wff.

Demonstration: Theorems 55, 56, and 18.

THEOREM 58: If $\vdash B_1 \wedge B_2 \wedge \ldots \wedge B_n$, then $\vdash B_1$ and $\vdash B_2$ and ... and $\vdash B_n$.

Demonstration: We use mathematical induction. The assertion is true if n is 1. Suppose that it is true when n is k; we show that the assertion is true when n is $k + 1$. By Theorem 55, $\vdash B_1 \wedge \ldots \wedge B_k \dot{\wedge} B_{k+1} \dot{\rightarrow} B_1 \wedge \ldots \wedge B_k$; we are assuming that $\vdash B_1 \wedge \ldots \wedge B_k \wedge B_{k+1}$. Hence by Theorem 7, $\vdash B_1 \wedge \ldots \wedge B_k$. Thus, by the induction assumption, $\vdash B_1$, $\vdash B_2$, ..., $\vdash B_k$. Again, by Theorem 57, $\vdash B_1 \wedge \ldots \wedge B_k \dot{\wedge} B_{k+1} \dot{\rightarrow} B_{k+1}$; and so $\vdash B_{k+1}$ by Theorem 7. This establishes the theorem.

THEOREM 59: $\vdash B_1 \wedge B_2 \wedge \ldots \wedge B_n$ iff $\vdash B_1$ and $\vdash B_2$ and ... and $\vdash B_n$.

Demonstration: Theorems 54 and 58

THEOREM 60: $\vdash A \vee C \rightarrow B \vee D$ whenever $\vdash A \rightarrow B$ and $\vdash C \rightarrow D$.

Demonstration:

$\vdash C \to D$ by assumption
$\vdash A \vee C \to A \vee D$ by Theorem 4
$\vdash A \vee D \to B \vee D$ since $\vdash A \to B$, Theorems 4, 18
$\vdash A \vee C \to B \vee D$ by Theorem 6

THEOREM 61: $\vdash A \wedge C \to B \wedge D$ whenever $\vdash A \to B$ and $\vdash C \to D$.

Demonstration:

$\vdash \mathscr{D}B \to \mathscr{D}A$ and $\vdash \mathscr{D}D \to \mathscr{D}C$ by Theorem 42
$\vdash \mathscr{D}B \vee \mathscr{D}D \to \mathscr{D}A \vee \mathscr{D}C$ by Theorem 60
$\vdash \mathscr{D}(\mathscr{D}A \vee \mathscr{D}C) \to \mathscr{D}(\mathscr{D}B \vee \mathscr{D}D)$ by Theorem 42
$\vdash A \wedge C \to B \wedge D$ definition of $\mathscr{D}$ and Theorem 18

THEOREM 62: $\vdash A \vee (B \wedge C) \to (A \vee B) \wedge (A \vee C)$ whenever A, B, and C are wff.

Demonstration:

$\vdash B \wedge C \to B$ and $\vdash B \wedge C \to C$ by Theorems 55 and 57
$\vdash A \vee (B \wedge C) \to A \vee B$ and $\vdash A \vee (B \wedge C) \to A \vee C$ by Theorem 4
$\vdash (A \vee (B \wedge C)) \wedge (A \vee (B \wedge C)) \to (A \vee B) \wedge (A \vee C)$ by Theorem 61
$\vdash A \vee (B \wedge C) \to (A \vee B) \wedge (A \vee C)$ by Theorem 18

THEOREM 63: $A \dot{\to} B \to C \equiv A \wedge B \to C$ whenever A, B, and C are wff.

Demonstration:

$A \dot{\to} B \to C = \sim A \dot{\vee} \sim B \vee C$
$\equiv \sim A \vee \sim B \dot{\vee} C$ by Theorem 48
$\equiv \sim \sim (\sim A \vee \sim B) \vee C$
$= \sim (A \wedge B) \vee C$
$= A \wedge B \to C$

THEOREM 64: $A \dot{\to} B \to C \equiv B \dot{\to} A \to C$ whenever A, B, and C are wff.

Demonstration:

$A \dot{\to} B \to C \equiv A \wedge B \to C$ by Theorem 63
$\equiv B \wedge A \to C$ by Theorem 20
$\equiv B \dot{\to} A \to C$ by Theorem 63

THEOREM 65: $\vdash B \wedge (A \vee C) \to A \vee (B \wedge C)$ whenever A, B, and C are wff.

Demonstration:

$\vdash B \dot{\to} C \to B \wedge C$ by Theorem 53
$\vdash C \to B \wedge C \dot{\to} A \vee C \to A \vee (B \wedge C)$ by (4)
$\vdash B \dot{\to} A \vee C \to A \vee (B \wedge C)$ by Theorem 6
$\vdash B \wedge (A \vee C) \to A \vee (B \wedge C)$ by Theorems 63 and 18

THEOREM 66: $\vdash (A \vee B) \wedge (A \vee C) \to A \vee (B \wedge C)$ whenever A, B, and C are wff.

Demonstration: $\vdash (A \vee B) \wedge (A \vee C) \rightarrow A \vee ((A \vee B) \wedge C)$ by Theorem 65
$\vdash C \wedge (A \vee B) \rightarrow A \vee (C \wedge B)$ by Theorem 65
$\vdash A \vee (C \wedge (A \vee B)) \rightarrow A \vee A \vee (C \wedge B)$ by Theorem 4
$\vdash A \vee ((A \vee B) \wedge C) \rightarrow A \vee (B \wedge C)$ by Theorem 18
$\vdash (A \vee B) \wedge (A \vee C) \rightarrow A \vee (B \wedge C)$ by Theorem 6

THEOREM 67: $A \vee (B \wedge C) \equiv (A \vee B) \wedge (A \vee C)$ whenever A, B, and C are wff.

Demonstration: Theorems 62 and 66.

THEOREM 68: $A \wedge (B \vee C) \equiv (A \wedge B) \vee (A \wedge C)$ whenever A, B, and C are wff.

Demonstration: Theorem 67 and duality.

EXERCISES

1. Show that $\vdash A \rightarrow (B \rightarrow A)$ whenever A and B are wff.
2. Show that $A \vee (B \rightarrow C) \equiv B \rightarrow A \vee C$ whenever A, B, and C are wff.
3. Prove that $A \dot{\rightarrow} A \rightarrow B \equiv A \rightarrow B$ whenever A and B are wff.
4. Show that $\vdash B \wedge (A \vee C) \rightarrow (A \vee B) \wedge (A \vee C)$ whenever A, B, and C are wff.
5. Prove that $\vdash A \rightarrow (B \rightarrow C) \dot{\rightarrow} (A \rightarrow B) \rightarrow (A \rightarrow C)$ whenever A, B, and C are wff.
6. Prove that $\vdash A \wedge B \rightarrow A \wedge C$ whenever $\vdash B \rightarrow C$.
7. Find the fallacy in the following argument: If $\vdash B \rightarrow C$, then $\vdash A \wedge B \rightarrow A \wedge C$; hence, by duality, $\vdash A \vee C \rightarrow A \vee B$; thus, $\vdash A \vee C \rightarrow A \vee B$ whenever $\vdash B \rightarrow C$
8. Prove Theorem 51 in detail.
9. Carry out the proof of Theorem 52.
10. Demonstrate Theorem 56.
11. We shall say that a wff A is *prime* iff the only connectives occurring in A are $\vee$ and $\sim$; furthermore, we require that $\sim$ occurs prefixed only to atomic wff. For example, $\mathbf{Y}$, $\mathbf{X} \vee \sim \mathbf{Y} \vee \sim \mathbf{Z}$, $\sim \mathbf{W}$ are prime; neither $\mathbf{X} \vee \sim \sim \mathbf{Y}$ nor $\mathbf{X} \wedge \mathbf{Y}$ is prime.
(a) Show that A is prime iff there exist wff $B_1, B_2, \ldots, B_n$ such that each

B_i is atomic or is the negation of an atomic wff, and $A = B_1 \vee B_2 \vee \ldots \vee B_n$. We shall say that each B_i is a *disjunct* of A.

(b) Show that a disjunct of a prime wff A, is also a component of A.

(c) Show that a prime wff A is provable if there exists an atomic wff, say x, such that both x and $\sim x$ are disjuncts of A.

(d) Suppose that A is prime, but that there is no atomic wff, say x, such that both x and $\sim x$ are disjuncts of A; show that A is *not* provable, *Hint:* show that A is not true by constructing an assignment of truth-values under which the truth-value of A is f.

9. The Completeness of the Propositional Calculus

The purpose of this section is to demonstrate that the class of all provable wff *is* the class of all true wff. We have already seen that the set of all provable wff is a subset of the set of all true wff; it remains to prove that the set of all true wff is a subset of the set of all provable wff.

The vital concept in this connection is the notion of a wff possessing the form $B_1 \wedge B_2 \wedge \ldots \wedge B_n$ where each B_i is prime. We shall say that the wff A is in *conjunctive* normal form iff A has the specified form. Thus, a wff is in conjunctive normal form iff it is the conjunction of a finite number of prime wff. Furthermore, we shall say that each B_i is a *conjunct* of $B_1 \wedge B_2 \ldots \wedge B_n$.

This concept is important because there is a simple test to decide of a given wff in conjunctive normal form, whether or not it is provable.

TEST: A wff in conjunctive normal form is provable iff given any conjunct of the wff, there is an atomic wff, say x, such that both x and $\sim x$ are disjuncts of the given conjunct.

Let us establish this test. Suppose that A is any wff in conjunctive normal form. By Theorem 59, A is provable iff each conjunct of A is provable. But each conjunct is a prime wff, and by No. 11 of the preceding exercises, a prime wff is provable iff there exists an atomic wff, say x, such that both x and $\sim x$ are disjuncts of the prime wff. We have established our Test.

Note that a wff in conjunctive normal form is established to be provable or not provable by *scanning* the given wff.

Let us prove now

THEOREM 69: Given any wff A, there is a wff B such that $A \equiv B$ and B is in conjunctive normal form.

Demonstration: First, note that $\mathcal{N}A$ involves only the connectives $\wedge$, $\vee$, $\sim$; furthermore, $\sim$ appears prefixed to atomic wff only. Thus, we must show that we can transform $\mathcal{N}A$ into an equivalent wff such that "$\wedge$" does not occur within the scope of **v**. This is really easy: we have only to apply Theorem 20 and Theorem 67, repeatedly if necessary. To see precisely how this works, we introduce a relevant concept: the *order* of a wff involving only the connectives $\wedge$, **v**, and $\sim$, and in which $\sim$ occurs prefixed only to atomic wff. We shall say that a wff of this form has order n iff there are exactly n "$\wedge$"s which lie within the scope of **v**, counting multiplicities. For example, $(\mathbf{X} \wedge \mathbf{Y}) \vee \mathbf{Z} \dot{\vee} \mathbf{W}$ has order 2, $(\mathbf{X} \wedge \mathbf{Y}) \dot{\vee} \mathbf{Z} \vee \mathbf{W}$ has order 1,

$$(\mathbf{X} \wedge \mathbf{Y} \wedge \mathbf{Z}) \vee (\sim \mathbf{Z} \wedge \mathbf{W})$$

has order 3,

$$\mathbf{X} \dot{\vee} (\mathbf{X} \wedge \mathbf{Y} \wedge \mathbf{Z}) \vee (\sim \mathbf{Z} \wedge \mathbf{W})$$

has order 6. Now suppose that $\mathscr{N}A$ has positive order; then $(C \wedge D) \vee E$ is a component of $\mathscr{N}A$, so that

$$\mathscr{N}A = \phi(C \wedge D) \vee E\theta.$$

By Theorem 67,

$$(C \wedge D) \vee E \equiv (C \vee E) \wedge (D \vee E);$$

hence, by Theorem 20,

$$\mathscr{N}A \equiv \phi(C \vee E) \wedge (D \vee E)\theta.$$

Clearly, $\phi(C \vee E) \wedge (D \vee E)\theta$ has smaller order than $\phi(C \wedge D) \vee E\theta$. We have demonstrated that given any wff with positive order, there exists an equivalent wff with smaller order. It follows from this that, given any wff with positive order, there exists an equivalent wff with order 0. But a wff that has order 0 is in conjunctive normal form. We have shown that, given any wff A, we can find a wff B in conjunctive normal form such that $\mathscr{N}A \equiv B$. Recalling Theorem 27, $\mathscr{N}A \equiv A$, and Theorem 19, we conclude that $A \equiv B$. This establishes Theorem 69.

Now, we can demonstrate that each true wff is provable. Let A be any true wff; then there is a wff B in conjunctive normal form such that $A \equiv B$. Hence, $\vdash A \rightarrow B$ and $\vdash B \rightarrow A$. Suppose that A is not provable; then B is not provable (Theorem 7). Therefore, by our test there is a conjunct of B that does not involve both an atomic wff and its negation. But then we can assign truth-values so that the truth-value of this conjunct is f, and so the truth-value of B is f. It follows that the truth-value of A is also f, under the given assignment of truth-values. Thus, A is not a true wff. This establishes that the class of all provable wff *is* the class of all true wff.

10. The Consequences of a Set of Wff

The aim of a theory of deduction is to enable us to characterize just how a statement is deduced from a given set of statements. We are now in a position to do this. Let K be any non-empty set of wff, and let B be any wff; we shall say that B is *deducible* from K, or that B is a *consequence* of K, iff there is a natural number n such that $\vdash A_1 \wedge A_2 \wedge \ldots \wedge A_n \rightarrow B$, where $\{A_1, A_2, \ldots, A_n\} \subset K$.

In other words, we require the existence of a *finite* number of wff in K whose conjunction entails B. We shall denote the statement "B is a consequence of K" by writing "$K \vdash B$". Let us formalize this important notion of a consequence of a non-empty set of wff K.

DEFINITION: $K \vdash B$ iff there exists a non-empty finite subset of K, say $\{A_1, A_2, \ldots, A_n\}$, such that $\vdash A_1 \wedge A_2 \wedge \ldots \wedge A_n \rightarrow B$.

For example, consider the set $\{\mathbf{Y}, \sim(\mathbf{Z} \vee \sim \mathbf{X})\}$. Since $\sim (\mathbf{Z} \vee \sim \mathbf{X}) \equiv \sim \mathbf{Z} \wedge \mathbf{X}$ and $\vdash \sim \mathbf{Z} \wedge \mathbf{X} \rightarrow \mathbf{X}$, we see that $\vdash \sim (\mathbf{Z} \vee \sim \mathbf{X}) \rightarrow \mathbf{X}$. Therefore, $\{\mathbf{Y}. \sim (\mathbf{Z} \vee \sim \mathbf{X})\} \vdash \mathbf{X}$.

As another illustration, consider the set $\{x \mid x \text{ is a proposition}\} = K$. Since $\vdash \mathbf{X} \wedge \mathbf{Y} \rightarrow \mathbf{X} \wedge \mathbf{Y}$ and $\{\mathbf{X}, \mathbf{Y}\} \subset K$, we see that $K \vdash \mathbf{X} \wedge \mathbf{Y}$.

We now establish a property of our concept.

THEOREM 70: $K \vdash A \wedge B$ whenever $K \vdash A$ and $K \vdash B$.

Demonstration: By assumption, there are non-empty, finite subsets of K, say $\{A_1, A_2, \ldots, A_n\}$ and $\{B_1, B_2, \ldots, B_m\}$, such that $\vdash A_1 \wedge A_2 \wedge \ldots \wedge A_n \rightarrow A$ and $\vdash B_1 \wedge B_2 \wedge \ldots \wedge B_m \rightarrow B$. Therefore, by Theorem 61, page 142

$$\vdash (A_1 \wedge A_2 \wedge \ldots \wedge A_n) \wedge (B_1 \wedge B_2 \wedge \ldots \wedge B_m) \rightarrow A \wedge B.$$

But $\{A_1, A_2, \ldots, A_n, B_1, B_2, \ldots, B_m\}$ is a finite subset of K. Hence, $K \vdash A \wedge B$.

Let us examine one more result.

THEOREM 71: Let K be a non-empty finite set of wff, say $\{A_1, A_2, \ldots, A_n\}$; then $K \vdash A$ iff $\vdash A_1 \wedge A_2 \wedge \ldots \wedge A_n \rightarrow A$.

Demonstration: (1) Suppose $K \vdash A$. Then there is a natural number, say t, such that $\vdash B_1 \wedge B_2 \wedge \ldots \wedge B_t \rightarrow A$ where

$$\{B_1, B_2, \ldots, B_t\} \subset \{A_1, A_2, \ldots, A_n\}.$$

In view of Theorems 57, 51, and 56, we see that

$$\vdash A_1 \wedge A_2 \wedge \ldots \wedge A_n \rightarrow B_1 \wedge B_2 \wedge \ldots \wedge B_t$$

Hence, by Theorem 6, page 122, $\vdash A_1 \wedge A_2 \wedge \ldots \wedge A_n \rightarrow A$.

(2) Suppose $\vdash A_1 \wedge A_2 \wedge \ldots \wedge A_n \rightarrow A$. Then, by definition,

$$\{A_1, A_2, \ldots, A_n\} \vdash A.$$

The connection between the theory of deduction for the propositional calculus and arguments—in the sense of Section 5 of Chapter 1—should now be clear.

5

The predicate calculus

1. Introduction

We have seen that the axiomatic method revolves around mathematical objects called algebraic systems. Indeed, algebraic systems are studied by means of the axiomatic method: in the first instance, by constructing certain families of algebraic systems, and then by demonstrating that given propositions are true in each algebraic system of a specified family.

Recall that a family of algebraic systems is characterized, or defined, by first stating, in general terms, the type or form that an algebraic system must possess in order to qualify for membership in the family, and then listing a number of propositions, called postulates, each of which must be true in an algebraic system of the specified type in order that the algebraic system be admitted to the family. Bearing this in mind, note that a proposition that is true in each algebraic system of a specified family is sometimes said to be a *consequence* of the postulates defining the given family. Obviously, there is a relationship between such a proposition and the postulates defining the family. The purpose of this chapter is to explore the nature of this relationship; in fact, we intend to provide a deduction-technique under which we can deduce that a given proposition is a consequence (in the above sense) of a given set of propositions *without* appealing to the family of algebraic systems defined by the same postulate-set.

Notice the difference in view-point! When proving that a given proposition is true in each algebraic system of a family (defined by a given postulate-set), one is thinking directly of the algebraic systems involved. On the other hand, in a theory of deduction the entire emphasis is on the given postulate-set, and one proves that a given proposition is a consequence of the postulate-set, by carrying out purely logical procedures, without considering the algebraic systems defined by the postulate-set. In the one case, the algebraic systems are uppermost in mind; in the other case, it is the postulate-set that is uppermost in mind. There is a certain "rough and ready" character to the first approach; one demonstrates that a given proposition is true in each algebraic system of the given family, by any means at hand. In a sense, there are no rules to the game; there are no restrictions on the method of proof. On the other hand, in a theory of deduction rules are of the essence. The game is carried on in a completely formalized manner and even within a formal language. The goal of a theory of deduction is to characterize the notion of a consequence of a set of propositions by purely formal techniques within the language of the theory of deduction and without involving the algebraic systems defined by the given set of propositions.

It is convenient to begin by making some simplifications. Our concept of an algebraic system is complicated—from a foundational point-of-view—because of the presence of both operators and relations. In mathematics it is clear that operators and relations are important, indeed vital, concepts. However, it is not difficult to see that any operator can be expressed by means of a suitably chosen relation. For example, the binary operator $\boldsymbol{+}$ on on the natural numbers is exemplified by the ternary relation on the natural numbers:

$$\{(a, b, c) \mid a \in N \wedge b \in N \wedge c \in N \wedge a + b = c\}.$$

Indeed, the only difference between this ternary relation on N and the binary operator $\boldsymbol{+}$ is in how we think of it! Of course, in the case of $\boldsymbol{+}$, we write

$$\boldsymbol{+} = \{(a, b, c) \mid a \in N \wedge b \in N \wedge a + b = c\}$$

where we regard "(a, b, c)" as being a name of the ordered pair $((a, b), c)$. Thus, $\boldsymbol{+}$ is a set of ordered pairs, whereas the ternary relation introduced above is a set of ordered triples. The point is that the mere device of replacing each ordered triple (a, b, c) appearing in the ternary relation by the associated ordered pair $((a, b), c)$, transforms the ternary relation into the desired binary operator. We see, then, that we can get along without operators, since any operator can be represented, in this way, by a relation. Thus, it is possible to simplify our notion of an algebraic system.

To emphasize this point let us introduce the term *structure*. By a structure we mean any ordered n^{tuple} whose first term is a non-empty set (called the *basic set* of the structure) and whose remaining terms are relations on the basic set or are members of the basic set. A structure must possess at least one relation. For example, the ordered triple $(\{0, 1\}, \{0\}, 0)$ is a structure whose basic set is $\{0, 1\}$ and whose second term is the unary relation $\{0\}$ and whose third term is 0, a member of the basic set.

In this chapter we shall present the formal language of the predicate calculus and define, in a completely formal manner, what we mean by a *consequence* of a set of propositions. In order to simplify the conceptual difficulties involved in the predicate calculus, we have based the development of this theory of deduction on Chapter 4. A word of caution: Do not attempt to read on unless you have mastered Chapter 4.

In Chapter 6 we shall prove that the set of all consequences of a given set of propositions, indeed is the set of propositions (i.e., "propositions" within the meaning of the predicate calculus) that are true in each structure of the family defined by the given set of propositions.

2. The Language of the Predicate Calculus

It is our intention to characterize the notion of a statement or proposition as used in much of mathematics. We shall require a stock of objects called *individuals* from which we can form the various basic sets needed for our structures; we shall require a stock of symbols to denote the various relations that may be involved in our structures; we shall call these symbols *predicates*. Since each relation has associated with it a natural number—the order of the relation—we shall associate a natural number with each predicate; we shall require three logical connectives ~, ∨, ∀; finally, we shall need parentheses to indicate punctuation. Thus, the symbols of the predicate calculus are as follows.

Individuals: **x**, **y**, **z**, . . . infinitely many
Predicates: **F**, **G**, **H**, . . . infinitely many

Each predicate is assigned a natural number, called the *order* of the predicate.

Connectives: **~**, **∨**, **∀**
Parentheses: **(** , **)**

Remember, the basic symbols of a formal system possess no intrinsic meaning or denotation; however, to make sense out of what we are doing, we have indicated the intended function of our basic symbols. As in the case of the propositional calculus, when we write down one of the above symbols, that symbol is the object we wish to denote. For this reason we are using boldface type for these symbols. In this sense, then, any two of the above symbols are equally meaningless.

We have said that each predicate is assigned a natural number; the idea is that a predicate to which n is assigned will correspond (in the ultimate interpretation) to an n^{ary} relation.

Our purpose is to create a language—the language of the predicate calculus—from the raw material provided by the above symbols. First, we state what is meant by an *expression* in the predicate calculus.

DEFINITION: The result of writing down a finite number of the above symbols, one after the other, is called an *expression*.

More precisely, each symbol of the predicate calculus is said to be an expression; furthermore, $\alpha\beta$ is an expression whenever α is an expression and β is one of our symbols. This is subject to the restriction that each expression is finite. Since zero is a finite number, we shall regard the result of writing down no symbols, to be an expression. That is,   is an expression.

For example, **G** is a symbol of the predicate calculus, and so **G** is an expression. Since **∀** is a symbol, it follows that **G∀** is an expression. Since **y** is a symbol, it follows that **G∀y** is an expression; again, we see that **G∀y(**, **G∀y(x**, **G∀y(x(**, **G∀y(x(∀**, **G∀y(x(∀∀**, **G∀y(x(∀∀F** are expressions.

On the other hand, none of the following is an expression:

$$\mathbf{X} \wedge \mathbf{Y}, \quad \exists\mathbf{x}(\mathbf{Fx}), \quad \begin{matrix}\forall\\ \mathbf{x}\\ \mathbf{F}\\ \mathbf{x}\end{matrix}, \quad [\mathbf{Fx}], \quad \mathbf{x} + \mathbf{y}, \quad \mathbf{x}^{\mathbf{y}}.$$

We shall say that an individual, say t, is *free* in an expression iff t occurs in the expression and **∀**t does not occur. For example, **y** is free in **∀x(Fy)**, whereas **x** is not free in this expression, in **Fz**, or in **∀x(Gxyz)**. We shall say that an individual, say t, is *bound* in an expression iff **∀**t occurs in the expression. For example, **y** is bound in the expressions **Fx∀y**, **∀y**, **∀∀y**, **xx∀∀yy**, **∀y(Fy)**, **(∀y(Fy))**; whereas **y** is not bound in the expressions **∀xy**, **y∀**, **∀Fy**.

Having defined expressions, we now select certain expressions which we call *well-formed formulae* or *wff* for short. To begin, we define what we mean by an *atomic* wff.

DEFINITION OF ATOMIC WFF: Let R be any predicate of order n, and let $t_1, t_2, \ldots, t_n$ be any n individuals (not necessarily distinct), then the expression $(Rt_1t_2 \ldots t_n)$ is said to be an atomic wff. These are the only atomic wff.

For example, if **G** has order 2, then **(Gxy)** and **(Gyy)** are atomic wff. On the other hand, **Gxy** and **(Gxyz)** and **(Gz)** are *not* atomic wff.

DEFINITION OF WFF: First, we say that each atomic wff is a wff; furthermore, if A is a wff, so is $(\sim A)$; if B and C are wff, so is $(B \vee C)$, provided that no individual is free in B and is bound in C or vice versa; moreover, if D is any wff and t is any individual which is free in D, then $(\forall tD)$ is a wff. D is said to be the *scope* of $\forall t$ in the wff $(\forall tD)$. These are the only wff.

For example, if **F** has order 1 and **G** has order 2, then **((Fx) ∨ (Gyy))** and **((Fy) ∨ (∀x(Gxy)))** are wff, whereas **(∀y(Gxz))** and **((Fx) ∨ (∀x(Gxz)))** are not wff.

Notice our use of capital letters at the beginning of the alphabet as variables for wff; furthermore, notice that these symbols are set in lightface type. This convention has the important advantage of bringing out the distinction between the symbols of the predicate calculus (which are set in boldface type), and the variables denoting wff (which are set in lightface type). Again, notice our use of lower case letters at the middle of the alphabet as variables for individuals; again, these symbols are set in lightface type.

Since each wff is an expression and each expression is finite, we see that

THEOREM. Each wff is finite.

We shall say that a wff that is not atomic is *composite*. Thus, **(∀y(Fy))** is composite. By the *length* of a composite wff, we mean the number of instances of connectives occurring in the wff. For example, **((~ (∀y(Fy))) ∨ (Gxy))** has length 3.

Again, we have the important notion of the *main connective* of a wff. We shall say that **~** is the main connective of the wff *A* iff there is a wff, say *B*, such that *A* is **(~** *B***)**; we shall say that **∨** is the main connective of the wff *A* iff there are wff, say *B* and *C*, such that *A* is **(B ∨ C)**; finally, we shall say that **∀** is the main connective of the wff *A* iff there exists a wff, say *D*, and an individual, say *t*, such that *A* is **(∀***tD***)**.

For example, **~** is the main connective of the wff **(~ ((Fx) ∨ (Gyz)))**, whereas **∀** is the main connective of the wff **(∀z((Fz) ∨ (Gxy)))**.

THEOREM: Each composite wff has exactly one main connective.

Demonstration: Consider the definition of wff.

We now state and prove our

FUNDAMENTAL THEOREM ABOUT WFF: Each wff has property *P* provided that

1. Each atomic wff has property *P*
2. **(~** *A***)** has property *P* whenever *A* is a wff with property *P*
3. **(***A* **∨** *B***)** has property *P* whenever *A* has property *P* and *B* has property *P*, provided **(***A* **∨** *B***)** is a wff
4. **(∀***tD***)** has property *P* whenever *D* has property *P*—provided that **(∀***tD***)** is a wff.

Demonstration: Let *P* be a property satisfying the four assumptions of the fundamental theorem, but such that not all wff possess property *P*. Consider the set *S* of all wff that do not possess property *P*; then *S* is non-empty and no atomic wff is a member of *S*. Since each composite wff has finite length, it follows that there is a natural number, say *k*, such that *k* is the length of a member of *S*, whereas no wff with length less than *k*, is a member of S. In other words, if there exists a wff which does not possess property P, then there must also exist a "shortest" wff which does not possess property P. Let A be any member of S with length k. Since A is composite, A possesses a main connective. There are three possibilities.

1. The main connective of A is $\sim$; then there is a wff, say B, such that A is $(\sim B)$. It follows that $B \bar{\in} S$ and so B has property P. Therefore, applying the second assumption of our fundamental theorem, A has property P. This contradiction demonstrates that the main connective of A is not $\sim$.
2. The main connective of A is $\vee$: then there are wff B and C such that A is $(B \vee C)$. Again, it follows that $B \bar{\in} S$ and $C \bar{\in} S$; hence, B has property P and C has property P. Applying the third assumption of our theorem, it follows that A has property P. This contradiction demonstrates that the main connective of A is not $\vee$.
3. The main connective of A is $\forall$: then there is a wff, say D, and an individual, say t, such that A is $(\forall t D)$. Clearly, $D \bar{\in} S$ and so D has property P. Applying the fourth assumption of our theorem, we see that A has property P. This contradiction demonstrates that the main connective of A is not $\forall$.

Since each composite wff possesses a main connective, and since the only possible main connectives are $\sim$, $\vee$, $\forall$, it follows that A is not a composite wff. Thus, the assumption that there exists a wff which does not have property P, is untenable. So our fundamental theorem is established.

EXERCISES

1. Which of the following are expressions?

(a) **G**	(b) **(G)**	(c) **(Gxy)**
(d) **{Gxy}**	(e) **)Gxy(**	(f) **Gx ~ y**
(g) **Gx, y**	(h) **G(x, y)**	(i) **GGG**

2. Assuming that **F** has order 1, **G** has order 2, and **H** has order 3, which of the following are wff?

(a) **Fz**	(b) **(Fz)**
(c) **Gxy**	(d) **(Gxy)**
(e) **G(x, y)**	(f) **(G(x, y))**
(g) **(Fxy)**	(h) **(Fy)**
(i) **~ (Fz)**	(j) **(~ Fz)**

(k) **(~ (Fz))**
(l) **(∀z(~ (Fz)))**
(m) **((Gxz) ∨ (∀z(Fz)))**
(n) **((Gxy) ∨ (∀z(Fz)))**
(o) **(∀z(Gxz)) ∨ (∀z(Fz)))**
(p) **((∀z(Gxz)) ∨ (∀z(Fz)))**
(q) **(∀y(F))**
(r) **(∀y((Fx) ∨ (Fy)))**
(s) **(∀y(∀z(Hxyz)))**
(t) **(∀y(∀z(Gxyz)))**
(u) **(∀x(∀y(∀z(Gxyz))))**
(v) **(∀x(∀y(~ (∀z(Hxyz)))))**
(w) **(∀z(∀y(∀x((Fx) ∨ (Gyz)))))**
(x) **(∀x(∀y(∀x((Fx) ∨ (Gyx)))))**

3. In which of the following expressions is **y** free, and in which of these expressions is **y** bound?

(a) **y**
(b) **Fy**
(c) **∀y**
(d) **z**
(e) **FyGxy∀**
(f) **FyGx∀y**
(g) **((∀xyz**
(h) **∨∀ ~ y**
(i) **Hxyz**
(j) **Hxyz ∨ F∀y**
(k) **((Hxyz) ~ (∀y(Fy)))**
(l) **((Hxxx) ~ (∀y(Fy)))**

4. Precisely what is meant by saying that a symbol occurs in a wff?

5. Prove that an atomic wff occurs in each wff.

6. Is it true that each composite wff has property *P*, given that

(1) **(~** *A***)** has property *P* whenever *A* is a composite wff with property *P*
(2) **(***B* **∨** *C***)** has property *P* whenever *B* and *C* are composite wff with property *P*, provided **(***B* **∨** *C***)** is a wff
(3) **(∀***tD***)** has property *P* whenever *D* is a composite wff with property *D*, provided **(∀***tD***)** is a wff

7. Let *L* be a mapping of the set of all wff into the set of real numbers, such that:

1. $L[A] = 0$ whenever *A* is atomic
2. $L[(\sim B)] = L[B]$ whenever *B* is a wff
3. $L[(C \vee D)] = L[C] + L[D]$ whenever *C* and *D* are wff
4. $L[(\forall tE)] = 1 + L[E]$ whenever *E* is a wff and *t* is free in *E*

Describe *L* in colloquial language. Prove that *L* is characterized by the given conditions.

8. Let *R* be a mapping of the set of all wff into the set of all wff, such that:

1. $R[A] = A$ whenever *A* is atomic
2. $R[(\sim B)] = (\sim R[B])$ whenever *B* is a wff
3. $R[(C \vee D)] = (R[C] \vee R[D])$ whenever *C* and *D* are wff

4. $R[(\forall tE)] = (\forall t((\sim (\mathrm{F}t)) \vee R[E]))$ whenever E is a wff and t is free in E

(a) Show that these four conditions characterize R.

(b) Compute $R[(\forall \mathrm{x}(\forall \mathrm{y}(\forall \mathrm{z}(\mathrm{Hxyz}))))]$.

(c) Characterize R in colloquial language.

3. Parentheses-omitting Conventions

As in the propositional calculus, the importance of parentheses in the predicate calculus is unquestioned. Nonetheless, the presence of many parentheses in a wff makes for poor readability. For example, consider the wff

$$(\sim ((\forall \mathrm{y}(\sim ((\mathrm{Fx}) \vee (\mathrm{Gxy})))) \vee (\sim (\mathrm{Gyy}))))$$

The main connective of this wff is not immediately apparent, since it does not strike the eye at first glance. Of course, one can easily work out which is the main connective of the wff; a careful inspection discloses that it is $\sim$. The point is that this fact is not immediately apparent to the eye. What we need is an improved notation. We want methods of *denoting* wff so that the main connective of a wff will stand out. In particular, we must avoid the danger of the eye becoming lost in a thicket of parentheses.

As in the case of the propositional calculus, we introduce additional symbols to help us denote wff. Let A and B be any wff of the predicate calculus; we agree to denote the wff $((\sim A) \vee B)$ by writing "$(A \rightarrow B)$", we agree to denote the wff $(\sim ((\sim A) \vee (\sim B)))$ by writing "$(A \wedge B)$", we agree to denote the wff $((A \rightarrow B) \wedge (B \rightarrow A)$ by writing "$(A \leftrightarrow B)$", and we agree to denote the wff $(\sim (\forall t(\sim A)))$ by writing "$(\exists tA)$", whenever t is an individual.

Again, we attribute a bracketing power to the connectives ,$\sim$ $\vee$, $\wedge$, $\rightarrow$, $\leftrightarrow$ in that precise order, as in the case of the propositional calculus; furthermore, we shall strengthen the bracketing power of a connective by dotting the connective. Note that the connectives $\forall$ and $\exists$ are not included in this convention. We have a special convention for these symbols. Let Q_1, Q_2, $\ldots$, Q_n be any finite sequence of the symbols $\forall$ and $\exists$, so that $Q_i = \forall$ or $Q_i = \exists$ for each i, and let A be any wff free of the symbols $\forall$ and $\exists$ and in which the n distinct individuals $t_1, t_2, \ldots, t_n$ are free. Then by "$Q_1t_1Q_2t_2 \ldots Q_nt_nA$" we denote the wff $(Q_1t_1(Q_2t_2 \ldots (Q_nt_nA) \ldots))$, so that Q_1 is the main connective of $Q_1t_1Q_2t_2 \ldots Q_nt_nA$. In case A is atomic, we shall sometimes omit the parentheses appearing in A.

For example, the wff $(\exists \mathrm{y}(\forall \mathrm{z}(\forall \mathrm{w}(\exists \mathrm{x}(\mathrm{Hxyzw})))))$ is denoted by "$\exists \mathrm{y}\forall \mathrm{z}\forall \mathrm{w}\exists \mathrm{x}\mathrm{Hxyzw}$", and the wff $(\forall \mathrm{x}(\exists \mathrm{y}(\forall \mathrm{w}((\mathrm{Fw}) \vee (\mathrm{Hxxyw})))))$ is denoted by "$\forall \mathrm{x}\exists \mathrm{y}\forall \mathrm{w}(\mathrm{Fw} \vee \mathrm{Hxxyw})$".

Notice in particular that the connectives $\forall$ and $\exists$ possess the weakest possible binding power. For example, "$\forall \mathrm{yFy} \vee \mathrm{Gx}$" denotes $((\forall \mathrm{y}(\mathrm{Fy})) \vee (\mathrm{Gx}))$, whereas the wff $(\forall \mathrm{y}((\mathrm{Fy}) \vee (\mathrm{Gx})))$ is denoted by "$\forall \mathrm{y}(\mathrm{Fy} \vee \mathrm{Gx})$".

EXERCISES

Indicate the main connective of the following wff by inserting parentheses:

1. $\forall y(Fx \vee Gxy) \rightarrow \exists zFz$
2. $\forall xFx \leftrightarrow \exists yGyy \wedge \exists yFy$
3. $\forall z(Fz \rightarrow Gxx) \vee Fy$
4. $\forall z \exists yGyz$
5. $\exists y \exists x(Fy \leftrightarrow Fx)$
6. $\exists y \exists xGyx \leftrightarrow Fz$
7. $\forall xGxy \vee \forall z(Fz \wedge Fz)$
8. $\forall yFy \dot{\rightarrow} Gxx \leftrightarrow Fx$
9. $Gxy \dot{\vee} Fz \rightarrow \forall wHxyw$

Write down the wff denoted by the following (use only the connectives $\sim, \vee, \forall$):

10. $\exists xFx \rightarrow Fy$
11. $\exists x(Fx \rightarrow Fy)$
12. $\exists x(Fx \vee Fy)$
13. $\forall x \exists yGxy$
14. $\forall x \exists y \forall zHxyz$
15. $\forall yGyy \wedge \exists xFx$
16. $\exists xFx \leftrightarrow \exists xGxx$
17. $\exists xFx \leftrightarrow \exists yFy$
18. $\exists x(Fx \leftrightarrow \exists yFy)$

Simplify the following wff.

19. $(\forall y(Fy))$
20. $(\forall x((Fx) \vee (Fy)))$
21. $(\forall z((Fz) \vee (Gyz)))$
22. $(\forall w((\sim (Fw)) \vee (Fw)))$

23. $(\sim(\forall y(\sim(Fy))))$

24. $((\sim(Gyx)) \vee (\forall z(Fz)))$

25. $(\forall y((\sim(Gyx)) \vee (\forall z(Fz))))$

26. $(\forall x(\forall y((\sim(Gyx)) \vee (\forall z(Fz)))))$

4. Some Syntactical Transforms

As in the propositional calculus, by a syntactical transform we mean a mapping of the set of all wff into the set of all wff. We shall find it convenient, when discussing the notion of a *proof*, to have available a particular family of syntactical transforms.

First, given individuals s and t, let us introduce a syntactical transform which associates with a given wff, say A, the wff obtained from A by interchanging s and t throughout A; we shall denote the resulting wff by "$I_t^s A$". It is clear just which wff is denoted by "$I_t^s A$"; nonetheless, it is helpful to define the syntactical transform I_t^s in the step-by-step manner which apes the permitted construction steps.

DEFINITION OF I_t^s:

1. $$I_t^s(Hx_1 \ldots x_n) = Hz_1 \ldots z_n \text{ where } z_i = \begin{cases} s \text{ if } x_i = t \\ t \text{ if } x_i = s \\ x_i \text{ otherwise} \end{cases}$$

2. $$I_t^s(\sim A) = \sim I_t^s A$$

3. $$I_t^s(A \vee B) = (I_t^s A) \vee (I_t^s B)$$

4. $$I_t^s(\forall u A) = \begin{cases} \forall s I_t^s A \text{ if } u = t \\ \forall t I_t^s A \text{ if } u = s \\ \forall u I_t^s A \text{ otherwise} \end{cases}$$

In fact, we have defined a *family* of syntactical transforms, since s and t may be any individuals. By applying our fundamental theorem about wff, it is easy to show that the four properties of I_t^s displayed above, actually define a unique syntactical transform.

To illustrate, we compute $I_x^y(Gxz \vee \forall yHxyz)$.

Now,

$$\begin{aligned} I_x^y(Gxz \vee \forall yHxyz) &= (I_x^y Gxz) \vee I_x^y(\forall yHxyz) && \text{by 3} \\ &= Gyz \vee I_x^y(\forall yHxyz) && \text{by 1} \\ &= Gyz \vee \forall x I_x^y Hxyz && \text{by 4} \\ &= Gyz \vee \forall xHyxz && \text{by 1} \end{aligned}$$

In a similar way, it is easy to see that

$$I_w^z(\forall xFx \vee \forall w\forall zGwz) = \forall xFx \vee \forall z\forall wGzw.$$

In terms of I^s_t, we now define the syntactical transform S^s_t that we will need when introducing the notion of a proof in a later section.

DEFINITION OF S^s_t:

1. $S^s_t(Hx_1 \ldots x_n) = Hz_1 \ldots z_n$ where $z_i = \begin{cases} s \text{ if } x_i = t \\ x_i \text{ if } x_i \neq t \end{cases}$

2. $S^s_t(\sim A) = \sim S^s_t A$

3. $S^s_t(A \vee B) = (S^s_t A) \vee (S^s_t B)$

4. $S^s_t(\forall u A) = \begin{cases} \forall t A \text{ if } u = t \\ \forall t I^s_t A \text{ if } u = s \\ \forall u S^s_t A \text{ otherwise} \end{cases}$

Let us see the effect of S^s_t on a wff. Clearly, each free instance of t is replaced by s; each bound s not in the scope of $\forall t$ is replaced by t; and each bound t in the scope of $\forall s$ is replaced by s. For example,

$$S^{\mathbf{x}}_{\mathbf{w}}(\forall \mathbf{z} \forall \mathbf{y} \mathbf{Gyz} \vee \sim (\forall \mathbf{x} \forall \mathbf{w}(\mathbf{Fx} \vee \mathbf{Fw})))$$
$$= \forall \mathbf{z} S^{\mathbf{x}}_{\mathbf{w}}(\forall \mathbf{w} \mathbf{Gwz}) \vee \sim (S^{\mathbf{x}}_{\mathbf{w}}(\forall \mathbf{x} \forall \mathbf{w}(\mathbf{Fx} \vee \mathbf{Fw})))$$
$$= \forall \mathbf{z} \forall \mathbf{w} \mathbf{Gwz} \vee \sim (\forall \mathbf{w} I^{\mathbf{x}}_{\mathbf{w}}(\forall \mathbf{w}(\mathbf{Fx} \vee \mathbf{Fw})))$$
$$= \forall \mathbf{z} \forall \mathbf{w} \mathbf{Gwz} \vee \sim (\forall \mathbf{w} \forall \mathbf{x}(\mathbf{Fw} \vee \mathbf{Fx})).$$

Notice, that again we have defined a *family* of syntactical transforms, since the s and t of the definition may be any individuals. It may be helpful to read S^s_t as "substitute s for t". We shall see that this transform enables us to introduce the notion of a *proof* fairly efficiently.

EXERCISES

Simplify the following:

1. $I^{\mathbf{y}}_{\mathbf{x}}(\mathbf{Fx} \vee \sim (\mathbf{Gxy} \vee \mathbf{Hzyx}))$
2. $I^{\mathbf{z}}_{\mathbf{w}}(\forall \mathbf{w}(\mathbf{Hxyw} \vee \mathbf{Fz}))$
3. $S^{\mathbf{z}}_{\mathbf{w}}(\forall \mathbf{w}(\mathbf{Hxyw} \vee \mathbf{Fz}))$
4. $S^{\mathbf{z}}_{\mathbf{x}}(\mathbf{Fx} \vee \forall \mathbf{y}(\mathbf{Gxy} \vee \forall \mathbf{z} \mathbf{Hxyz}))$
5. $S^{\mathbf{y}}_{\mathbf{x}}(\mathbf{Fx} \vee \forall \mathbf{y}(\mathbf{Gxy} \vee \forall \mathbf{z}(\mathbf{Hxyz})))$
6. $S^{\mathbf{x}}_{\mathbf{y}}(\mathbf{Fx} \vee \forall \mathbf{y}(\mathbf{Gxy} \vee \forall \mathbf{z} \mathbf{Hxyz}))$
7. Show that $I^s_t(A \wedge B) = I^s_t(A) \wedge I^s_t(B)$ and $S^s_t(A \wedge B) = S^s_t(A) \wedge S^s_t(B)$ whenever A and B are wff and s and t are individuals.

8. Show that $I_t^s(A \to B) = I_t^s(A) \to I_t^s(B)$ and $S_t^s(A \to B) = S_t^s(A) \to S_t^s(B)$ whenever A and B are wff, and s and t are individuals.

9. Show that $I_t^s(A \leftrightarrow B) = I_t^s(A) \leftrightarrow I_t^s(B)$ and $S_t^s(A \leftrightarrow B) = S_t^s(A) \leftrightarrow S_t^s(B)$ whenever A and B are wff, and s and t are individuals.

10. Show that $I_{\mathbf{x}}^{\mathbf{y}}(\exists tA) = \begin{cases} \exists \mathbf{y} I_{\mathbf{x}}^{\mathbf{y}}A & \text{if } t = \mathbf{x} \\ \exists \mathbf{x} I_{\mathbf{x}}^{\mathbf{y}}A & \text{if } t = \mathbf{y} \\ \exists t I_{\mathbf{x}}^{\mathbf{y}}A & \text{otherwise} \end{cases}$

and $S_{\mathbf{x}}^{\mathbf{y}}(\exists tA) = \begin{cases} \exists \mathbf{x} A & \text{if } t = \mathbf{x} \\ \exists \mathbf{x} I_{\mathbf{x}}^{\mathbf{y}}A & \text{if } t = \mathbf{y} \\ \exists t S_{\mathbf{x}}^{\mathbf{y}}A & \text{otherwise.} \end{cases}$

Simplify the following:

11. $I_{\mathbf{x}}^{\mathbf{y}}(\mathbf{Fw} \wedge \exists \mathbf{x} \forall \mathbf{y} \exists \mathbf{z} \mathbf{Hxyzw})$

12. $S_{\mathbf{x}}^{\mathbf{y}}(\mathbf{Fw} \wedge \exists \mathbf{x} \forall \mathbf{y} \exists \mathbf{z} \mathbf{Hxyzw})$

13. $I_{\mathbf{w}}^{\mathbf{z}}(\forall \mathbf{x} \forall \mathbf{y} \exists \mathbf{z} \forall \mathbf{w} \mathbf{Hxyzw})$

14. $S_{\mathbf{w}}^{\mathbf{z}}(\forall \mathbf{x} \forall \mathbf{y} \exists \mathbf{z} \forall \mathbf{w} \mathbf{Hxyzw})$

15. $S_{\mathbf{z}}^{\mathbf{w}}(\forall \mathbf{x} \forall \mathbf{y} \exists \mathbf{z} \forall \mathbf{w} \mathbf{Hxyzw})$

16. Prove that $I_t^t A = A$ whenever A is a wff and t is an individual.

17. Prove that $S_t^t A = A$ whenever A is a wff and t is an individual.

18. Prove that $I_t^s I_s^t A = A$ whenever A is a wff and s and t are individuals.

19. Prove that $I_t^s I_t^s A = A$ whenever A is a wff and s and t are individuals.

20. Prove that $I_t^s = I_s^t$ whenever s and t are individuals.

21. Prove that $S_t^s \neq S_s^t$ unless $s = t$.

22. Prove that $I_t^s S_v^u A = S_v^u I_t^s A$ whenever A is a wff, provided that s, t, u, and v are all different individuals.

23. Prove that $I_t^s S_u^s A = S_u^t I_t^s A$ whenever A is a wff, provided that s is not bound in A and u is free in A.

24. Show that $S_t^s S_s^t A = S_t^s A$ whenever A is a wff, provided that s and t are free in A.

25. Let T_t^s be a mapping of the set of all wff into the set of all expressions, defined as follows:

   1. $T_t^s(Hx_1 \ldots x_n) = Hz_1 \ldots z_n$ where $z_i = \begin{cases} s \text{ if } z_i = t \\ x_i \text{ if } z_i \neq t \end{cases}$
   2. $T_t^s(\sim A) = \sim T_t^s A$

3. $T_t^s(A \vee B) = T_t^s(A) \vee T_t^s(B)$

4. $T_t^s(\forall uA) = \begin{cases} \forall tA \text{ if } u = t \\ \forall tT_s^t A \text{ if } u = s \\ \forall uT_t^s A \text{ otherwise} \end{cases}$

(a) Show that $T_t^s(A \wedge B) = T_t^s(A) \wedge T_t^s(B)$.
(b) Show that $T_t^s(A \rightarrow B) = T_t^s(A) \rightarrow T_t^s(B)$.
(c) Show that $T_t^s(A \leftrightarrow B) = T_t^s(A) \leftrightarrow T_t^s(B)$.

(d) Show that $T_t^s(\exists uA) = \begin{cases} \exists tA \text{ if } u = t \\ \exists tT_s^t A \text{ if } u = s \\ \exists uT_t^s A \text{ otherwise} \end{cases}$

(e) Show that $T_{\mathbf{x}}^{\mathbf{y}}$ is *not* a syntactical transform. (*Hint:* Find a wff, say B, such that $T_{\mathbf{x}}^{\mathbf{y}}B$ is not a wff).

26. Prove that $I_{\mathbf{x}}^{\mathbf{y}}A$ is a wff whenever A is a wff.

27. Prove that $S_{\mathbf{x}}^{\mathbf{y}}A$ is a wff whenever A is a wff.

28. Demonstrate the following variant of the fundamental theorem about wff. Each wff has property P if:

(1) each atomic wff has property P

(2) $\sim B$ has property P whenever B has property P

(3) $C \vee D$ has property P whenever C has property P and D has property P, and $C \vee D$ is a wff.

(4) $\forall tE$ has property P provided $S_t^s E$ has property P whenever s is an individual, and $\forall tE$ is a wff.

5. Structures, Swff, and Models

The language of the predicate calculus, introduced in this chapter, is intended to characterize the notion of a *statement* in mathematics. To make this quite clear and to bring out the intended significance of the various symbols appearing in a wff, we now present the notion of a *model* of a wff.

As we have suggested, we shall be concerned with algebraic systems involving relations but no operators; we shall call them *structures*. Now consider a wff, say A, and a structure, say $\mathcal{S}$; we shall say that A is *defined* in $\mathcal{S}$ iff each predicate of order n occurring in A is correlated with an n^{ary} relation of $\mathcal{S}$, and each individual which is free in A, is correlated with a displayed member of the basic set of $\mathcal{S}$. Of course, two predicates in A, which possess the same order, may be correlated with the same relation in $\mathcal{S}$, and two free individuals in A may be correlated with the same displayed member of the basic set of $\mathcal{S}$.

For example, consider the wff

(i) $$\forall \mathbf{x}(\mathbf{Fx}) \rightarrow \mathbf{Fz} \vee \forall \mathbf{x} \exists \mathbf{y} \mathbf{Gxy}$$

and the structure

(I) $$(\{a, b\}, \{a\}, \{(a, a), (b, b)\}, a)$$

whose basic set is $\{a, b\}$, and which involves two relations—the unary relation $\{a\}$ and the binary relation $\{(a, a), (b, b)\}$—and also involves one displayed member of the basic set—namely, a.

There is only one way of defining the given wff (i) in the given structure (I): we shall associate the unary relation $\{a\}$ with the predicate **F**, we shall associate the binary relation $\{(a, a), (b, b)\}$ with the predicate **G**, and we shall associate the displayed member of the basic set a with **z**, the individual which is free in (i). In other words, we introduce a mapping μ of $\{\mathbf{F}, \mathbf{G}, \mathbf{z}\}$ onto $\{\{a\}, \{(a, a), (b, b)\}, a\}$ such that $\mu\mathbf{F} = \{a\}$, $\mu\mathbf{G} = \{(a, a), (b, b)\}$ and $\mu\mathbf{z} = a$. Under μ, then, (i) is defined in (I).

We shall make essential use of the mapping μ in a moment. First, however, we need to make precise the language of a structure; that is, we must characterize the family of propositions (in the sense of Chapter I) that are meaningful within the frame-work of a given structure. We shall call any such proposition, a *structural well-formed formula*, or *swff* for short.

In defining the notion of a swff, we shall make use of our "substituting" transform S_t^s of Section 4; this means that we must extend S_t^s so that it applies to the language of structures as well as to the language of the predicate calculus.

Some examples may make this clear:

$$S_b^{\mathbf{y}}(\mathbf{x} \vee \forall b\mathbf{R}a) = \mathbf{x} \vee \forall \mathbf{y}\mathbf{R}a,$$

and $$S_a^{\mathbf{x}}((\mathbf{R}ba) \vee (\mathbf{T}a)) = (\mathbf{R}b\mathbf{x}) \vee (\mathbf{T}\mathbf{x}).$$

We now define what we mean by a swff. Let $\mathcal{S}$ be any structure with basic set S. Let **R** be any n^{ary} relation which is a term of $\mathcal{S}$, and let $(a_1, a_2, \ldots, a_n)$ be any ordered n^{tuple} of members of S; then we shall say that $(Ra_1a_2 \ldots a_n)$ is a swff. If A and B are swff, so are $(\sim A)$ and $(A \vee B)$. Suppose that $a \in S$ and suppose that D is any swff in which a occurs; let s be any individual of the predicate calculus which does not occur in D; then we say that $(\forall s S_a^s D)$ is a swff. These are the only swff. All this is subject to the restriction that each swff is finite. Here, the symbols "$\sim$", "$\vee$", and "$\forall$" denote the logical connectives discussed in Chapter 1, not the symbols introduced on page 149.

To illustrate our notion of swff, let us consider the structure (I) above; we denote the unary relation $\{a\}$ by **T** and the binary relation $\{(a, a), (b, b)\}$

by **R**. Then (Raa), (Rab), (Rba), (Rbb), (Ta), (Tb) are swff. Again, $(\sim(Raa))$ and $((Ta) \vee (\sim(Raa)))$ are swff. Thus, $(\forall \mathbf{x}(R\mathbf{x}b))$ is a swff, since $S_a^{\mathbf{x}}(Rab) = (R\mathbf{x}b)$. It is easy to see that each of the following is a swff

$$(\forall \mathbf{z}(T\mathbf{z})), (\forall \mathbf{z}(\sim(T\mathbf{z}))), ((Tb) \vee (\sim(\forall \mathbf{y}(T\mathbf{y})))), (\forall \mathbf{y}(\forall \mathbf{x}(R\mathbf{x}\mathbf{y}))).$$

It is convenient to introduce the usual parentheses-omitting conventions; for example, the swff $(\sim(\forall \mathbf{y}(\sim(T\mathbf{y}))))$ is denoted by "$\exists \mathbf{y}T\mathbf{y}$", the swff $((\sim(Ta)) \vee (Rbc))$ is denoted by "$Ta \rightarrow Rbc$", so that we introduce as abbreviations, as usual, the symbols "$\wedge$", "$\rightarrow$", "$\leftrightarrow$", "$\exists$". Notice that these symbols denote the logical connectives discussed in Chapter 1, not the symbols introduced on page 154.

Finally, we introduce the idea of a swff *holding* in a structure, say $\mathcal{S}$. The definition is as follows.

1. We shall say that the swff $Ra_1a_2 \ldots a_n$ holds in $\mathcal{S}$ iff $(a_1, a_2, \ldots, a_n) \in \mathbf{R}$ provided that **R** is a term of $\mathcal{S}$, **R** is an n^{ary} relation, and $(a_1, a_2, \ldots, a_n)$ is an ordered n^{tuple} of members of the basic set of $\mathcal{S}$.
2. We shall say that the swff $\sim A$ holds in $\mathcal{S}$ iff A does not hold in $\mathcal{S}$.
3. We shall say that the swff $B \vee C$ holds in $\mathcal{S}$ iff B holds in $\mathcal{S}$ or C holds in $\mathcal{S}$.
4. We shall say that the swff $\forall sD$ holds in $\mathcal{S}$ iff $S_s^a D$ holds in $\mathcal{S}$ whenever a is a member of the basic set of $\mathcal{S}$. (*Note:* "$S_s^a D$" denotes the swff obtained from D by replacing each instance of s by a.)

We shall illustrate this definition in a moment. First, notice that if a wff, say A, is defined in a structure, say $\mathcal{S}$, under a mapping μ; then the array of symbols obtained from A by replacing each predicate and free individual that occurs in A by its image in $\mathcal{S}$ under μ, and replacing **~** by "$\sim$", **v** by "$\vee$", **∀** by "$\forall$", **(** by "(", and **)** by ")", is a swff. We shall denote this swff by "μA". To illustrate, we return to our example (i) above:

$$\mu(\forall \mathbf{x}(\mathbf{Fx}) \rightarrow \mathbf{Fz} \vee \forall \mathbf{x}\exists \mathbf{y}\mathbf{Gxy}) = \forall \mathbf{x}(T\mathbf{x}) \rightarrow Ta \vee \forall \mathbf{x}\exists \mathbf{y}R\mathbf{xy}$$

Clearly, $\forall \mathbf{x}(T\mathbf{x}) \rightarrow Ta \vee \forall \mathbf{x}\exists \mathbf{y}R\mathbf{xy}$ is a swff; let us show that this swff holds in the structure (I). We examine the swff $\forall \mathbf{x}(T\mathbf{x})$ first; $S_{\mathbf{x}}^a T\mathbf{x}$ is Ta, which holds in (I), but $S_{\mathbf{x}}^b T\mathbf{x}$ is Tb, which does not hold in (I). Hence, the swff $\forall \mathbf{x}(T\mathbf{x})$ does not hold in (I). It now follows that the swff $\sim \forall \mathbf{x}(T\mathbf{x})$ holds in (I), and so the given swff $\forall \mathbf{x}(T\mathbf{x}) \rightarrow Ta \vee \forall \mathbf{x}\exists \mathbf{y}R\mathbf{xy}$ holds in (I). As a further illustration, we show that the swff $\forall \mathbf{x}\exists \mathbf{y}R\mathbf{xy}$ holds in (I). Now, $S_{\mathbf{x}}^a \exists \mathbf{y}R\mathbf{xy} = \exists \mathbf{y}Ra\mathbf{y}$; since $S_{\mathbf{y}}^a Ra\mathbf{y}$ holds in (I), it follows that $\exists \mathbf{y}Ra\mathbf{y}$ holds in (I). Similarly, $S_{\mathbf{x}}^b \exists \mathbf{y}R\mathbf{xy} = \exists \mathbf{y}Rb\mathbf{y}$; again, $S_{\mathbf{y}}^b Rb\mathbf{y}$ holds in (I), and so $\exists \mathbf{y}Rb\mathbf{y}$ holds in (I). This means that the given swff $\forall \mathbf{x}\exists \mathbf{y}Rx\mathbf{y}$ holds in (I).

Here are some more definitions. We shall say that a structure, say $\mathcal{S}$, is a *model* of a wff, say A, under a given mapping μ iff A is defined in $\mathcal{S}$ under μ, and the swff μA holds in the structure $\mathcal{S}$.

We can extend this definition quite easily. Suppose that K is a set of wff, each of which is defined in a given structure $\mathcal{S}$ under a given mapping μ.

Then we shall say that the structure $\mathcal{S}$ is a *model of K* under the given mapping μ iff $\mathcal{S}$ is a model of each member of K under μ.

For example, consider the set of wff $\{\forall \mathbf{xGxx}, \mathbf{Fz} \vee \forall \mathbf{xFx}, \mathbf{Gzz}\}$, the structure (I) above, and the mapping μ presented above. Clearly,

$$\mu\forall \mathbf{xGxx} = \forall \mathbf{x}R\mathbf{xx}, \quad \mu(\mathbf{Fz} \vee \forall \mathbf{xFx}) = Ta \vee \forall \mathbf{x}T\mathbf{x}, \quad \mu\mathbf{Gzz} = Raa$$

But the swff $\forall \mathbf{x}R\mathbf{xx}$ holds in (I); the swff $Ta \vee \forall \mathbf{x}T\mathbf{x}$ holds in (I), since Ta holds in (I); and the swff Raa holds in (I). Thus, the structure (I) is a model of $\{\forall \mathbf{xGxx}, \mathbf{Fz} \vee \forall \mathbf{xFx}, \mathbf{Gzz}\}$ under the mapping μ.

Now for the vital concept of a *true* wff. We shall say that a wff of the predicate calculus, say A, is *true* iff the swff μA holds in each structure in which A is defined. To be quite precise, we mean that if $\mathcal{S}$ is any structure and μ is any mapping, then the swff μA holds in the structure $\mathcal{S}$ whenever A is defined in $\mathcal{S}$ under the mapping μ. Thus, A is true iff $\mathcal{S}$ is a model of A under μ whenever A is defined in $\mathcal{S}$ under μ.

It is easily seen, for example, that the wff $\forall \mathbf{y}(\mathbf{Fy}) \rightarrow \mathbf{Fx}$ is true; in this regard, note that the wff $\forall \mathbf{y}(\mathbf{Fy}) \rightarrow \mathbf{Fx}$ is defined only in structures in which a member of the basic set is displayed as a term.

Recalling that the basic set of each structure is non-empty, we readily see that the wff $\forall \mathbf{y}(\mathbf{Fy}) \rightarrow \exists \mathbf{x}(\mathbf{Fx})$ is true.

We shall now establish two important facts about true wff.

THEOREM 1: If A is true and $A \rightarrow B$ is true, then B is true.

Demonstration: Let $\mathcal{S}$ be any structure and let μ be any mapping under which B is defined in $\mathcal{S}$. We must show that the swff μB holds in $\mathcal{S}$. Consider the wff A; there are two possibilities: either (1) A is defined in $\mathcal{S}$ under μ, or (2) A is not defined in $\mathcal{S}$ under μ.

(1) Assume that A is defined in $\mathcal{S}$ under μ. Then the swff μA and $\mu(A \rightarrow B)$ both hold in $\mathcal{S}$, by assumption. But $\mu(A \rightarrow B)$ is $\mu A \rightarrow \mu B$. Therefore, μB holds in $\mathcal{S}$.

(2) Assume that A is not defined in $\mathcal{S}$ under μ. This means that there are predicates occurring in A that are not assigned an image in $\mathcal{S}$ under μ, or there are individuals free in A that are not assigned an image in $\mathcal{S}$ under μ. If necessary, we extend the structure $\mathcal{S}$ to a larger structure $\mathcal{S}'$ by adjoining to $\mathcal{S}$ relations of the required order, say $\mathbf{H}_1, \mathbf{H}_2, \ldots, \mathbf{H}_k$ as required; furthermore, we arbitrarily choose a member of the basic set, say a, to be the image of each individual free in A which does not already possess an image under μ. In this way, the mapping μ is extended to a mapping μ' under which A is defined in $\mathcal{S}'$. Of course, $\mu'\alpha = \mu\alpha$ in case $\mu\alpha$ exists. Recalling that the wff A and $A \rightarrow B$ are both true by assumption, we see that the swff $\mu'A$ and $\mu'A \rightarrow \mu'B$ both hold in the structure $\mathcal{S}'$. Therefore, $\mu'B$ holds in $\mathcal{S}'$. But $\mu'B = \mu B$; thus μB holds in $\mathcal{S}'$, and so μB holds in $\mathcal{S}$.

We have demonstrated that if B is defined in a structure, then the corresponding swff holds in that structure. Thus, B is true.

THEOREM 2: $A \to \forall tB$ is true provided that $A \to B$ is true, t is free in B, and t does not occur in A.

Demonstration: We are given that the wff $A \to B$ is true and wish to show that, if $A \to \forall tB$ is a wff, then it is also true. Let $\mathcal{S}$ be any structure and let μ be any mapping under which $A \to \forall tB$ is defined in $\mathcal{S}$. We must show that the swff $\mu(A \to \forall tB)$ holds in $\mathcal{S}$. Clearly, $\mu(A \to \forall tB)$ is $\mu A \to \mu(\forall tB)$. If μA does not hold in $\mathcal{S}$, there is nothing to prove. Hence, we assume that μA holds in $\mathcal{S}$. This means we must show that $\mu(\forall tB)$ holds in $\mathcal{S}$. Let a be any member of the basic set of $\mathcal{S}$; let us show that the swff $\mu(S_t^a B)$ holds in $\mathcal{S}$. To this purpose, consider the mapping μ' obtained from μ as follows:

$$\mu'\alpha = \begin{cases} a \text{ if } \alpha = t \\ \mu\alpha \text{ otherwise} \end{cases}$$

and consider the structure $\mathcal{S}'$ obtained from $\mathcal{S}$ by displaying a as a special term. Since $A \to B$ is true and is defined in $\mathcal{S}'$ under μ', we know that the swff $\mu'(A \to B)$ holds in $\mathcal{S}'$. That is, $\mu'A \to \mu'B$ holds in $\mathcal{S}'$. But $\mu'A = \mu A$, since t does not occur in A. Therefore, the swff $\mu'A$ holds in $\mathcal{S}'$, and so the swff $\mu'B$ holds in $\mathcal{S}'$. But $\mu'B = \mu(S_t^a B)$! Therefore, $\mu(S_t^a B)$ holds in $\mathcal{S}'$; hence, $\mu(S_t^a B)$ holds in $\mathcal{S}$.

We have demonstrated that the swff $\mu(S_t^a B)$ holds in $\mathcal{S}$ whenever a is a member of the basic set of $\mathcal{S}$. This means that the swff $\mu(\forall tB)$ holds in $\mathcal{S}$, and so the swff $\mu(A \to \forall tB)$ holds in $\mathcal{S}$. We conclude that the wff $A \to \forall tB$ is true. This establishes Theorem 2.

EXERCISES

1. Consider the structure $(\{a, b\}, \{a\}, \{(a, a), (b, b)\}, a, b)$ and the wff $\forall \mathbf{x}(\mathbf{Fx}) \to \mathbf{Fz} \lor \forall \mathbf{x} \exists \mathbf{y} \mathbf{Gxy}$.
   (a) Construct two different mappings under each of which the given wff is defined in the given structure.
   (b) In each case, write down the swff that results. Do these swff hold in the given structure?
2. Consider the structure $(\{a, b, c\}, \{(a, a), (b, b), (c, c)\}, c)$ and the wff $\forall \mathbf{y} \mathbf{Gyy} \land \exists \mathbf{y} \mathbf{Gyz}$.
   (a) Construct a mapping under which the given wff is defined in the given structure.
   (b) Show that the resulting swff holds in the structure.

(c) Construct a structure and a mapping such that $\forall \mathbf{y}G\mathbf{yy} \wedge \exists \mathbf{y}G\mathbf{yz}$ is defined in your structure under your mapping, but the resulting swff does not hold in your structure.

3. Consider the structure $(\{0, 1\}, \{(0, 1), (1, 0)\}, \{(0, 0)\})$ and the wff $\exists \mathbf{x}\exists \mathbf{y}G\mathbf{xy}$.
   (a) Show that the given wff can be defined in the given structure in two ways.
   (b) Prove that in either case, the resulting swff holds in the given structure.

4. Consider the structure $(\{0, 1, 2\}, \{(0, 0), (1, 1)\}, 1)$ and the wff $\forall \mathbf{x}G\mathbf{xx}$.
   (a) Construct a mapping under which the given wff is defined in the given structure.
   (b) Show that the resulting swff does not hold in the given structure.
   (c) Construct a structure in which $\forall \mathbf{x}G\mathbf{xx}$ can be defined under an appropriate mapping and such that the resulting swff holds in the structure.
   (d) Write down a swff which holds in the structure of this problem.

5. Simplify the following:
   (a) $S_a^{\mathbf{x}}(Rab)$ (b) $S_b^{\mathbf{x}}(Rab)$
   (c) $S_a^{\mathbf{y}}(Rab)$ (d) $S_b^{\mathbf{y}}(Rab)$
   (e) $S_c^{\mathbf{x}}(Rcc \vee \forall \mathbf{y}Gyc)$ (f) $S_b^{\mathbf{x}}(T\mathbf{x} \rightarrow Gba)$
   (g) $S_{\mathbf{x}}^{c}(R\mathbf{x} \wedge \sim T\mathbf{yx})$ (h) $S_{\mathbf{x}}^{c}(S_c^{\mathbf{x}}(Gca))$.

6. Given that A and B are swff constructed with reference to a structure $\mathcal{S}$, prove that:
   (a) the swff $A \wedge B$ holds in $\mathcal{S}$ iff A holds in $\mathcal{S}$ and B holds in $\mathcal{S}$
   (b) the swff $A \rightarrow B$ holds in $\mathcal{S}$ iff A does not hold in $\mathcal{S}$ or B holds in $\mathcal{S}$
   (c) the swff $A \leftrightarrow B$ holds in $\mathcal{S}$ iff both A and B hold in $\mathcal{S}$, or neither holds in $\mathcal{S}$
   (d) the swff $\exists tA$ holds in $\mathcal{S}$ iff there is a member of the basic set of $\mathcal{S}$, say a, such that the swff $S_t^a A$ holds in $\mathcal{S}$.

7. Show that each of the following swff holds in the structure (I) of the text:
   (a) $\forall \mathbf{x}(R\mathbf{xx})$ (b) $\exists \mathbf{y}(Ra\mathbf{y})$
   (c) $\exists \mathbf{y}(T\mathbf{y})$ (d) $Ta \rightarrow Raa$
   (e) $Ta \wedge Raa$ (f) $Ta \leftrightarrow Raa$
   (g) $\forall \mathbf{x}(T\mathbf{x}) \rightarrow \forall \mathbf{x}\forall \mathbf{y}(R\mathbf{xy})$ (h) $\sim (\forall \mathbf{x}\forall \mathbf{y}(R\mathbf{xy}))$
   (i) $\forall \mathbf{z}(T\mathbf{z} \rightarrow Ra\mathbf{z})$ (j) $\forall \mathbf{z}(T\mathbf{z} \vee Rb\mathbf{z})$

8. Which of the following swff hold in the structure $(\{0, 1, 2\}, \mathbf{U}, \mathbf{V}, \mathbf{W}, 0)$, given that $\mathbf{U} = \{1, 2\}$, $\mathbf{V} = \{(0, 1), (0, 2)\}$, $\mathbf{W} = \{(0, 1, 0), (0, 1, 1), (0, 1, 2)\}$:
   (a) $U1$ (b) $\sim U1$
   (c) $U2 \vee V11$ (d) $U2 \wedge V11$

(e) $\forall x(Ux)$ (f) $\sim \forall x(Ux)$
(g) $\forall x(Ux \to V0x)$ (h) $V10$
(i) $W001 \wedge V02$ (j) $U2 \wedge V01 \dot{\wedge} W011$
(k) $\forall x \forall y(Vxy \wedge \sim Uy \to Wxyy)$ (l) $\exists y(U1 \to V0y \wedge W0yy)$

9. Show that the structure of Exercise 8 is a model of each of the following wff:

(a) $\exists x(Fx)$ (b) $\forall x(Fx \to Gyx)$
(c) $\forall x \exists y(Fx \vee Gxy)$ (d) $\forall x \forall y(Fx \wedge Gxy \to Hxyx)$
(e) $\forall x \forall y(Gxy \wedge Hxyx \to Fy)$ (f) $\forall x \forall y(Gxy \wedge Hxyx \to \sim Fx)$
(g) $\forall y(Gwy \wedge Hwyw \to Hwyy)$ (h) $\forall y(Hwyy \to Hwyw)$
(i) $\forall y \exists x(Hwxy)$ (j) $\forall x \forall y \forall z(Gxy \wedge Gyz \to Hxyz)$
(k) $\exists x \forall y(Hwxy)$ (l) $\exists x \exists y \forall w(Hxyw)$

10. Show that the structure $(\{a, b\}, \{b\}, \{(a, b), (b, a)\}, a)$ is a model of the set of wff $\{\exists yGxy, \exists yFy, \forall w(Fw \vee Gwx), \forall z \exists y(Gzy), \forall z \exists y(Gzy \wedge Gyz)\}$.

11. (a) Given that A is a wff, t is an individual that is free in A, and s is an individual that is bound in $\forall tA$, show that $\forall tA \to S_t^s A$ is *not* a wff.
(b) Given that $\forall tA$ is a wff, and s is an individual which is not bound in $\forall tA$, show that $\forall tA \to S_t^s A$ is a wff.
(c) Prove that $\forall tA \to S_t^s A$ is true, given that t is free in A and s is not bound in $\forall tA$.

6. The Concept of a Proof

Once again, by a *proof* in the predicate calculus, we mean a finite sequence of wff of the predicate calculus that possesses certain formal properties. Our object is to characterize the set of all *true* wff by using only the formal devices available within the language of the predicate calculus, without referring to structures in any way. The general pattern that we shall follow is exactly the pattern to which we were exposed in the study of the propositional calculus.

To begin, we note that if A, B, and C are any wff of the predicate calculus, then each of the following is true, provided, of course, that it is a wff: $A \vee A \to A$, $A \to A \vee B$, $A \vee B \to B \vee A$, $A \to B \dot{\to} C \vee A \to C \vee B$. For example, let us show that the wff $A \to A \vee B$ is true. Suppose that this wff is defined in a given structure $\mathcal{S}$ under a mapping μ. We must show that the swff $\mu(A \to A \vee B)$ holds in $\mathcal{S}$. The swff mentioned can be simplified, and it is easily seen to be $\mu A \to \mu A \vee \mu B$. There are two possibilities regarding the swff μA: either μA holds in $\mathcal{S}$ or μA does not hold in $\mathcal{S}$. In the former case, it follows that the swff $\mu A \vee \mu B$ holds in $\mathcal{S}$, and so the swff $\mu A \to \mu A \vee \mu B$ holds in $\mathcal{S}$. In the latter case, the swff $\sim \mu A$ holds in $\mathcal{S}$, and so again $\mu A \to \mu A \vee \mu B$ holds in $\mathcal{S}$. This demonstrates that the swff $\mu(A \to A \vee B)$ holds in $\mathcal{S}$; it follows that the wff $A \to A \vee B$ is true. The remaining three wff referred to above are easily shown to be true by a similar argument.

In Exercise 11, on page 165, we observed that $\forall tA \to S_t^s A$ is true, provided it is a wff. Clearly, $\forall tA \to S_t^s A$ is a wff iff t is free in A, s is not bound in A, and s and t are distinct individuals. (Notice that $\forall tA \to A$ is not a wff.) In other words, $\forall tA \to S_t^s A$ is true whenever A is a wff, t is free in A, and s is not bound in $\forall tA$.

We shall base our notion of a *proof* on the five true wff discussed here and on two rules of inference, which we shall discuss shortly. Actually, it is five *types* or *families* of wff that we are involved with, not merely five wff. To make this quite clear, we shall sometimes say that a wff, say E, has the *form* $A \to A \vee B$. By this we mean there exist wff A and B such that E *is* $A \to A \vee B$. What is involved is the set $\{A \to A \vee B \mid A \text{ and } B \text{ are wff}\}$; our statement that the wff E has the form $A \to A \vee B$ merely asserts that the wff E is a member of the above set.

Thus, our notion of proof involves the following five sets of wff:

(1) $\{A \vee A \to A \mid A \text{ is a wff}\}$
(2) $\{A \to A \vee B \mid A, B, \text{ and } A \vee B \text{ are wff}\}$
(3) $\{A \vee B \to B \vee A \mid A, B, \text{ and } A \vee B \text{ are wff}\}$
(4) $\{A \to B \mathbin{\dot{\to}} C \vee A \to C \vee B \mid A, B, \text{ and } A \vee B \mathbin{\dot{\vee}} C \text{ are wff}\}$
(5) $\{\forall tA \to S_t^s A \mid A \text{ is a wff, } t \text{ is free in } A\text{, and } s \text{ is not bound in } \forall tA\}$.

Now, we turn to rules of inference. We have already observed (Theorem 1 on page 162) that the wff B is true whenever the wff A and $A \to B$ are true. Of course, this is our rule of inference, Modus Ponens. Similarly (Theorem 2, on page 163) $A \to \forall tB$ is true whenever $A \to B$ is true, provided that these are both wff. We shall make use of these rules of inference in characterizing our important notion of a proof, which we now define.

DEFINITION: A finite sequence of wff is called a *proof* iff each term of the sequence, say E, possesses one of the five forms

I (1) $A \vee A \to A$
(2) $A \to A \vee B$
(3) $A \vee B \to B \vee A$
(4) $A \to B \mathbin{\dot{\to}} C \vee A \to C \vee B$
(5) $\forall tA \to S_t^s A$

or else

II (i) there is a wff, say D, such that the wff D and $D \to E$ both precede E in the sequence

or (ii) E has the form $A \to \forall tB$ and is preceded in the sequence by $A \to B$.

The five sets of wff referred to under I are known as *axiom schemes*, while the two statements appearing under II are called *rules of inference*.

To illustrate the important concept of a proof, consider the following finite sequence of wff, where **F** has order one:

$$\underset{(2)}{\mathbf{Fw} \to \mathbf{Fw} \vee \mathbf{Fw}}, \quad \underset{(1)}{\mathbf{Fw} \vee \mathbf{Fw} \to \mathbf{Fw}},$$

$$\underset{(4)}{\mathbf{Fw} \vee \mathbf{Fw} \to \mathbf{Fw} \mathrel{\dot{\to}} \sim \mathbf{Fw} \vee (\mathbf{Fw} \vee \mathbf{Fw}) \to \sim \mathbf{Fw} \vee \mathbf{Fw}},$$

$$\underset{(i)}{\sim \mathbf{Fw} \vee (\mathbf{Fw} \vee \mathbf{Fw}) \to \sim \mathbf{Fw} \vee \mathbf{Fw}}, \quad \underset{(i)}{\sim \mathbf{Fw} \vee \mathbf{Fw}}$$

where the insertion under each of the terms of this sequence indicates the appropriate axiom scheme or rule of inference to justify the presence of the term in the proof. Since we shall be referring to this proof in a moment, let us agree to denote it by "P_1".

Consider an individual other than **w**, say **z**, and let "P_2" denote the proof obtained from P_1 by replacing **w** throughout by **z**. It is easily seen that the finite sequence obtained by juxtaposing two proofs is again a proof; thus, the finite sequence obtained by writing down P_1 followed by P_2 is a proof. Consider the following finite sequence of wff:

$$P_1, P_2, \quad \underset{(2)}{\sim \mathbf{Fw} \vee \mathbf{Fw} \to (\sim \mathbf{Fw} \vee \mathbf{Fw}) \vee \sim (\sim \mathbf{Fz} \vee \mathbf{Fz})},$$

$$\underset{(i)}{(\sim \mathbf{Fw} \vee \mathbf{Fw}) \vee \sim (\sim \mathbf{Fz} \vee \mathbf{Fz})},$$

$$\underset{(3)}{(\sim \mathbf{Fw} \vee \mathbf{Fw}) \vee \sim (\sim \mathbf{Fz} \vee \mathbf{Fz}) \to \sim (\sim \mathbf{Fz} \vee \mathbf{Fz}) \vee (\sim \mathbf{Fw} \vee \mathbf{Fw})},$$

$$\underset{(i)}{\sim \mathbf{Fz} \vee \mathbf{Fz} \to \sim \mathbf{Fw} \vee \mathbf{Fw}}, \quad \underset{(ii)}{\sim \mathbf{Fz} \vee \mathbf{Fz} \to \forall \mathbf{w}(\sim \mathbf{Fw} \vee \mathbf{Fw})},$$

$$\underset{(i)}{\forall \mathbf{w}(\sim \mathbf{Fw} \vee \mathbf{Fw})}.$$

As indicated by the insertions, this sequence satisfies the formal requirements of a proof, and so it is a proof.

Having defined the notion of a proof in the predicate calculus, we now introduce the concept of a *provable* wff. This is the concept that really interests us; later we shall prove that the set of all provable wff is precisely the set of all true wff. For the moment, however, consider the

DEFINITION: We shall say that a wff, say C, is *provable* iff there is a proof whose last term is C.

For example, the wff $\forall \mathbf{w}(\sim \mathbf{Fw} \vee \mathbf{Fw})$ is provable, since we have constructed a proof whose last term is $\forall \mathbf{w}(\sim \mathbf{Fw} \vee \mathbf{Fw})$. It is easy to construct a proof whose last term is the wff $\forall \mathbf{x}(\sim \mathbf{Fx} \vee \mathbf{Fx})$, so this wff is provable.

Of course, the wff $\forall \mathbf{w} A \rightarrow S^{\mathbf{z}}_{\mathbf{w}} A$ is provable; it is easy to construct a proof whose last term is $\forall \mathbf{w} A \rightarrow S^{\mathbf{z}}_{\mathbf{w}} A$, given that A is a wff, **w** is free in A, and **z** is not bound in $\forall \mathbf{w} A$.

As in the propositional calculus, we shall denote the statement "C is provable" by prefixing the symbol "$\vdash$" to C; thus "$\vdash C$" means "C is provable". Furthermore, suppose that $\vdash C$; then there exists at least one proof whose last term is the wff C. We shall call any such proof, *a proof of C*. For example, P_1 is a proof of $\sim \mathbf{Fw} \vee \mathbf{Fw}$, and P_2 is a proof of $\sim \mathbf{Fz} \vee \mathbf{Fz}$.

Analogous to our fundamental theorem about wff, we have the important

FUNDAMENTAL THEOREM ABOUT PROVABLE WFF: Each provable wff has property P provided that:

1. each member of each axiom scheme has property P
2. if A and $A \rightarrow B$ are both provable and both have property P, then B has property P
3. if $A \rightarrow B$ is provable, has property P, and t is any individual free in B but not occurring in A, then $A \rightarrow \forall tB$ has property P.

Demonstration: Let P be a property satisfying the assumptions of the theorem. Suppose that there is a provable wff that does not have property P, say C. Now consider any proof of C. Clearly, each term of this finite sequence is a provable wff; furthermore, since there is a term of the sequence that does not have property P, there must be a first such term, say E. So E does not have property P, whereas each term of the sequence that precedes E does possess property P. Now we apply the assumptions of our theorem. By 1, E is not a member of an axiom scheme. Since E is a term of a proof and is not a member of an axiom scheme, the presence of E in the proof is justified only by a rule of inference. There are two possibilities:

(i) there is a wff, say D, such that the wff D and $D \rightarrow E$ precede E in the given proof.

But by the second assumption of our theorem, E has property P, since both D and $D \rightarrow E$ are provable and possess property P.

(ii) E has the form $A \rightarrow \forall tB$ and is preceded in the sequence by the wff $A \rightarrow B$.

It follows that $A \rightarrow B$ is provable and has property P; furthermore, the individual t is free in B and does not occur in A. Therefore, by the third assumption of our theorem, $A \rightarrow \forall tB$ has property P.

Having demonstrated that the wff E possesses property P, we have arrived at a contradiction. This means that the initial assumption of our demonstration is false; thus, each provable wff possesses property P.

THEOREM 3: Each provable wff is true.

Demonstration: We apply our fundamental theorem about provable wff. But we have already seen that a member of any axiom scheme is true, and we have established Theorems 1 and 2 on page 162. This demonstrates Theorem 3.

THEOREM 4: $\vdash A \vee \sim A$ whenever A is a wff.

Demonstration: See the pattern leading up to Theorem 9 on page 122.

THEOREM 5: $\vdash \forall tA$ whenever $\vdash A$ and t is an individual that is free in A.

Demonstration: We construct a proof of $\forall tA$. Let π_1 be a proof of A, and let π_2 be a proof of $\mathbf{F}s \vee \sim \mathbf{F}s$, where $\mathbf{F}$ is a predicate of order one, and s is an individual that does not occur in A. Then the finite sequence

$$\pi_1, \pi_2, \qquad A \rightarrow A \vee \sim (\mathbf{F}s \vee \sim \mathbf{F}s), \qquad A \vee \sim (\mathbf{F}s \vee \sim \mathbf{F}s),$$
$$A \vee \sim (\mathbf{F}s \vee \sim \mathbf{F}s) \rightarrow \sim (\mathbf{F}s \vee \sim \mathbf{F}s) \vee A,$$
$$\mathbf{F}s \vee \sim \mathbf{F}s \rightarrow A, \qquad \mathbf{F}s \vee \sim \mathbf{F}s \rightarrow \forall tA, \qquad \forall tA$$

is a proof of $\forall tA$.

EXERCISES

1. (a) Demonstrate Theorem 4.
   (b) Given that $\vdash A$, show that $\vdash B \vee A$ provided $B \vee A$ is a wff.
2. Given that $\vdash A \rightarrow B$ and $\vdash B \rightarrow C$, show that $\vdash A \rightarrow C$.
3. Given that A is a wff, show that $\vdash A \rightarrow \sim\sim A$ and $\vdash \sim\sim A \rightarrow A$.
4. Given that $\vdash A \rightarrow B$, show that $\vdash \sim B \rightarrow \sim A$.
5. Show that $\vdash A \rightarrow B$ iff $\vdash \sim B \rightarrow \sim A$.
6. Show that $A \vee C \rightarrow B \vee D$ is provable, provided it is a wff, and that $\vdash A \rightarrow B$ and $\vdash C \rightarrow D$.
7. Show that $\vdash S^s_t A \rightarrow \exists tA$ provided A is a wff, t is free in A, and s is not bound in $\exists tA$.
8. Show that $\vdash \forall tA \rightarrow \exists tA$ whenever t is free in A and A is a wff.

9. Given that $\forall t(A \vee B) \to A \vee S^s_t B$ is a wff and that s and t do not occur in A, show that:
   (a) $\vdash \forall t(A \vee B) \to A \vee S^s_t B$
   (b) $\vdash \forall t(A \vee B) \to \sim\sim A \vee S^s_t B$
   (c) $\vdash \forall t(A \vee B) \to A \vee \forall s S^s_t B$
   (d) $\vdash A \to \forall t(A \vee B)$
   (e) $\vdash A \vee \forall t B \to A \vee S^s_t B$
   (f) $\vdash A \vee \forall t B \to \forall s(A \vee S^s_t B)$

10. Given that s and t are free in A, $\mathbf{x}$ and $\mathbf{y}$ do not occur in A, and that $s \neq t$, show that:
   (a) $\forall s \forall t A \to \forall t S^{\mathbf{x}}_s A$
   (b) $\forall t S^{\mathbf{x}}_s A \to S^{\mathbf{y}}_t S^{\mathbf{x}}_s A$
   (c) $\forall s \forall t A \to \forall \mathbf{x} S^{\mathbf{y}}_t S^{\mathbf{x}}_s A$
   (d) $\forall s \forall t A \to \forall \mathbf{y} \forall \mathbf{x} S^{\mathbf{y}}_t S^{\mathbf{x}}_s A$

11. Given that $\vdash A \to B$, t is free in B and t does not occur in A, show that $\vdash A \to \forall t B$.

12. Given that $\vdash A \to B$, t is free in A and t does not occur in B, show that $\vdash \exists t A \to B$.

13. Show that $A \wedge C \to B \wedge D$ is provable, provided it is a wff, and that $\vdash A \to B$, and $\vdash C \to D$. *Hint:* Use Exercises 4 and 6.

14. Show that $A \to B \wedge C$ is provable, provided it is a wff, and that $\vdash A \to B$, and $\vdash A \to C$.

7. Some Results About Proofs and Provable Wff

The purpose of this section is to gain some familiarity with the notions of a proof and of a provable wff by establishing two fairly simple results first and then considering a highly important and sophisticated property of proofs.

THEOREM 6: $\vdash \forall t A \to \forall s S^s_t A$ and $\vdash \forall s S^s_t A \to \forall t A$ provided these are wff and s is not in A.

Demonstration: Since s does not occur in A, $\vdash \forall t A \to S^s_t A$ by I (5); therefore, $\vdash \forall t A \to \forall s S^s_t A$ by II (ii). Again, t does not occur in $S^s_t A$, since t is free in A; hence, by I (5), $\vdash \forall s S^s_t A \to S^t_s(S^s_t A)$, that is $\vdash \forall s S^s_t A \to A$. Thus, by II (ii), $\vdash \forall s S^s_t A \to \forall t A$ since t does not occur in $\forall s S^s_t A$ and is free in A.

Later we shall demonstrate that the restriction on s can be eliminated; this will require, however, a penetrating analysis.

THEOREM 7: If $\vdash A \to B$ and s is an individual, free in both A and B, then $\vdash \forall sA \to \forall sB$.

Demonstration: Let t be an individual which is in neither A nor B. Then $\vdash \forall tS^t_sA \to A$ by I (5); therefore, $\vdash \forall tS^t_sA \to B$ since $\vdash A \to B$. But s is free in B and does not occur in $\forall tS^t_sA$, hence $\vdash \forall tS^t_sA \to \forall sB$. Also, $\vdash \forall sA \to \forall tS^t_sA$ by Theorem 6; thus, $\vdash \forall sA \to \forall sB$.

We now consider a sophisticated property of proofs.

THEOREM 8: If $A_1, A_2, \ldots, A_n$ is a proof, then $I^s_tA_1, I^s_tA_2, \ldots, I^s_tA_n$ is a proof whenever s and t are individuals.

Demonstration: Suppose that $I^s_tA_1, I^s_tA_2, \ldots, I^s_tA_n$ is not a proof; then there is a smallest natural number k such that $I^s_tA_1, I^s_tA_2, \ldots, I^s_tA_k$ is not a proof. Noting that $I^s_tA_1, I^s_tA_2, \ldots, I^s_tA_{k-1}$ is a proof, we see that the wff $I^s_tA_k$, and so the wff A_k, is of special significance. We concentrate our attention on the provable wff A_k and the proof $A_1, A_2, \ldots, A_k$. There are three possibilities.

(1) A_k is a member of an axiom scheme. We shall show that $I^s_tA_k$ is also a member of an axiom scheme.

$$I^s_t(A \lor A \to A) = I^s_tA \lor I^s_tA \to I^s_tA$$

$$I^s_t(A \to A \lor B) = I^s_tA \to I^s_tA \lor I^s_tB$$

$$I^s_t(A \lor B \to B \lor A) = I^s_tA \lor I^s_tB \to I^s_tB \lor I^s_tA$$

$$I^s_t(A \to B \mathrel{\dot{\to}} C \lor A \to C \lor B) = I^s_tA \to I^s_tB \mathrel{\dot{\to}} I^s_tC \lor I^s_tA \to I^s_tC \lor I^s_tB$$

$$I^s_t(\forall uA \to S^v_uA) = \forall uI^s_tA \to I^s_tS^v_uA = \forall uI^s_tA \to S^v_uI^s_tA$$

if s, t, u, v are all different.

$$I^s_t(\forall uA \to S^s_uA) = \forall uI^s_tA \to I^s_tS^s_uA = \forall uI^s_tA \to S^t_uI^s_tA$$

if s, t, u are all different, since s is not bound in A and u is free in A.

$$I^s_t(\forall tA \to S^v_tA) = \forall sI^s_tA \to I^s_tS^v_tA = \forall sI^s_tA \to S^v_sI^s_tA$$

if s, t, v are all different.

$$I^s_t(\forall tA \to S^s_tA) = \forall sI^s_tA \to I^s_tS^s_tA = \forall sI^s_tA \to S^t_sI^s_tA$$

Thus, if A_k is a member of an axiom scheme, then so is $I^s_tA_k$.

(2) A_k is preceded in the given proof by A_i and $A_i \to A_k$. Then $I^s_tA_k$ is preceded by $I^s_tA_i$ and $I^s_tA_i \to I^s_tA_k$ in the finite sequence $I^s_tA_1, I^s_tA_2, \ldots, I^s_tA_k$.

(3) $A_k = B \rightarrow \forall uC$ and A_k is preceded in the given proof by $B \rightarrow C$. Clearly, $I^s_t A_k = I^s_t B \rightarrow I^s_t \forall uC$; essentially, there are two possibilities.

(a) Assume that $u \neq t$ and $u \neq s$. Then $I^s_t A_k = I^s_t B \rightarrow \forall u I^s_t C$. But $I^s_t(B \rightarrow C) = I^s_t B \rightarrow I^s_t C$, and u is free in $I^s_t C$ and does not occur in $I^s_t B$; hence, $I^s_t B \rightarrow \forall u I^s_t C$ is justified by II (ii).

(b) Assume that $u = s$. Then $I^s_t A_k = I^s_t B \rightarrow \forall t I^s_t C$, and $I^s_t A_k$ is preceded by $I^s_t B \rightarrow I^s_t C$. But t is not in $I^s_t B$ and t is free in $I^s_t C$; hence, $I^s_t B \rightarrow \forall t I^s_t C$ is justified by II (ii).

We have demonstrated that $I^s_t A_1, I^s_t A_2, \ldots, I^s_t A_k$ is a proof. This establishes Theorem 8.

COROLLARY 1: $\vdash I^s_t A$ whenever $\vdash A$ and s and t are any individuals.

COROLLARY 2: If $\vdash A$ and t is an individual not in A, then there is a proof of A in which t does not occur.

Demonstration: Consider a proof of A. Since only a finite number of symbols occurs in a given proof, there is an individual, say s, which is not in the proof. Now construct a sequence of wff from the given proof by applying I^s_t to each wff in the proof. The resulting sequence is free of t; furthermore, by Theorem 8, this sequence is a proof of A.

EXERCISES

1. Show that $\vdash \exists tA \rightarrow \exists s S^s_t A$ and $\vdash \exists s S^s_t A \rightarrow \exists tA$ provided they are wff and s does not occur in A.
2. Given that $\vdash A \rightarrow B$ and s is an individual free in both A and B, show that $\vdash \exists sA \rightarrow \exists sB$.
3. Establish Corollary 1 directly by appealing to the fundamental theorem about provable wff.
4. Show that $\vdash \forall t S^t_s A \rightarrow S^t_s S^u_s A$, given that t is bound in A, s is free in A, and u is not bound in A.
5. Show that $\vdash \forall t I^s_t A \rightarrow S^u_s A$, given that t is bound in A, s is free in A, and u is not bound in A.
6. Show that $\vdash S^s_t A$, given that $\vdash A$ and t is free in A.
7. Show that $\vdash S^s_t A$, given that $\vdash A$ and t does not occur in A.

8. Show that $\vdash S_t^s A$, given that $\vdash A$, t is bound in A, and s is not bound in A.
9. Find a wff, say A, such that $\mathbf{x}$ is bound in A, $\mathbf{y}$ is bound in A, $S_{\mathbf{x}}^{\mathbf{y}}A \neq A$ and $S_{\mathbf{x}}^{\mathbf{y}}A \neq I_{\mathbf{x}}^{\mathbf{y}}A$.
10. Given that A is a provable wff in which none of the individuals $t_1, t_2, \ldots, t_m$ occurs, show that there is a proof of A in which none of the individuals $t_1, t_2, \ldots, t_m$ occurs.
11. Find a member of an axiom scheme, say A, such that $S_{\mathbf{x}}^{\mathbf{y}}A$ is *not* a member of an axiom scheme.
12. Given that $A_1, A_2, \ldots, A_n$ is a proof, show that $S_{\mathbf{x}}^{\mathbf{y}}A_1, S_{\mathbf{x}}^{\mathbf{y}}A_2, \ldots, S_{\mathbf{x}}^{\mathbf{y}}A_n$ is not necessarily a proof.

8. Components and Wff-Builders

We now introduce the notion of a component of a wff in order to facilitate the study of wff and provable wff. The intuitive idea is that a wff, say B, is a component of a wff A iff there exist expressions ϕ and θ such that the expression $\phi B\theta$ is the wff A. Either or both of ϕ and θ may be empty.

This concept is defined formally as follows.

DEFINITION: 1. Let A be an atomic wff. Then the wff A is the only component of A.

2. The components of $\sim B$ are $\sim B$ and each component of B.
3. The components of $C \vee D$ are $C \vee D$, each component of C, and each component of D.
4. The components of $\forall tE$ are $\forall tE$ and each component of E.

For example, the components of $\sim \forall \mathbf{y}(\mathbf{Fy} \vee \mathbf{Gxy})$ are the following wff: $\sim \forall \mathbf{y}(\mathbf{Fy} \vee \mathbf{Gxy})$, $\forall \mathbf{y}(\mathbf{Fy} \vee \mathbf{Gxy})$, $\mathbf{Fy} \vee \mathbf{Gxy}$, $\mathbf{Fy}$, and $\mathbf{Gxy}$.

We establish some properties of components.

THEOREM 9: The wff C is a component of A whenever C is a component of B and B is a component of A.

Demonstration: We shall show that each wff, say A, has the property that any component of a component of A is again a component of A. Applying our fundamental theorem about wff, we must show that:

(1) each atomic wff has the property
(2) $\sim B$ has the property whenever B has the property
(3) $C \vee D$ has the property whenever C has the property and D has the property
(4) $\forall tE$ has the property whenever E has the property.

(1) Let A be any atomic wff. The only component of A is A; hence, A is the only component of a component of A. But A is a component of A. Thus, each atomic wff possesses the stated property.

(2) Suppose that B has the property; we shall show that $\sim B$ has the property. The components of $\sim B$ are $\sim B$ and the components of B. Suppose F is a component of a component of $\sim B$; then either F is a component of $\sim B$ or F is a component of a component of B. In the latter case, F is a component of B, by assumption. Hence, in either case F is a component of $\sim B$.

(3) We leave this case as an exercise.

(4) Suppose that E has the property and t is free in E; we shall show that $\forall tE$ possesses the property. Now, the components of $\forall tE$ are $\forall tE$ and the components of E. Let F be any component of a component of $\forall tE$; then either F is a component of $\forall tE$ or F is a component of a component of E. In the latter case, F is a component of E, by assumption. Hence, in either case, F is a component of $\forall tE$. This demonstrates Theorem 9.

We show now that our formal definition has captured the intended idea.

THEOREM 10: Let A be any wff and let B be any component of A. Then there are expressions ϕ and θ such that $A = \phi B\theta$.

Demonstration: We show that each wff possesses the stated property by applying our fundamental theorem about wff.

(1) Let A be any atomic wff. Let B be any component of A; then B is A. Hence, $A = \phi B\theta$ where ϕ and θ are empty.

(2) Suppose that C has the property; we shall show that $\sim C$ has the property. Let B be any component of $\sim C$; if B is $\sim C$ itself, then ϕ and θ are empty. Now suppose that B is a component of C; by assumption, there exist expressions ϕ and θ such that C is $\phi B\theta$; hence, $\sim C$ is $(\sim \phi B\theta)$. Thus, $\sim C$ has the property.

(3) We leave this case as an exercise.

(4) Suppose that E has the property and t is free in E; we shall show that $\forall tE$ possesses the property. Let B be any component of $\forall tE$. If B is $\forall tE$ itself, then ϕ and θ are empty. Suppose B is a component of E; by assumption, there exist expressions ϕ and θ such that E is $\phi B\theta$. Therefore, $\forall tE$ is $(\forall t\phi B\theta)$. Thus, $\forall tE$ has the stated property. This establishes Theorem 10.

It remains to establish the converse of Theorem 10. This is not easy! We must first improve our knowledge of the *structure* of wff; in particular, we need to understand the role of parentheses in a wff.

DEFINITION: The *mate* of a particular left-hand parenthesis occurring in a wff is the first right-hand parenthesis to its right such that an equal number of left-hand parentheses and right-hand parentheses occur in between.

DEFINITION: The *mate* of a particular right-hand parenthesis occurring in a wff is the first left-hand parenthesis to its left such that an equal number of left-hand parentheses and right-hand parentheses occur in between.

For example, the parentheses of the following wff are mated as indicated:

(~ ((∀x(Fx)) ∨ (~ (Gyy))))
a bc d dc e f feba

[the *same* letter is placed under two parentheses iff they are mated].

THEOREM 10-1: Each wff possesses an equal number of left-hand and right-hand parentheses.

Demonstration: Apply the Fundamental Theorem about Wff.

THEOREM 10-2: Counting from left to right, the number of instances of left-hand parentheses in a wff is in excess of the number of instances of right-hand parentheses in the wff, until the final right-hand parenthesis is reached.

Demonstration: Apply the Fundamental Theorem about Wff.

THEOREM 10-3: Each parenthesis occurring in a wff possesses a mate.

Demonstration: Apply the Fundamental Theorem about Wff (use Theorem 10-2).

THEOREM 10-4: No two parentheses of a wff have the same mate.

Demonstration: Apply the Fundamental Theorem about Wff (use Theorem 10-2).

THEOREM 10-5: The first and last parentheses of a wff are mated.

Demonstration: Theorem 10-3 and Theorem 10-2.

We can now establish the converse of Theorem 10.

THEOREM 10-6: Let A and B be any wff, and let ϕ and θ be any expressions such that $A = \phi B\theta$; then B is a component of A.

Demonstration: We apply the Fundamental Theorem about Wff.

(1) Let A be any atomic wff. Clearly, if B is a wff such that $A = \phi B\theta$, then B is A; so, B is a component of A.

(2) Suppose that C has the property; we shall show that (~ C) has the property. Let B be a wff such that (~ C) $= \phi B\theta$. If $C = \phi_1 B\theta_1$, then B is a component of C by assumption; hence, B is a component of (~ C). If B is not contained within C, then $B =$ (~ α where α is contained within C). Since B is a wff it follows from Theorem 10-5 that $\alpha = C$) so that

$B = (\sim C)$; otherwise, the first parenthesis of B has no mate. Thus, B is a component of $(\sim C)$.

(3) Suppose D and E have the property; here, an argument similar to that of (2) establishes that $(D \vee E)$ has the property.

(4) Suppose F has the property and t is an individual free in F; again, an argument similar to that of (2) establishes that $(\forall tF)$ has the property. This establishes our theorem.

The expressions ϕ and θ referred to in Theorems 10 and 10-6 are not necessarily wff. For example, consider the wff **(∀y((Fx) ∨ (Gxy)))**, which we have written out in full. Notice that one component of this wff is the wff **(Fx)**; in this case, ϕ is **(∀y(** and θ is **∨(Gxy)))**.

Let us turn our attention from the component of a wff to the accompanying two expressions.

DEFINITION: We say that $[\phi, \theta]$ is a *wff-builder* iff there exists a wff A such that $\phi A\theta$ is a wff.

Of course, if ϕ and θ are both empty then $[\phi, \theta]$ is a wff-builder. Again, let ϕ be **(∀x** and let θ be **)**; then $[\phi, \theta]$ is a wff-builder, since **(∀x(Fx))** is a wff.

We now consider the vital property of wff-builders.

THE SUBSTITUTION THEOREM: Let $[\phi, \theta]$ be any wff-builder, and suppose that $\vdash A \rightarrow B$ and $\vdash B \rightarrow A$; then either $\vdash \phi A\theta \rightarrow \phi B\theta$ and $\vdash \phi B\theta \rightarrow \phi A\theta$, or else these are not wff.

Demonstration: Let A and B be wff such that $\vdash A \rightarrow B$ and $\vdash B \rightarrow A$. Our theorem asserts that each wff C has the property that if A is a component of C, so that C is $\phi A\theta$, then $\vdash \phi A\theta \rightarrow \phi B\theta$ and $\vdash \phi B\theta \rightarrow \phi A\theta$, provided these are wff. We apply our fundamental theorem about wff.

(1) Let C be any atomic wff such that A is a component of C. Then A is C, so that ϕ and θ are empty. Thus, $\phi B\theta$ is B. Hence, we must show that $\vdash A \rightarrow B$ and $\vdash B \rightarrow A$. But this is so by assumption.

(2) Suppose that C has the property; we shall show that $\sim C$ has the property. Clearly, if $\sim C$ is A, then $\sim C$ has the property. Also, if $A \neq \sim C$ and A is not a component of C, then A is not a component of $\sim C$; hence, in this case $\sim C$ has the property. Finally, we suppose that A is a component of C. Then $C = \phi A\theta$; but $\vdash \phi A\theta \rightarrow \phi B\theta$ and $\vdash \phi B\theta \rightarrow \phi A\theta$, since C has the property. Recalling that $\vdash \sim E \rightarrow \sim D$ whenever $\vdash D \rightarrow E$, we conclude that $\vdash \sim \phi B\theta \rightarrow \sim \phi A\theta$ and $\vdash \sim \phi A\theta \rightarrow \sim \phi B\theta$. Thus, $\sim C$ has the property.

(3) We leave this case as an exercise.

(4) Suppose that E has the property and t is free in E; we shall show that $\forall tE$ has the property. Clearly, we are primarily concerned with the case in which A is a component of E. Then $E = \phi A\theta$; moreover, $\vdash \phi A\theta \rightarrow \phi B\theta$

and $\vdash\phi B\theta \rightarrow \phi A\theta$ by assumption. Noting that t is free in $\phi A\theta$, we see that t is not bound in $\phi B\theta$. There are two possibilities:

(a) t is free in $\phi B\theta$. Then t is free in both $\phi A\theta$ and $\phi B\theta$; hence, by Theorem 7, $\vdash\forall t\phi A\theta \rightarrow \forall t\phi B\theta$ and $\vdash\forall t\phi B\theta \rightarrow \forall t\phi A\theta$.

(b) t does not occur in $\phi B\theta$. Then $\forall t\phi A\theta \rightarrow \forall t\phi B\theta$ is not a wff. Hence, $\forall tE$ possesses the stated property whenever E has the property and t is free in E.

This establishes the substitution theorem.

COROLLARY 1: If $\vdash C$ and $\forall tA$ is a component of C—so $C = \phi\forall tA\theta$—then $\vdash\phi\forall sS_t^sA\theta$ provided this is a wff and s is not in A.

Demonstration: Theorem 6 and the substitution theorem.

COROLLARY 2: $\vdash\forall tA \rightarrow \forall sS_t^sA$ and $\vdash\forall sS_t^sA \rightarrow \forall tA$ provided these are wff.

Demonstration: By Theorem 6, we need consider only the case in which s occurs in A. Since $\forall tA \rightarrow \forall sS_t^sA$ is a wff, we conclude that s is bound in $\forall tA$. There are two possibilities:

(a) s is t. Then S_t^sA is A and $\forall sS_t^sA$ is $\forall tA$. But $\vdash C \rightarrow C$ whenever C is a wff.

(b) $s \neq t$, Then s is bound in A. Let u be an individual that does not occur in A; then $\vdash\forall tA \rightarrow \forall uS_t^uA$ by Theorem 6. Applying Corollary 1, we can now, in effect, replace each bound s in $\forall uS_t^uA$ by t, since t does not occur in $\forall uS_t^uA$; this is achieved by replacing each component of $\forall uS_t^uA$ with the form $\forall vC$ by $\forall tS_v^tC$ (note that t does not occur in C). Hence, $\vdash\forall tA \rightarrow I_t^v\forall uS_t^uA$. In the same way, applying Corollary 1 again, we replace all "u"s occuring in $I_t^v\forall uS_t^uA$ by s—we can do this because s does not occur in $I_t^v\forall uS_t^uA$. So $\vdash\forall tA \rightarrow I_v^uI_t^v\forall uS_t^uA$; but $I_v^uI_t^v\forall uS_t^uA$ is $\forall vS_t^vA$. Thus, $\vdash\forall tA \rightarrow \forall vS_t^vA$.

Now we prove that $\vdash\forall vS_t^vA \rightarrow \forall tA$, given that t is free in A and v is bound in A. But $\vdash\forall vS_t^vA \rightarrow \forall tS_v^tS_t^vA$ by our preceding result, that is $\vdash\forall vS_t^vA \rightarrow \forall tA$. This establishes Corollary 2.

COROLLARY 3: If $\vdash\phi\forall tA\phi$, then $\vdash\phi\forall vS_t^vA\theta$ provided $\phi\forall vS_t^vA\theta$ is a wff.

As in the propositional calculus, it is useful to introduce a binary relation on the set of all wff of the predicate calculus. This relation is denoted by "$\equiv$" and is defined as follows:

DEFINITION OF $\equiv$: $A \equiv B$ iff $\vdash A \rightarrow B$ and $\vdash B \rightarrow A$.

For example, $C \equiv \sim\sim C$ whenever C is a wff, $\forall tE \equiv \forall sS_t^sE$ provided s is not free in E and t is free in E.

We shall read "$A \equiv B$" as "A is *equivalent* to B".

Our substitution theorem, which is the fundamental theorem about wff-builders, asserts that replacing a component of a given wff by a wff equivalent to it produces a wff equivalent to the given wff. In symbols, $\phi A\theta \equiv \phi B\theta$ whenever $A \equiv B$ and $\phi A\theta \to \phi B\theta$ is a wff. Rewriting the substitution theorem in this language, we obtain

THE SUBSTITUTION THEOREM: If $A \equiv B$ then $\phi A\theta \equiv \phi B\theta$ whenever $\phi A\theta \to \phi B\theta$ is a wff.

Though we read "$\equiv$" as "equivalent", we should realize that our binary relation $\equiv$ is *not* an equivalence relation. It is easy to see that $\equiv$ is reflexive and symmetric; however, $\equiv$ is not transitive. To see this, observe that

$$\mathbf{Fx} \vee \sim \mathbf{Fx} \equiv \forall \mathbf{yFy} \to \mathbf{Fz} \quad \text{and} \quad \forall \mathbf{yFy} \to \mathbf{Fz} \equiv \forall \mathbf{xFx} \to \mathbf{Fz}$$

yet

$$\mathbf{Fx} \vee \sim \mathbf{Fx} \equiv \forall \mathbf{xFx} \to \mathbf{Fz} \qquad \text{is false,}$$

since

$$\mathbf{Fx} \vee \sim \mathbf{Fx} \dot{\to} \forall \mathbf{xFx} \to \mathbf{Fz}$$

is not a wff.

To illustrate the power of Corollary 3, we now establish

THEOREM 12: $\vdash \forall s \forall tA \to \forall t \forall sA$ provided this is a wff.

Demonstration: Let A be any wff in which the distinct individuals s and t are free. Let u and v be any individuals that do not occur in A. Then $\vdash \forall s \forall tA \to \forall tS^u_sA$ and $\vdash \forall tS^u_sA \to S^v_tS^u_sA$ by I (5). Thus $\vdash \forall s \forall tA \to S^v_tS^u_sA$. Hence, $\vdash \forall s \forall tA \to \forall uS^v_tS^u_sA$ and so $\vdash \forall s \forall tA \to \forall v \forall uS^v_tS^u_sA$ by II (ii). Now we apply Corollary 3, replacing the component $\forall v \forall uS^v_tS^u_sA$ by $\forall tS^t_v \forall uS^v_tS^u_sA$; but $\forall tS^t_v \forall uS^v_tS^u_sA = \forall t \forall uS^u_sA$; thus, $\vdash \forall s \forall tA \to \forall t \forall uS^u_sA$. Finally, by Corollary 3, we replace $\forall uS^u_sA$ by $\forall sS^s_uS^u_sA$; but $\forall sS^s_uS^u_sA = \forall sA$. Hence, $\vdash \forall s \forall tA \to \forall t \forall sA$.

As another illustration of Corollary 3, we establish

THEOREM 12: $\vdash \forall t(A \wedge B) \to A \wedge \forall tB$ whenever this is a wff.

Demonstration: We assume that $\forall t(A \wedge B) \to A \wedge \forall tB$ is a wff; in particular, this means that the individual t does not occur in A and is free in B. Choose an individual, say s, which does not occur in the wff $A \wedge B$; then

	$\vdash \forall s(A \wedge S^s_tB) \to S^t_s(A \wedge S^s_tB)$	by I (5),
i.e.,	$\vdash \forall s(A \wedge S^s_tB) \to A \wedge B$	
but	$\vdash A \wedge B \to B$	
Therefore	$\vdash \forall s(A \wedge S^s_tB) \to B$	by Exercise 2, page 169
hence,	$\vdash \forall s(A \wedge S^s_tB) \to \forall tB$	by Exercise 11, page 170
Therefore	$\vdash \forall tS^t_s(A \wedge S^s_tB) \to \forall tB$	by Corollary 3, page 177
i.e.,	$\vdash \forall t(A \wedge B) \to \forall tB.$	

It is easily seen that

$$\vdash \forall t(A \wedge B) \rightarrow A$$

[Note that $\vdash \forall t(A \wedge B) \rightarrow A \wedge S_t^s B$ and $\vdash A \wedge S_t^s B \rightarrow A$]; hence

$$\vdash \forall t(A \wedge B) \rightarrow A \wedge \forall tB \quad \text{by Exercise 14, page 170}$$

This establishes Theorem 12.

EXERCISES

1. List the components of $\exists \mathbf{x}(\mathbf{Fx} \vee \mathbf{Gxy})$.
2. List the components of $\exists \mathbf{x}(\mathbf{Fx} \wedge \mathbf{Gxy})$.
3. List the components of $\forall \mathbf{y} \exists \mathbf{x}(\mathbf{Fx} \wedge \mathbf{Gxy})$.
4. Establish Case (3) of Theorem 9.
5. Establish Case (3) of Theorem 10.
6. Show that [(~,)] is a wff-builder.
7. Show that [((**Fx**) **v**,)] is a wff-builder.
8. Show that [((**Fx**) **v** (~,))] is a wff-builder.
9. Is [(,)] a wff-builder?
10. Show that $\vdash \phi \exists s S_t^s A \theta$, provided this is a wff, s is not in A, and $\vdash \phi \exists t A \theta$.
11. Show that $\exists tA \equiv \exists s S_t^s A$ provided $\exists tA \rightarrow \exists s S_t^s A$ is a wff.
12. Show that $\vdash \phi \exists s S_t^s A \theta$ if this is a wff and $\vdash \phi \exists t A \theta$.
13. Show that $\equiv$ is reflexive and symmetric.
14. Establish Case (3) of Theorem 11.
15. Show that $\vdash S_t^s A$ whenever $\vdash A$, s is bound in A, and t is bound in A.
16. Show that $\vdash S_t^s A$ whenever $\vdash A$, and s and t are any individuals.
17. Show that $\vdash \phi B \theta$ whenever $\vdash \phi A \theta$, $A \equiv B$ and $\phi A \theta \rightarrow \phi B \theta$ is a wff.
18. Show that $\vdash A \vee \forall tB \rightarrow \forall t(A \vee B)$, provided this is a wff.
19. Show that $A \vee \forall tB \equiv \forall t(A \vee B)$, provided $A \vee \forall tB \rightarrow \forall t(A \vee B)$ is a wff.
20. Show that $A \rightarrow \forall tB \equiv \forall t(A \rightarrow B)$, provided $A \rightarrow \forall tB \dot{\rightarrow} \forall t(A \rightarrow B)$ is a wff.
21. Show that $\vdash \forall t(A \wedge B) \rightarrow \forall tA \wedge \forall tB$, provided this is a wff.
22. Show that $\forall tA \wedge \forall tB \equiv \forall t(A \wedge B)$, provided $\forall tA \wedge \forall tB \rightarrow \forall t(A \wedge B)$ is a wff.
23. Show that $\vdash \forall t(A \rightarrow B) \dot{\rightarrow} \forall tA \rightarrow \forall tB$, provided this is a wff.

24. Show that $\vdash \forall t(A \leftrightarrow B) \dot{\rightarrow} \forall tA \leftrightarrow \forall tB$, provided this is a wff.

25. Show that $\vdash \forall t(A \rightarrow B) \dot{\rightarrow} \exists tA \rightarrow \exists tB$, provided this is a wff.

26. Show that $\vdash \exists s \forall tA \rightarrow \forall t \exists sA$, provided this is a wff.

27. Show that $\sim \forall tA \equiv \exists t \sim A$ whenever t is free in A. (Apply the substitution theorem to Exercise 3 on page 169.)

28. Show that $\vdash A \wedge \forall tB \rightarrow \forall t(A \wedge B)$, provided this is a wff.

29. Show that $A \wedge \forall tB \equiv \forall t(A \wedge B)$, provided $A \wedge \forall tB \rightarrow \forall t(A \wedge B)$ is a wff.

30. Show that $\sim \exists tA \equiv \forall t(\sim A)$ whenever t is free in A.

31. Show that $A \vee B \equiv B \vee A$, provided $A \vee B$ is a wff.

32. Show that $A \vee (B \vee C) \equiv (A \vee B) \vee C$, provided $A \vee (B \vee C)$ is a wff.

33. Show that $\sim (A \vee B) \equiv \sim A \wedge \sim B$, provided $A \vee B$ is a wff.

34. Show that $\forall s \forall tA \equiv \forall t \forall sA$, provided $\forall s \forall tA$ is a wff.

9. Duality

In Section 3 we introduced the symbols "$\wedge$" and "$\exists$", ostensibly as part of a parentheses-omitting program. It turns out, as with the propositional calculus, that these symbols are "dual" to the fundamental connectives $\vee$ and $\forall$. For example, let "E" denote the wff $\mathbf{Fx} \vee \forall \mathbf{y}(\mathbf{Gyy} \wedge \sim \mathbf{Fy})$; then

$$\begin{aligned} \sim \mathbf{E} &= \sim (\mathbf{Fx} \vee \forall \mathbf{y}(\mathbf{Gyy} \wedge \sim \mathbf{Fy})) \\ &\equiv \sim \mathbf{Fx} \wedge \sim \forall \mathbf{y}(\mathbf{Gyy} \wedge \sim \mathbf{Fy}) \\ &= \sim \mathbf{Fx} \wedge \sim \forall \mathbf{y}(\sim (\sim \mathbf{Gyy} \vee \sim \sim \mathbf{Fy})) \\ &= \sim \mathbf{Fx} \wedge \exists \mathbf{y}(\sim \mathbf{Gyy} \vee \sim \sim \mathbf{Fy}) \\ &\equiv \sim \mathbf{Fx} \wedge \exists \mathbf{y}(\sim \mathbf{Gyy} \vee \mathbf{Fy}). \end{aligned}$$

This demonstrates that

$$\sim \mathbf{Fx} \wedge \exists \mathbf{y}(\sim \mathbf{Gyy} \vee \mathbf{Fy}) \equiv \sim (\mathbf{Fx} \vee \forall \mathbf{y}(\mathbf{Gyy} \wedge \sim \mathbf{Fy})).$$

Notice that these wff—namely,

$$\mathbf{Fx} \vee \forall \mathbf{y}(\mathbf{Gyy} \wedge \sim \mathbf{Fy}) \quad \text{and} \quad \sim \mathbf{Fx} \wedge \exists \mathbf{y}(\sim \mathbf{Gyy} \vee \mathbf{Fy}),$$

are closely related in form. In fact, one can be obtained from the other by carrying out the following transformations:

(1) interchange the symbols $\vee$ and "$\wedge$"
(2) interchange the symbols $\forall$ and "$\exists$"

(3) if an atomic wff has prefixed to it an odd number of ~'s, throw out all these ~'s; if an atomic wff has prefixed to it an even number of ~'s, insert one ~ in place of these ~'s.

In order to investigate this phenomenon of "duality", we consider certain syntactical transforms—first, the *normal form* of a wff, a syntactical transform which we denote by "$\mathcal{N}$".

DEFINITION OF $\mathcal{N}$:

(1) $$\mathcal{N}A = A \text{ if } A \text{ is atomic}$$

(2) $$\mathcal{N}(\sim A) = \begin{cases} \sim A \text{ if } A \text{ is atomic} \\ \mathcal{N}B \text{ if } A = \sim B \\ \mathcal{N}(\sim C) \wedge \mathcal{N}(\sim D) \text{ if } A = C \vee D \\ \exists t(\mathcal{N}(\sim E)) \text{ if } A = \forall tE \end{cases}$$

(3) $$\mathcal{N}(C \vee D) = \mathcal{N}C \vee \mathcal{N}D$$

(4) $$\mathcal{N}(\forall tE) = \forall t(\mathcal{N}E).$$

For example,

$$\begin{aligned} \mathcal{N}(\sim \forall \mathbf{xFx} \vee \sim \forall \mathbf{x}\forall \mathbf{y}(\sim \mathbf{Gxy})) &= \mathcal{N}(\sim \forall \mathbf{xFx}) \vee \mathcal{N}(\sim \forall \mathbf{x}\forall \mathbf{y}(\sim \mathbf{Gxy})) \\ &= \exists \mathbf{x}(\mathcal{N}(\sim \mathbf{Fx})) \vee \exists \mathbf{x}(\mathcal{N}(\sim \forall \mathbf{y} \sim \mathbf{Gxy})) \\ &= \exists \mathbf{x}(\sim \mathbf{Fx}) \vee \exists \mathbf{x}\exists \mathbf{y}\mathcal{N}(\sim \sim \mathbf{Gxy}) \\ &= \exists \mathbf{x}(\sim \mathbf{Fx}) \vee \exists \mathbf{x}\exists \mathbf{y}\mathcal{N}\mathbf{Gxy} \\ &= \exists \mathbf{x}(\sim \mathbf{Fx}) \vee \exists \mathbf{x}\exists \mathbf{y}\mathbf{Gxy}. \end{aligned}$$

We shall now establish the basic properties of $\mathcal{N}$.

THEOREM 13: $\sim \mathcal{N}B \equiv \mathcal{N}(\sim B)$ whenever B is a wff.

Demonstration: We apply our fundamental theorem about wff.

(1) Let A be any atomic wff. Then $\mathcal{N}A$ is A and $\mathcal{N}(\sim A)$ is $\sim A$; hence, $\sim \mathcal{N}A$ is $\mathcal{N}(\sim A)$, and so $\sim \mathcal{N}A \equiv \mathcal{N}(\sim A)$.

(2) Suppose that C is a wff with the property; then $\sim \mathcal{N}C \equiv \mathcal{N}(\sim C)$. We want to show that $\sim \mathcal{N}(\sim C) \equiv \mathcal{N}(\sim \sim C)$. But $\mathcal{N}(\sim \sim C)$ is $\mathcal{N}C$ by definition, and $\mathcal{N}(\sim C) \equiv \sim \mathcal{N}C$ by assumption. Therefore,

$$\sim \mathcal{N}(\sim C) \equiv \mathcal{N}C,$$

but $\mathcal{N}C \equiv \mathcal{N}(\sim \sim C)$; hence, $\sim \mathcal{N}(\sim C) \equiv \mathcal{N}(\sim \sim C)$.

(3) Suppose that D and E each possess the property; then $\sim \mathcal{N}D \equiv \mathcal{N}(\sim D)$ and $\sim \mathcal{N}E \equiv \mathcal{N}(\sim E)$. We want to show that

$$\sim \mathcal{N}(D \vee E) \equiv \mathcal{N}(\sim (D \vee E)).$$

But

$$\begin{aligned} \mathcal{N}(\sim (D \vee E)) = \mathcal{N}(\sim D) \wedge \mathcal{N}(\sim E) &= \sim (\sim \mathcal{N}(\sim D) \vee \sim \mathcal{N}(\sim E)) \\ &\equiv \sim (\sim \sim \mathcal{N}D \vee \sim \sim \mathcal{N}E) \\ &\equiv \sim (\mathcal{N}D \vee \mathcal{N}E), \end{aligned}$$

and $$\sim \mathcal{N}(D \vee E) = \sim (\mathcal{N}D \vee \mathcal{N}E)$$

by definition. Thus, $\sim \mathcal{N}(D \vee E) \equiv \mathcal{N}(\sim (D \vee E))$.

(4) Suppose that A has the property and t is free in A. We shall show that $\forall tA$ has the property. Now,

$$\mathcal{N}(\sim \forall tA) = \exists t(\mathcal{N}(\sim A)) \equiv \exists t(\sim \mathcal{N}A)$$

by assumption, and $\sim \mathcal{N}(\forall tA) = \sim \forall t\mathcal{N}A$ by definition, and $\sim \forall t\mathcal{N}A \equiv \exists t(\sim \mathcal{N}A)$; thus, $\sim \mathcal{N}(\forall tA) \equiv \mathcal{N}(\sim \forall tA)$.

This establishes Theorem 13.

THEOREM 14: $\mathcal{N}A \equiv A$ whenever A is a wff.

Demonstration: We apply our fundamental theorem about wff.

(1) Let A be any atomic wff. Then $\mathcal{N}A$ is A; and hence $\mathcal{N}A \equiv A$.

(2) Suppose that C is a wff with the property; then $\mathcal{N}C \equiv C$. We shall show that $\sim C$ has the property. But $\mathcal{N}(\sim C) \equiv \sim \mathcal{N}C$ by Theorem 13, and $\mathcal{N}C \equiv C$ by assumption; therefore, $\sim \mathcal{N}C \equiv \sim C$ and so $\mathcal{N}(\sim C) \equiv \sim C$.

(3) Suppose that D and E each possess the property; then $\mathcal{N}D \equiv D$ and $\mathcal{N}E \equiv E$. We shall show that $D \vee E$ has the property. But $\mathcal{N}(D \vee E) = \mathcal{N}D \vee \mathcal{N}E \equiv D \vee E$ by the substitution theorem.

(4) Suppose that A has the property and t is free in A; then $\mathcal{N}A \equiv A$. But $\mathcal{N}(\forall tA) = \forall t(\mathcal{N}A) \equiv \forall tA$ by the substitution theorem. Thus, $\forall tA$ has the property.

THEOREM 15: $\mathcal{N}(A \to B) \equiv \mathcal{N}A \to \mathcal{N}B$ whenever $A \to B$ is a wff.

Demonstration: $\mathcal{N}(A \to B) \equiv A \to B$ and $\mathcal{N}A \to \mathcal{N}B \equiv A \to B$ by Theorem 14.

THEOREM 16: $\vdash \mathcal{N}A$ whenever $\vdash A$.

Demonstration: $\vdash A \to \mathcal{N}A$, since $\mathcal{N}A \equiv A$; but $\vdash A$. Therefore, $\vdash \mathcal{N}A$.

THEOREM 17: $\mathcal{N}A \equiv \mathcal{N}B$ whenever $A \equiv B$.

Demonstration: Apply Theorem 14.

We now introduce another syntactical transform $\mathcal{M}$ designed first to transform a wff into normal form, and then to interchange $\vee$ and "$\wedge$" throughout, to interchange $\forall$ and "$\exists$" throughout, and finally to replace each instance of an atomic wff, say W, by $\sim W$, and then discarding any even number of $\sim$'s that occur prefixed to W.

DEFINITION OF $\mathcal{M}$:

(1) $$\mathcal{M}A = \sim A \text{ if } A \text{ is atomic}$$

(2) $$\mathcal{M}(\sim A) = \begin{cases} A \text{ if } A \text{ is atomic} \\ \mathcal{M}B \text{ if } A = \sim B \\ \mathcal{M}(\sim B) \vee \mathcal{M}(\sim C) \text{ if } A = B \vee C \\ \forall t\mathcal{M}(\sim E) \text{ if } A = \forall tE \end{cases}$$

(3) $$\mathcal{M}(A \vee B) = \mathcal{M}A \wedge \mathcal{M}B$$
(4) $$\mathcal{M}(\forall tA) = \exists t(\mathcal{M}A)$$

For example,

$$\begin{aligned}\mathcal{M}(\sim \forall \mathrm{xFx} \vee \sim \forall \mathrm{x}\forall \mathrm{y}(\sim \mathrm{Gxy})) &= \mathcal{M}(\sim \forall \mathrm{xFx}) \wedge \mathcal{M}(\sim \forall \mathrm{x}\forall \mathrm{y} \sim \mathrm{Gxy})\\ &= \forall \mathrm{x}\mathcal{M}(\sim \mathrm{Fx}) \wedge \forall \mathrm{x}\mathcal{M}(\sim \forall \mathrm{y} \sim \mathrm{Gxy})\\ &= \forall \mathrm{xFx} \wedge \forall \mathrm{x}\forall \mathrm{y}(\mathcal{M}(\sim \sim \mathrm{Gxy}))\\ &= \forall \mathrm{xFx} \wedge \forall \mathrm{x}\forall \mathrm{y}(\mathcal{M}\mathrm{Gxy})\\ &= \forall \mathrm{xFx} \wedge \forall \mathrm{x}\forall \mathrm{y}(\sim \mathrm{Gxy})\end{aligned}$$

We now establish some properties of the syntactical transform $\mathcal{M}$.

THEOREM 18: $\mathcal{M}(\sim A) \equiv \sim \mathcal{M}A$ whenever A is a wff.

Demonstration: We apply our fundamental theorem about wff.

(1) Let A be any atomic wff. Then $\mathcal{M}A$ is $\sim A$ and $\mathcal{M}(\sim A)$ is A; thus, $\sim \mathcal{M}A$ is $\sim \sim A$, and so $\sim \mathcal{M}A \equiv \mathcal{M}(\sim A)$.

(2) Suppose that B is a wff with the property; then $\mathcal{M}(\sim B) \equiv \sim \mathcal{M}B$. We shall show that $\sim B$ has the property. Now, $\mathcal{M}(\sim \sim B) = \mathcal{M}B$ by definition, and $\sim \mathcal{M}(\sim B) \equiv \sim \sim \mathcal{M}B$ by assumption. Thus, $\mathcal{M}(\sim \sim B) \equiv \sim \mathcal{M}(\sim B)$.

(3) Suppose that C and D are wff with the property; then $\mathcal{M}(\sim C) \equiv \sim \mathcal{M}C$ and $\mathcal{M}(\sim D) \equiv \sim \mathcal{M}D$. We shall show that $C \vee D$ possesses the property.

But $$\mathcal{M}(\sim (C \vee D)) = \mathcal{M}(\sim C) \vee \mathcal{M}(\sim D) \quad \text{by definition}$$
$$\equiv \sim \mathcal{M}C \vee \sim \mathcal{M}D \quad \text{by Theorem 11}$$
and $$\sim \mathcal{M}(C \vee D) = \sim (\mathcal{M}C \wedge \mathcal{M}D) \quad \text{by definition}$$
$$\equiv \sim \mathcal{M}C \vee \sim \mathcal{M}D$$

(4) Suppose that E has the property and t is free in E; then $\mathcal{M}(\sim E) \equiv \sim \mathcal{M}E$. We shall show that $\forall tE$ has the property. But

$$\mathcal{M}(\sim \forall tE) = \forall t(\mathcal{M}(\sim E)) \quad \text{by definition}$$
$$\equiv \forall t(\sim \mathcal{M}E) \quad \text{by assumption}$$
and $$\sim \mathcal{M}(\forall tE) = \sim \exists t(\mathcal{M}E) \quad \text{by definition}$$
$$\equiv \forall t(\sim \mathcal{M}E)$$

This establishes Theorem 18.

THEOREM 19: $\mathcal{M}A \equiv \sim A$ whenever A is a wff.

Demonstration: We apply our fundamental theorem about wff.

(1) Let A be any atomic wff; then $\mathcal{M}A = \sim A$ by definition. Thus $\mathcal{M}A \equiv \sim A$.

(2) Suppose that B is a wff with the property; then $\mathcal{M}B \equiv \sim B$. We shall show that $\sim B$ has the property. But $\mathcal{M}(\sim B) \equiv \sim \mathcal{M}B$ by Theorem 18, and $\sim \mathcal{M}B \equiv \sim \sim B$ by assumption; thus, $\mathcal{M}(\sim B) \equiv \sim \sim B$.

(3) This case is left as an exercise.

(4) Suppose that E has the property and t is free in E; then $\mathscr{M}E \equiv \sim E$. We shall show that $\forall tE$ has the property. But

$$\mathscr{M}(\forall tE) = \exists t(\mathscr{M}E) \quad \text{by definition}$$
$$\equiv \exists t(\sim E) \quad \text{by the substitution theorem and assumption}$$

and

$$\sim \forall tE \equiv \exists t(\sim E).$$

This establishes Theorem 19.

COROLLARY: $\mathscr{M}(\mathscr{M}A) \equiv A$ whenever A is a wff.

Demonstration: $\mathscr{M}(\mathscr{M}A) \equiv \sim \mathscr{M}A \equiv \sim \sim A \equiv A$ by Theorem 19.

The following theorem is the basis of the principle of duality, which we shall consider later.

THEOREM 20: $\mathscr{M}A \equiv \mathscr{M}B$ whenever $A \equiv B$.

Demonstration: Since $A \equiv B$, it follows that $\sim A \equiv \sim B$. But $\sim A \equiv \mathscr{M}A$ and $\sim B \equiv \mathscr{M}B$ by Theorem 19; hence, $\mathscr{M}A \equiv \mathscr{M}B$ by the substitution theorem.

We require one more syntactical transform $\mathscr{R}$, which has the function of reversing the effect of $\mathscr{M}$ on atomic wff.

DEFINITION OF $\mathscr{R}$

(1) $$\mathscr{R}A = \sim A \text{ if } A \text{ is atomic}$$

(2) $$\mathscr{R}(\sim A) = \begin{cases} A \text{ if } A \text{ is atomic} \\ \mathscr{R}B \text{ if } A = \sim B \\ \sim \mathscr{R}A \text{ otherwise} \end{cases}$$

(3) $$\mathscr{R}(A \vee B) = \mathscr{R}A \vee \mathscr{R}B$$

(4) $$\mathscr{R}(\forall tA) = \forall t(\mathscr{R}A)$$

For example,

$$\begin{aligned}\mathscr{R}(\sim \forall \mathrm{x}\mathrm{Fx} \vee \sim \forall \mathrm{x}\forall \mathrm{y}(\sim \mathrm{Gxy})) &= \mathscr{R}(\sim \forall \mathrm{x}\mathrm{Fx}) \vee \mathscr{R}(\sim \forall \mathrm{x}\forall \mathrm{y} \sim \mathrm{Gxy}) \\ &= \sim \mathscr{R}(\forall \mathrm{x}\mathrm{Fx}) \vee \sim \mathscr{R}(\forall \mathrm{x}\forall \mathrm{y} \sim \mathrm{Gxy}) \\ &= \sim \forall \mathrm{x}(\mathscr{R}\mathrm{Fx}) \vee \sim \forall \mathrm{x}(\mathscr{R}(\forall \mathrm{y} \sim \mathrm{Gxy})) \\ &= \sim \forall \mathrm{x}(\sim \mathrm{Fx}) \vee \sim \forall \mathrm{x}\forall \mathrm{y}(\mathscr{R}(\sim \mathrm{Gxy})) \\ &= \sim \forall \mathrm{x}(\sim \mathrm{Fx}) \vee \sim \forall \mathrm{x}\forall \mathrm{y}\mathrm{Gxy}\end{aligned}$$

In short, the effect of $\mathscr{R}$ on a wff is to replace each atomic wff, say W, by $\sim W$, and then to discard any even number of $\sim$'s which occur prefixed to W. Thus, we can cancel the effect of $\mathscr{M}$ on atomic wff (up to equivalence) by applying $\mathscr{R}$ after applying $\mathscr{M}$.

We now establish some properties of the syntactical transform $\mathscr{R}$.

THEOREM 21: $\mathscr{R}(\sim A) \equiv \sim \mathscr{R}A$ whenever A is a wff.

Demonstration: Apply the fundamental theorem about wff.

THEOREM 22: $\mathscr{R}(A \rightarrow B) \equiv \mathscr{R}A \rightarrow \mathscr{R}B$.

Demonstration: $\mathscr{R}(\sim A \vee B) = \mathscr{R}(\sim A) \vee \mathscr{R}B \equiv \sim \mathscr{R}A \vee \mathscr{R}B$.

THEOREM 23: $\mathscr{R}(S^s_t A) = S^s_t(\mathscr{R}A)$ whenever A is a wff, and s and t are any individuals.

Demonstration: Apply the fundamental theorem about wff.

THEOREM 24: $\vdash \mathscr{R}A$ if $\vdash A$.

Demonstration: Apply the fundamental theorem about provable wff.

THEOREM 25: $\mathscr{R}A \equiv \mathscr{R}B$ whenever $A \equiv B$.

Demonstration: Since $\vdash A \rightarrow B$, it follows from Theorem 24 that $\vdash \mathscr{R}(A \rightarrow B)$, and so $\vdash \mathscr{R}A \rightarrow \mathscr{R}B$ by Theorem 22. Similarly, we see that $\vdash \mathscr{R}B \rightarrow \mathscr{R}A$.

Finally, we are in a position to introduce the *dual* of a wff. By the dual of A we mean the wff obtained from A by interchanging $\vee$ and "$\wedge$" throughout A, and by interchanging $\forall$ and "$\exists$" throughout A. The dual of A is denoted by "$\mathscr{D}A$"; the syntactical transform $\mathscr{D}$ is defined formally as follows:

DEFINITION OF $\mathscr{D}$:

(1) $$\mathscr{D}A = A \text{ if } A \text{ is atomic}$$

(2) $$\mathscr{D}(\sim A) = \begin{cases} \sim A \text{ if } A \text{ is atomic} \\ \mathscr{D}B \text{ if } A = \sim B \\ \mathscr{D}(\sim B) \vee \mathscr{D}(\sim C) \text{ if } A = B \vee C \\ \forall t \mathscr{D}(\sim D) \text{ if } A = \forall t D \end{cases}$$

(3) $$\mathscr{D}(A \vee B) = \mathscr{D}A \wedge \mathscr{D}B$$

(4) $$\mathscr{D}(\forall t A) = \exists t(\mathscr{D}A)$$

For example, $\mathscr{D}(\sim(\sim \forall \mathbf{x}\mathbf{Fx} \vee \sim \forall \mathbf{x} \forall \mathbf{y} \sim \mathbf{Gxy}))$

$$\begin{aligned} &= \mathscr{D}(\sim\sim \forall \mathbf{x}\mathbf{Fx}) \wedge \mathscr{D}(\sim\sim \forall \mathbf{x}\forall \mathbf{y} \sim \mathbf{Gxy}) \\ &= \mathscr{D}(\forall \mathbf{x}\mathbf{Fx}) \vee \mathscr{D}(\forall \mathbf{x}\forall \mathbf{y} \sim \mathbf{Gxy}) \\ &= \exists \mathbf{x}(\mathscr{D}\mathbf{Fx}) \vee \exists \mathbf{x}(\mathscr{D}(\forall \mathbf{y} \sim \mathbf{Gxy})) \\ &= \exists \mathbf{x}\mathbf{Fx} \vee \exists \mathbf{x}\exists \mathbf{y}\mathscr{D}(\sim \mathbf{Gxy}) \\ &= \exists \mathbf{x}\mathbf{Fx} \vee \exists \mathbf{x}\exists \mathbf{y}(\sim \mathbf{Gxy}) \end{aligned}$$

THEOREM 26: $\mathscr{D}(\sim A) \equiv \sim \mathscr{D}A$ whenever A is a wff.

Demonstration: Apply our fundamental theorem about wff.

We intend to prove that $\mathscr{R}(\mathscr{M}A) \equiv \mathscr{D}A$ whenever A is a wff. First, we establish.

THEOREM 27: $\mathscr{R}(\mathscr{M}(\sim A)) \equiv \sim \mathscr{R}(\mathscr{M}A)$ whenever A is a wff.

Demonstration: By Theorem 18, $\mathscr{M}(\sim A) \equiv \sim \mathscr{M}A$; therefore, by Theorem 25,

$$\mathscr{R}(\mathscr{M}(\sim A)) \equiv \mathscr{R}(\sim \mathscr{M}A)$$

But, by Theorem 21, $\mathscr{R}(\sim \mathscr{M}A) \equiv \sim \mathscr{R}(\mathscr{M}A)$; hence,

$$\mathscr{R}(\mathscr{M}(\sim A)) \equiv \sim \mathscr{R}(\mathscr{M}A).$$

THEOREM 28: $\mathscr{R}(\mathscr{M}(\sim A)) \equiv \mathscr{D}(\sim A)$ whenever A is a wff.

Demonstration: We apply the fundamental theorem about wff.

(1) Let A be any atomic wff; then $\mathscr{D}(\sim A) = \sim A$, and $\mathscr{R}(\mathscr{M}(\sim A)) = \mathscr{R}A = \sim A$.

(2) Suppose that B is a wff with the property; then $\mathscr{R}(\mathscr{M}(\sim B)) \equiv \mathscr{D}(\sim B)$. We shall show that

$$\mathscr{R}(\mathscr{M}(\sim \sim B)) \equiv \mathscr{D}(\sim \sim B).$$

But
$$\begin{aligned} \mathscr{R}(\mathscr{M}(\sim \sim B)) &\equiv \sim \mathscr{R}(\mathscr{M}(\sim B)) && \text{by Theorem 27} \\ &\equiv \sim \mathscr{D}(\sim B) && \text{by assumption} \\ &\equiv \mathscr{D}(\sim \sim B) && \text{by Theorem 26} \end{aligned}$$

(3) Suppose that B and C each possess the property; then $\mathscr{R}(\mathscr{M}(\sim B)) \equiv \mathscr{D}(\sim B)$ and $\mathscr{R}(\mathscr{M}(\sim C)) \equiv \mathscr{D}(\sim C)$. We shall show that

$$\mathscr{R}(\mathscr{M}(\sim (B \vee C))) \equiv \mathscr{D}(\sim (B \vee C)).$$

$$\begin{aligned} \text{But} \quad \mathscr{R}(\mathscr{M}(\sim (B \vee C))) &= \mathscr{R}(\mathscr{M}(\sim B) \vee \mathscr{M}(\sim C)) && \text{by definition} \\ &= \mathscr{R}(\mathscr{M}(\sim B)) \vee \mathscr{R}(\mathscr{M}(\sim C)) && \text{by definition} \\ &\equiv \mathscr{D}(\sim B) \vee \mathscr{D}(\sim C) && \text{by assumption} \\ \text{and} \quad \mathscr{D}(\sim (B \vee C)) &= \mathscr{D}(\sim B) \vee \mathscr{D}(\sim C) && \text{by definition} \end{aligned}$$

(4) Suppose that E has the property and t is free in E; then $\mathscr{R}(\mathscr{M}(\sim E)) \equiv \mathscr{D}(\sim E)$. We shall show that $\mathscr{R}(\mathscr{M}(\sim \forall tE)) \equiv \mathscr{D}(\sim \forall tE)$.

$$\begin{aligned} \text{But} \quad \mathscr{R}(\mathscr{M}(\sim \forall tE)) &= \mathscr{R}(\forall t\mathscr{M}(\sim E)) = \forall t(\mathscr{R}(\mathscr{M}(\sim E))) \\ &\equiv \forall t\mathscr{D}(\sim E), \\ \text{and} \quad \mathscr{D}(\sim \forall tE) &= \forall t\mathscr{D}(\sim E). \end{aligned}$$

This establishes Theorem 28.

THEOREM 29: $\mathscr{R}(\mathscr{M}A) \equiv \mathscr{D}A$ whenever A is a wff.

Demonstration: Since $\sim \sim A \equiv A$, $\mathscr{M}(\sim \sim A) \equiv \mathscr{M}A$ by Theorem 20;
therefore, $\mathscr{R}(\mathscr{M}(\sim \sim A)) \equiv \mathscr{R}(\mathscr{M}A)$ by Theorem 25.
But $\mathscr{D}(\sim \sim A) \equiv \mathscr{R}(\mathscr{M}(\sim \sim A))$ by Theorem 28;
and $\mathscr{D}(\sim \sim A) = \mathscr{D}A$ by definition.
Therefore, $\mathscr{R}(\mathscr{M}A) \equiv \mathscr{D}A$.

This establishes Theorem 29.

We can now state and prove the important

PRINCIPLE OF DUALITY: $\mathscr{D}A \equiv \mathscr{D}B$ whenever $A \equiv B$.

Demonstration: Assume that $A \equiv B$; then $\mathscr{M}A \equiv \mathscr{M}B$ by Theorem 20. Therefore, by Theorem 25, $\mathscr{R}(\mathscr{M}A) \equiv \mathscr{R}(\mathscr{M}B)$. Hence, $\mathscr{D}A \equiv \mathscr{D}B$ by Theorem 29.

THEOREM 30: $\mathscr{D}(A \wedge B) = \mathscr{D}A \vee \mathscr{D}B$ whenever $A \wedge B$ is a wff.

Demonstration: $A \wedge B = \sim(\sim A \vee \sim B)$; therefore,

$$\mathscr{D}(A \wedge B) = \mathscr{D}(\sim\sim A) \vee \mathscr{D}(\sim\sim B)$$
$$= \mathscr{D}A \vee \mathscr{D}B$$

THEOREM 31: $\mathscr{D}(\exists tE) = \forall t\mathscr{D}E$ whenever $\exists tE$ is a wff.

Demonstration: $\mathscr{D}(\sim \forall t \sim E) = \forall t\mathscr{D}(\sim\sim E) = \forall t\mathscr{D}E$.

THEOREM 32: $\mathscr{D}(\mathscr{D}A) \equiv A$ whenever A is a wff.

Demonstration: We apply our fundamental theorem about wff.

(1) Let A be any atomic wff; then $\mathscr{D}A = A$, and so $\mathscr{D}(\mathscr{D}A) = \mathscr{D}A = A$.

(2) Suppose that B is a wff with the property; then $\mathscr{D}(\mathscr{D}B) \equiv B$. We shall show that $\sim B$ has the property.

But $\mathscr{D}(\mathscr{D}(\sim B)) \equiv \mathscr{D}(\sim \mathscr{D}B) \equiv \sim \mathscr{D}(\mathscr{D}B)$ by Theorem 26

$\equiv \sim B$ by assumption

(3) Suppose that C and D each possesses the property; then $\mathscr{D}(\mathscr{D}C) \equiv C$ and $\mathscr{D}(\mathscr{D}D) \equiv D$. We shall show that $C \vee D$ has the property.

But $\mathscr{D}(\mathscr{D}(C \vee D)) = \mathscr{D}(\mathscr{D}C \wedge \mathscr{D}D)$ by definition

$= \mathscr{D}(\mathscr{D}C) \vee \mathscr{D}(\mathscr{D}D)$ by Theorem 30

$\equiv C \vee D$ by assumption

(4) Suppose that E has the property and t is free in E; then $\mathscr{D}(\mathscr{D}E) \equiv E$. We shall show that $\forall tE$ has the property. But $\mathscr{D}(\mathscr{D}\forall tE) = \mathscr{D}(\exists t\mathscr{D}E) = \forall t(\mathscr{D}(\mathscr{D}E)) \equiv \forall tE$.

This establishes Theorem 32.

THEOREM 33: $\vdash \mathscr{D}B \rightarrow \mathscr{D}A$ whenever $\vdash A \rightarrow B$.

Demonstration: Assume that $\vdash A \rightarrow B$; then $\vdash \sim B \rightarrow \sim A$. Hence,

	$\vdash \mathscr{M}B \rightarrow \mathscr{M}A$	by Theorem 19
thus,	$\vdash \mathscr{R}(\mathscr{M}B \rightarrow \mathscr{M}A)$	by Theorem 24
and so	$\vdash \mathscr{R}(\mathscr{M}B) \rightarrow \mathscr{R}(\mathscr{M}A)$	by Theorem 22
Hence,	$\vdash \mathscr{D}B \rightarrow \mathscr{D}A$	by Theorem 29

To illustrate the power of the Principle of Duality, we demonstrate

THEOREM 34: $A \wedge \exists tB \equiv \exists t(A \wedge B)$, provided $A \wedge \exists tB \rightarrow \exists t(A \wedge B)$ is a wff.

Demonstration: By Exercise 19 on page 179, $\mathscr{D}A \vee \forall t\mathscr{D}B \equiv \forall t(\mathscr{D}A \vee \mathscr{D}B)$ under the assumption of our theorem. Applying the principle of duality, we obtain

$$\mathscr{D}(\mathscr{D}A \vee \forall t\mathscr{D}B) \equiv \mathscr{D}(\forall t(\mathscr{D}A \vee \mathscr{D}B))$$

that is, $\mathscr{D}(\mathscr{D}A) \wedge \exists t\mathscr{D}(\mathscr{D}B) \equiv \exists t(\mathscr{D}(\mathscr{D}A) \wedge \mathscr{D}(\mathscr{D}B))$

hence, $A \wedge \exists tB \equiv \exists t(A \wedge B)$ by Theorem 32 and the substitution theorem

To illustrate Theorem 33, we establish

THEOREM 35: $\vdash \exists tA \wedge \forall tB \rightarrow \exists t(A \wedge B)$ provided this is a wff.

Demonstration: By Exercise 25 on page 180,

$$\vdash \forall t(\sim \mathscr{D}A \rightarrow \mathscr{D}B) \dot{\rightarrow} \exists t(\sim \mathscr{D}A) \rightarrow \exists t\mathscr{D}B$$

under the assumption of our theorem. Applying Theorem 33, we obtain

$$\vdash \mathscr{D}(\exists t(\sim \mathscr{D}A) \rightarrow \exists t\mathscr{D}B) \rightarrow \mathscr{D}(\forall t(\sim \mathscr{D}A \rightarrow \mathscr{D}B))$$

Hence, $\vdash \sim \mathscr{D}(\exists t(\sim \mathscr{D}A)) \wedge \mathscr{D}(\exists t\mathscr{D}B) \rightarrow \exists t\mathscr{D}(\sim \mathscr{D}A \rightarrow \mathscr{D}B)$ by Theorem 26

that is, $\vdash \sim \forall t\mathscr{D}(\sim \mathscr{D}A) \wedge \forall t\mathscr{D}(\mathscr{D}B) \rightarrow \exists t(\mathscr{D}(\sim \sim \mathscr{D}A) \wedge \mathscr{D}(\mathscr{D}B))$

and so $\vdash \sim (t\forall \sim \mathscr{D}(\mathscr{D}A)) \wedge \forall t\mathscr{D}(\mathscr{D}B) \rightarrow \exists t(\mathscr{D}(\mathscr{D}A) \wedge \mathscr{D}(\mathscr{D}B))$

by Theorem 26 and the substitution theorem

Hence, $\vdash \sim \forall t(\sim A) \wedge \forall tB \rightarrow \exists t(A \wedge B)$

by Theorem 32 and the substitution theorem

that is, $\vdash \exists tA \wedge \forall tB \rightarrow \exists t(A \wedge B)$

EXERCISES

Simplify the following wff:

1. $\mathscr{N}(\sim \mathbf{Fx} \vee \forall \mathbf{yGyy})$
2. $\mathscr{N}(\sim \mathbf{Fx} \vee \forall \mathbf{y}(\mathbf{Fy} \wedge \mathbf{Gyy}))$
3. $\mathscr{N}(\exists \mathbf{y}(\mathbf{Fy} \vee \mathbf{Gyy}))$
4. $\mathscr{N}(\sim \sim \sim \sim (\mathbf{Fx} \vee \mathbf{Gyy}))$
5. $\mathscr{M}(\sim \mathbf{Fx} \vee \forall \mathbf{yFy})$
6. $\mathscr{M}(\sim \mathbf{Fx} \vee \forall \mathbf{y}(\mathbf{Fy} \wedge \mathbf{Gyy}))$
7. $\mathscr{M}(\exists \mathbf{y}(\mathbf{Fy} \vee \mathbf{Gyy}))$

8. $\mathscr{R}(\sim \mathbf{Fx} \vee \forall \mathbf{yGyy})$
9. $\mathscr{R}(\exists \mathbf{y}(\mathbf{Fy} \vee \mathbf{Gyy}))$
10. $\mathscr{R}(\sim\sim\sim\sim (\mathbf{Fx} \vee \mathbf{Gyy}))$
11. $\mathscr{D}(\sim \mathbf{Fx} \vee \forall \mathbf{y}(\mathbf{Fy} \vee \mathbf{Gyy}))$
12. $\mathscr{D}(\exists \mathbf{y}(\mathbf{Fx} \vee \mathbf{Gyy}))$
13. $\mathscr{D}(\sim\sim\sim\sim (\mathbf{Fx} \vee \mathbf{Gyy}))$
14. $\mathscr{R}(\mathscr{M}(\sim \mathbf{Fx} \vee \forall \mathbf{y}(\mathbf{Fy} \vee \mathbf{Gyy})))$
15. $\mathscr{R}(\mathscr{M}(\exists \mathbf{y}(\mathbf{Fx} \vee \mathbf{Gyy})))$
16. $\mathscr{M}(\mathscr{R}(\sim \mathbf{Fx} \vee \forall \mathbf{y}(\mathbf{Fy} \vee \mathbf{Gyy})))$
17. $\mathscr{M}(\mathscr{R}(\exists \mathbf{y}(\mathbf{Fx} \vee \mathbf{Gyy})))$
18. $\mathscr{D}(\mathscr{D}(\sim (\mathbf{Fx} \vee \mathbf{Gyy})))$
19. Show that $\mathscr{N}(\mathscr{N}A) \equiv A$ whenever A is a wff.
20. Find a wff, say A, such that $\mathscr{N}(\mathscr{N}A) \neq A$.
21. Show that $\mathscr{M}(\mathscr{M}(A \vee B)) = \mathscr{M}(\mathscr{M}A) \vee \mathscr{M}(\mathscr{M}B)$ whenever $A \vee B$ is a wff.
22. Establish Case (3) of Theorem 19.
23. Establish Theorem 21.
24. Establish Theorem 23.
25. Establish Theorem 24.
26. Establish Theorem 26.
27. Find a wff, say A, such that $\mathscr{M}(\mathscr{R}A) \neq \mathscr{R}(\mathscr{M}A)$.
28. Apply Theorem 33 to show that $\vdash \exists tA \vee \exists tB \rightarrow \exists t(A \vee B)$, provided this is a wff.
29. By applying the principle of duality, show that $\exists tA \vee \exists tB \equiv \exists t(A \vee B)$, provided $\exists tA \vee \exists tB \rightarrow \exists t(A \vee B)$ is a wff.
30. By applying the principle of duality, show that $A \vee \exists tB \equiv \exists t(A \vee B)$, provided $A \vee \exists tB \rightarrow \exists t(A \vee B)$ is a wff.
31. Show that $A \wedge B \equiv B \wedge A$, provided $A \wedge B$ is a wff.
32. Show that $A \wedge (B \wedge C) \equiv (A \wedge B) \wedge C$, provided $A \wedge (B \wedge C)$ is a wff.
33. Prove Theorem 29 by applying the fundamental theorem about wff.

10. Prenex Normal Form *

Consider a wff, say A, which may or may not involve quantifiers. The purpose of this section is to establish the existence of a wff equivalent to A and possessing a very special form.

The technique which enables us to establish our result is based upon six results previously obtained, which we now gather together for convenience.

Let C and D be any wff, and t any individual such that $C \vee \forall t D \rightarrow \forall t(C \vee D)$ is a wff; then

(1)	$C \wedge \forall t D \equiv \forall t(C \wedge D)$	Theorem 12, page 178
(2)	$C \vee \forall t D \equiv \forall t(C \vee D)$	Exercise 19, page 179
(3)	$C \wedge \exists t D \equiv \exists t(C \wedge D)$	Theorem 34, page 188
(4)	$C \vee \exists t D \equiv \exists t(C \vee D)$	Exercise 30, page 189
(5)	$\sim \forall t C \equiv \exists t(\sim C)$	Exercise 27, page 180
(6)	$\sim \exists t C \equiv \forall t(\sim C)$	Exercise 30, page 180

For example, consider the wff $(\forall y\mathrm{F}y \vee \mathrm{F}x) \vee \sim (\forall w\mathrm{G}ww \vee \sim \forall y\mathrm{F}y)$, which we shall denote by "A". Then

$A \equiv (\forall y\mathrm{F}y \vee \mathrm{F}x) \vee \sim (\forall w\mathrm{G}ww \vee \sim \forall z\mathrm{F}z)$	by the substitution theorem
$\equiv (\forall y\mathrm{F}y \vee \mathrm{F}x) \vee (\sim \forall w\mathrm{G}ww \wedge \sim \sim \forall z\mathrm{F}z)$	by Exercise 33, page 180 and the substitution theorem
$\equiv \forall y\mathrm{F}y \vee (\mathrm{F}x \vee (\exists w(\sim \mathrm{G}ww) \wedge \forall z\mathrm{F}z))$	by (5), Exercise 32, page 180 and the substitution theorem
$\equiv y(\forall \mathrm{F}y \vee (\mathrm{F}x \vee (\exists w(\sim \mathrm{G}ww) \wedge \forall z\mathrm{F}z)))$	by (2), Exercise 31, page 180, and the substitution theorem
$\equiv \forall y(\mathrm{F}y \vee (\mathrm{F}x \vee (\exists w(\sim \mathrm{G}ww \wedge \forall z\mathrm{F}z))))$	by (3), Exercise 31, page 180 and the substitution theorem
$\equiv \forall y((\mathrm{F}y \vee \mathrm{F}x) \vee (\exists w\forall z(\sim \mathrm{G}ww \wedge \mathrm{F}z)))$	by (3) and the substitution theorem
$\equiv \forall y\exists w((\mathrm{F}y \vee \mathrm{F}x) \vee \forall z(\sim \mathrm{G}ww \wedge \mathrm{F}z))$	by (4) and the substitution theorem
$\equiv \forall y\exists w\forall z((\mathrm{F}y \vee \mathrm{F}x) \vee (\sim \mathrm{G}ww \wedge \mathrm{F}z))$	by (2) and the substitution theorem

Denote $\forall y\exists w\forall z((\mathrm{F}y \vee \mathrm{F}x) \vee (\sim \mathrm{G}ww \wedge \mathrm{F}z))$ by "B". Notice that the first step in the reduction of A to B consists in applying Corollary 2, page 177, repeatedly until a wff is obtained in which no individual is quantified more than once. The next step is to ensure that $\sim$ appears attached only to quantifier-free wff. Finally, by repeated applications of (1), (2), (3), (4), and the substitution theorem, the quantifiers are placed together at the left-hand side of the resulting wff. Observe that B consists of a block of quantifiers, called the *prefix* of B, followed by a quantifier-free wff, called the *matrix* of B. Here, the prefix of B is **∀y∃w∀z**, and the matrix of B is **((Fy ∨ Fx) ∨ (~ Gww ∧ Fz))**.

DEFINITION: A wff, say C, is said to be in *prenex normal form* iff there is a natural number n, $n \geq 1$, n quantifiers $Q_1, Q_2, \ldots, Q_n$ (where each Q_j is ∀ or "∃"), and n distinct individuals $t_1, t_2, \ldots, t_n$, together with a quantifier-free wff, say D, such that $C = Q_1t_1Q_2t_2 \ldots Q_nt_nD$.

Thus, each wff in prenex normal form possesses both a prefix and a matrix.

Applying our definition, it is easy to establish

LEMMA 1: If E is in prenex normal form and t is free in E, then $\forall tE$ is in prenex normal form, and $\exists tE$ is in prenex normal form.

LEMMA 2: $\sim (Q_1t_1Q_2t_2 \ldots Q_nt_nD) \equiv q_1t_1q_2t_2 \ldots q_nt_n(\sim D)$

where $$q_i = \begin{cases} \forall \text{ if } Q_i = \text{“}\exists\text{”} \\ \text{“}\exists\text{” if } Q_i = \forall \end{cases} \qquad i = 1, 2, \ldots, n$$

Demonstration: Mathematical induction on n.

Clearly, Lemma 2 states that given any wff in prenex normal form, say C, there is a wff in prenex normal form, say E, such that $\sim C \equiv E$; furthermore, t is free in E iff t is free in $\sim C$, whenever t is an individual.

LEMMA 3: Suppose that $A \vee B$ is a wff, A is in prenex normal form, and B is in prenex normal form. Then there is a wff in prenex normal form, say E, such that $A \vee B \equiv E$; furthermore, t is free in E iff t is free in $A \vee B$, whenever t is an individual.

Demonstration: By assumption, there are natural numbers r and n such that

$$A = Q_1s_1Q_2s_2 \ldots Q_rs_rA' \quad \text{and} \quad B = Q'_1t_1Q'_2t_2 \ldots Q'_nt_nB'$$

where A' and B' are quantifier-free. In view of Corollary 2, page 177, and the substitution theorem, we may assume that no individual is bound in both A and B. By mathematical induction on n, it is easy to see that

$$Q_1s_1Q_2s_2 \ldots Q_rs_rA' \vee Q'_1t_1Q'_2t_2 \ldots Q'_nt_nB'$$
$$\equiv Q'_1t_1Q'_2t_2 \ldots Q'_nt_nQ_1s_1Q_2s_2 \ldots Q_rs_r(A' \vee B'),$$

applying (2) or (4). This establishes Lemma 3.

LEMMA 4: If A is any quantifier-free wff, there is a wff in prenex normal form, say E, such that $A \equiv E$; furthermore, t is free in E iff t is free in A, whenever t is an individual.

Demonstration: Let s be any individual which does not occur in A, and suppose that **F** has order one. We shall show that $A \equiv \forall s(A \wedge (\mathbf{F}s \vee \sim \mathbf{F}s))$.

Clearly,	$\vdash \mathbf{F}s \vee \sim \mathbf{F}s$	by Theorem 4, page 169
therefore	$\vdash A \rightarrow \mathbf{F}s \vee \sim \mathbf{F}s$	by Exercise 1(b), page 169
also, $\vdash A \rightarrow A$, hence		
	$\vdash A \wedge A \rightarrow A \wedge (\mathbf{F}s \vee \sim \mathbf{F}s)$	by Exercise 13, page 170
thus	$\vdash A \rightarrow A \wedge (\mathbf{F}s \vee \sim \mathbf{F}s)$	by the substitution theorem
and so	$\vdash A \rightarrow \forall s(A \wedge (\mathbf{F}s \vee \sim \mathbf{F}s))$	by Exercise 11, page 170.

Now let t be an individual that does not occur in $A \vee \mathbf{F}s$; then

	$\vdash \forall s(A \wedge (\mathbf{F}s \vee \sim \mathbf{F}s)) \rightarrow A \wedge (\mathbf{F}t \vee \sim \mathbf{F}t)$	by I (5)
but	$\vdash A \wedge (\mathbf{F}t \vee \sim \mathbf{F}t) \rightarrow A$	
therefore	$\vdash \forall s(A \wedge (\mathbf{F}s \vee \sim \mathbf{F}s)) \rightarrow A$	
Thus,	$A \equiv \forall s(A \wedge (\mathbf{F}s \vee \sim \mathbf{F}s))$	

This establishes Lemma 4.

We are now in a position to establish an important generalization of Lemma 4, called the

FUNDAMENTAL THEOREM ABOUT PRENEX NORMAL FORM: If A is any wff, there is a wff in prenex form, say E, such that $A \equiv E$; furthermore, t is free in E iff t is free in A, whenever t is an individual.

Demonstration: We apply our fundamental theorem about wff. The property of wff involved is this: a wff, say A, has the property iff there exists a wff in prenex normal form, say E, and involving the same free individuals as does A, such that $A \equiv E$.

(1) By Lemma 4, each atomic wff has the property.

(2) Suppose B is a wff with the property; then there exists a wff E in prenex normal form and involving the same free individuals as does B, such that $B \equiv E$. By our substitution theorem, $\sim B \equiv \sim E$, and by Lemma 2, $\sim E \equiv D$ where D is in prenex normal form and involves the same free individuals as does $\sim E$. Hence, $\sim B$ has the property.

(3) Suppose C and D are wff with the property; then $C \equiv C'$ where C' is in prenex normal form and involves the same free individuals as does C, and $D \equiv D'$ where D' is in prenex normal form and involves the same free individuals as does D. We shall show that $C \vee D$ possesses the property, provided $C \vee D$ is a wff. But

$$C \vee D \equiv C' \vee D' \quad \text{by the substitution theorem}$$

$$\equiv E \quad \text{by Lemma 3}$$

where E is in prenex normal form and involves the same free individuals as does $C' \vee D'$. Thus, $C \vee D$ possesses the property.

(4) Suppose B has the property and s is free in B. Then there exists a wff in prenex normal form, say E, which involves the same free individuals as does B, such that $B \equiv E$. Therefore, by the substitution theorem, $\forall sB \equiv \forall sE$. By Lemma 1, $\forall sE$ is in prenex normal form; furthermore, $\forall sE$ involves the same free individuals as does $\forall sB$. Thus, $\forall sB$ possesses the property. This establishes our Theorem.

Given a wff, say E, in prenex normal form, it is convenient to denote E by "$P(M)$", where "P" represents the prefix of E, and "M" represents the matrix of E. By the *length* of the prefix of E, we shall mean the natural number n such that $P = Q_1t_1Q_2t_2 \ldots Q_nt_n$. In this way, a natural number is associated with each wff in prenex normal form—namely, the length of the prefix of the wff. To illustrate, note that Lemma 3 states that

$$P_1(M_1) \vee P_2(M_2) \equiv P_2P_1(M_1 \vee M_2)$$

which is easily established by mathematical induction over the length of P_2.

EXERCISES

Reduce each of the following wff to prenex normal form:

1. **Fy ∨ ∀xGxy**
2. **~ (Fy ∨ ∀xGxy)**
3. **∃yFy ∨ ∀xGxx**
4. **∃yFy ∧ ∀yGyy**
5. **∀yFy ∧ ∀yGyy**
6. **~ (∀yFy ∧ ∀yGyy)**
7. **(∀xFx ∧ ∀x∃yGxy) ∨ ∀yHyyy**
8. **(∀xFx ∧ ∀x∃yGxy) ∨ ∀x∃y∀zHxyz**

Construct a wff in prenex normal form equivalent to:

9. **Fz**
10. **~ Fz**
11. **Fz ∧ ~ Fz**
12. **Fz ∨ ~ Fz**

13. Given A, does there exist more than one wff E such that E is in prenex normal form, $A \equiv E$, and E involves the same free individuals as does A?

14. Show that $A \equiv A \wedge B$, given that $A \wedge B$ is a wff and $\vdash B$.

15. Given a wff A, show that there is a wff in prenex normal form, say E, which does *not* involve the same free individuals as does A, and such that $A \equiv E$.

16. Show that $P_1(M_1) \vee P_2(M_2) \equiv P_1P_2(M_1 \vee M_2)$, given that

$$P_1(M_1) \vee P_2(M_2) \rightarrow P_1P_2(M_1 \vee M_2)$$

is a wff.

11. The Consequences of a Set of Wff

The aim of a theory of deduction is to enable us to characterize just how a statement is deduced from a given set of statements. We are now in a position to do this. Let K be any non-empty set of wff, and let B be any wff; we shall say that B is *deducible* from K or that B is a *consequence* of K iff there is a natural number n such that $\vdash A_1 \wedge A_2 \wedge \ldots \wedge A_n \rightarrow B$, where $\{A_1, A_2, \ldots, A_n\} \subset K$.

In other words, we require the existence of a *finite* number of wff in K whose conjunction entails B. We shall denote the statement "B is a consequence of K" by "$K \vdash B$". Let us formalize this important notion of a consequence of a non-empty set of wff K.

DEFINITION: $K \vdash B$ iff there exists a non-empty finite subset of K, say $\{A_1, A_2, \ldots, A_n\}$, such that $\vdash A_1 \wedge A_2 \wedge \ldots \wedge A_n \rightarrow B$.

For example, consider the set $\{\forall \mathbf{w}(\mathbf{Fw}), \mathbf{Gxy})\}$. Since $\vdash \mathbf{Gxy} \wedge \forall \mathbf{wFw} \rightarrow \forall \mathbf{w}(\mathbf{Gxy} \wedge \mathbf{Fw})$, we can write $\{\forall \mathbf{w}(\mathbf{Fw}), \mathbf{Gxy}\} \vdash \forall \mathbf{w}(\mathbf{Gxy} \wedge \mathbf{Fw})$. Similarly, $\vdash \forall \mathbf{wFw} \rightarrow \mathbf{Fz}$; therefore, $\{\forall \mathbf{w}(\mathbf{Fw}), \mathbf{Gxy}\} \vdash \mathbf{Fz}$.

As another illustration, consider the set $\{\forall t\mathbf{F}t \mid t \text{ is an individual}\}$. Since $\vdash \forall \mathbf{yFy} \rightarrow \mathbf{Fx}$, we see that $\{\forall t\mathbf{F}t \mid t \text{ is an individual}\} \vdash \mathbf{Fx}$. Again, $\vdash \forall \mathbf{xFx} \wedge \forall \mathbf{yFy} \rightarrow \forall \mathbf{xFx} \wedge \forall \mathbf{yFy}$; therefore,

$$\{\forall t\mathbf{F}t \mid t \text{ is an individual}\} \vdash \forall \mathbf{xFx} \wedge \forall \mathbf{yFy}.$$

We now establish one property of our concept.

THEOREM 36: $K \vdash A \wedge B$ whenever $K \vdash A$ and $K \vdash B$.

Demonstration: By assumption, there are finite subsets of K say $\{A_1, A_2, \ldots, A_n\}$ and $\{B_1, B_2, \ldots, B_m\}$, such that $\vdash A_1 \wedge A_2 \wedge \ldots \wedge A_n \rightarrow A$ and $\vdash B_1 \wedge B_2 \wedge \ldots \wedge B_m \rightarrow B$. Therefore, $\vdash (A_1 \wedge \ldots \wedge A_n) \wedge (B_1 \wedge \ldots \wedge B_m) \rightarrow A \wedge B$. But $\{A_1, A_2, \ldots, A_n, B_1, B_2, \ldots, B_m\}$ is a finite subset of K. Hence, $K \vdash A \wedge B$.

Having defined the notion of a consequence of a set of statements, it is natural to consider all the consequences of a set of statements. Let K be any non-empty set of wff. Then by "$C[K]$" we denote the set of all consequences of K.

DEFINITION: $C[K]$ is $\{A \mid K \vdash A\}$.

For example, suppose that K is a non-empty set of wff such that $K \vdash B$ and $K \vdash \sim B$. Then $K \vdash B \wedge \sim B$ by Theorem 36; it follows that $K \vdash A$ whenever A is a wff. Thus, $C[K]$ is $\{A \mid A$ is a wff$\}$, the set of all wff.

Two important definitions follow. We assume that K is a non-empty set of wff.

DEFINITION: We say that K is *contradictory* iff $C[K]$ is the set of all wff.

DEFINITION: We say that K is *consistent* iff K is not contradictory.

Obviously, our definition of a contradictory set is not easily applied to the question of determining whether a given set of wff is contradictory. Fortunately, there is a very simple criterion that does the job.

THEOREM 37: K is contradictory iff there is a wff, say B, such that $K \vdash B$ and $K \vdash \sim B$.

Demonstration: (1) Suppose that K is contradictory. Then $K \vdash B$ and $K \vdash \sim B$ whenever B is a wff.

(2) Suppose that B is a wff such that $K \vdash B$ and $K \vdash \sim B$. Then $K \vdash B \wedge \sim B$ by Theorem 36; hence $K \vdash A$ whenever A is a wff, since $\vdash B \wedge \sim B \rightarrow A$.

This establishes Theorem 37.

THEOREM 38: Suppose K_1 is contradictory and $K_1 \subset K_2$. Then K_2 is contradictory.

Demonstration: Applying Theorem 37, there exists a wff, say B, such that $K_1 \vdash B$ and $K_1 \vdash \sim B$. Since $K_1 \subset K_2$, it follows that $K_2 \vdash B$ and $K_2 \vdash \sim B$. Hence, by Theorem 37, K_2 is contradictory.

COROLLARY: If K is consistent, then each non-empty subset of K is consistent.

THEOREM 39: K is consistent if each non-empty, finite subset of K is consistent.

Demonstration: Suppose that each non-empty, finite subset of K is consistent, yet K is contradictory. By Theorem 37, there is a wff, say B, such that $K \vdash B$ and $K \vdash \sim B$. Therefore, there are finite subsets of K, say K_1 and K_2, such that $K_1 \vdash B$ and $K_2 \vdash \sim B$. Now consider $K_1 \cup K_2$. Clearly, this is a finite subset of K; furthermore, $K_1 \cup K_2 \vdash B$ and $K_1 \cup K_2 \vdash \sim B$. Hence, by Theorem 37, $K_1 \cup K_2$ is contradictory. We have arrived at a contradiction; thus, our assumption that K is contradictory is false.

COROLLARY: K is consistent iff each non-empty, finite subset of K is consistent.

EXERCISES

1. Let K be any non-empty set of wff; show that $K \vdash A$ whenever $\vdash A$.
2. If $K \vdash A$, is A necessarily provable?
3. Show that $\vdash A \rightarrow B$ iff $\{A\} \vdash B$.
4. Given that $K \vdash A$ and $\vdash A \rightarrow B$, show that $K \vdash B$.
5. Given that $K \vdash A$ and $K \cup \{A\} \vdash B$; prove that $K \vdash B$.
6. Given that $K_1 \vdash A$ and $K_2 \vdash B$, prove that $K_1 \cup K_2 \vdash A \wedge B$.
7. Given that $K_1 \vdash A$ and $K_1 \subset K_2$, show that $K_2 \vdash A$.
8. Given that K is a non-empty set of wff such that $K \vdash \mathbf{Fx} \wedge \sim \mathbf{Fx}$, show that $K \vdash A$ whenever A is a wff.
9. Show that $K \vdash A$ whenever $A \in K$.
10. Show that $K \subset C[K]$.
11. Show that $C[C[K]] = C[K]$.
12. Show that $C[K_1] \cup C[K_2] \subset C[K_1 \cup K_2]$.
13. Are $C[K_1] \cup C[K_2]$ and $C[K_1 \cup K_2]$ necessarily the same?
14. Show that $A \in C[K]$ whenever $\vdash A$.
15. Given that A is a wff with the property that $K \vdash A$ whenever K is a non-empty set of wff, show that $\vdash A$.
16. Show that $\{A\}$, where A is a wff, is contradictory iff $\vdash \sim A$.
17. Construct a contradictory set such that each of its non-empty subsets is contradictory.
18. Given that K is consistent and $A \in K$, show that $K \cup \{\sim A\}$ is contradictory.

6

The completeness of the predicate calculus

1. The Extended Completeness Theorem

The *extended completeness theorem* is the bridge connecting mathematical logic and abstract algebra. Abstract algebra is the study of classes of algebraic systems; mathematical logic is the study of the pure theory of deduction, completely divorced from algebra. The extended completeness theorem establishes that, within limits, the two disciplines are two aspects of the same thing—two sides of the one coin. Some comments on the general picture may be helpful at this stage. First, let us consider the general method of abstract algebra. A class of algebraic systems is specified by describing the type of algebraic system in the class (i.e., by stating the kinds of operators or relations involved and the number of members of the basic set that are displayed), and then by listing certain statements, called postulates, which are true in each algebraic system of the class. In the algebraic method, the chief effort is to prove theorems about the class of algebraic systems specified in the above manner. This is achieved by considering an algebraic system of the specified type in which the listed postulates are true and showing that the stated theorem is true in that particular algebraic system. Since the only assumption made about the algebraic system considered is that it is a member of the specified class, one concludes that the stated theorem is true in each algebraic system of the class. Here, the algebraic system is uppermost in our thoughts and plays a key role in the technique.

On the other hand, in mathematical logic the algebraic system, or structure, plays no role at all. Attention is concentrated on the postulates defining the class of algebraic systems under investigation and on an abstract theory of deduction, which is used to characterize the consequences of the set of postulates. Thus, in mathematical logic the theorems of a theory are established by applying the theory of deduction to the postulates of the theory. Here, there is no involvement with structures; instead, the theory of deduction plays the key role.

We see that the two disciplines, mathematical logic and abstract algebra, have a common goal—to establish the theorems of a theory.

The purpose of this chapter is to demonstrate that the theory of deduction presented in Chapter 5 in fact achieves the desired goal. Some insight into the problem is obtained by considering the following three statements:

I. $\vdash A$ iff A is true.
II. $K \vdash A$ iff μA holds in $\mathcal{S}$ whenever $\mathcal{S}$ is a model of K under μ such that A is defined in $\mathcal{S}$ under μ.
III. K is consistent iff K possesses a model.

Each of these three statements in fact is correct. Statement I is known as Gödel's Completeness Theorem and was demonstrated by Gödel*, a brilliant logician, in a research paper published in 1930. Statements II and III are equivalent in the sense that either can be deduced from the other. Statement III is known as the extended completeness theorem and was demonstrated by the outstanding American logician and mathematician L. Henkin in a research paper published in 1949. Finally, we observe that Statements II and III are generalizations of Statement I in the sense that I can be deduced from either of II or III.

We begin by demonstrating the connection between II and III.

THEOREM 1: If III, then II.

Demonstration: (a) Given that $K \vdash A$, we shall show that μA holds in $\mathcal{S}$ whenever $\mathcal{S}$ is a model of K under μ such that A is defined in $\mathcal{S}$ under μ. If there does not exist a structure $\mathcal{S}$ possessing the specified properties, then there is nothing to prove. Assume, then, that $\mathcal{S}$ is a model of K under μ and that A is defined in $\mathcal{S}$ under μ; suppose, further, that μA does not hold in $\mathcal{S}$. Then $\mu(\sim A)$ holds in $\mathcal{S}$. Now consider the set $K \cup \{\sim A\}$. By III, $K \cup \{\sim A\}$ is consistent; but $K \cup \{\sim A\} \vdash A$, since $K \vdash A$, and $K \cup \{\sim A\} \vdash \sim A$. Thus, by Theorem 37, $K \cup \{\sim A\}$ is contradictory. This contradiction establishes that μA holds in $\mathcal{S}$.

(b) Given that μA holds in $\mathcal{S}$ whenever $\mathcal{S}$ is a model of K under μ such that A is defined in $\mathcal{S}$ under μ, we shall show that $K \vdash A$. Suppose that $K \vdash A$ is false; then $K \cup \{\sim A\}$ is consistent. Therefore, by III, $K \cup \{\sim A\}$

* K. Gödel, "Die Vollständigkeit der Axiome des logischen Funktionenkalküls", *Monatsheft für Mathematik und Physik*, vol. 37, 1930, pp. 349–360.

possesses a model, say $\mathcal{S}$. This means that there is a mapping μ such that $\mathcal{S}$ is a model of K under μ and $\mu(\sim A)$ holds in $\mathcal{S}$. This is a contradiction and we conclude that $K \vdash A$.

This establishes Theorem 1.

THEOREM 2: If II, then III.

Demonstration: (a) Given that K is consistent, we shall show that K possesses a model. Suppose that K does not possess a model; then $\mu(\mathbf{Fx} \wedge \sim \mathbf{Fx})$ holds in $\mathcal{S}$ whenever $\mathcal{S}$ is a model of K under μ and $\mathbf{Fx}$ is defined in $\mathcal{S}$ under μ. Hence, by II, $K \vdash \mathbf{Fx} \wedge \sim \mathbf{Fx}$; thus, K is contradictory. This contradiction establishes that K possesses a model.

(b) Given that K possesses a model, we shall show that K is consistent. Suppose that K is contradictory. Let $\mathcal{S}$ be a model of K under μ, and let B be any wff defined in $\mathcal{S}$ under μ. Then $K \vdash B \wedge \sim B$. Therefore, by II, $\mu(B \wedge \sim B)$ holds in $\mathcal{S}$. But $\mu(B \wedge \sim B)$ does not hold in $\mathcal{S}$. This contradiction establishes that K is consistent. So Theorem 2 is demonstrated.

Next we establish the connection between I and II.

THEOREM 3: If II, then I.

Demonstration: (a) Given that $\vdash A$, we shall show that A is true. Let $\mathcal{S}$ be any structure in which A is defined under μ, and let K be any non-empty set of wff such that $\mathcal{S}$ is a model of K under the same mapping μ. But $K \vdash A$, since $\vdash A$; therefore, by II, μA holds in $\mathcal{S}$. This demonstrates that A is true.

(b) Given that A is true, we shall show that $\vdash A$. Let $\mathcal{S}$ be any structure and μ any mapping such that A is defined in $\mathcal{S}$ under μ. Since A is true, μA holds in $\mathcal{S}$. Therefore, by II, $K \vdash A$ where $K = \{\sim A\}$. Hence, $\vdash \sim A \rightarrow A$; thus, $\vdash A$.

COROLLARY: If III, then I.

Demonstration: Theorems 1 and 3.

We are concerned with establishing the truth of III, the extended completeness theorem. To this purpose, we need two more concepts: the notion of a maximal-consistent set of wff and the notion of an $\exists$-complete set of wff. We shall consider these ideas in Sections 2 and 3.

EXERCISES

1. Establish the Corollary to Theorem 3 without using Theorem 3.
2. Given I and $K \vdash A$, show that μA holds in $\mathcal{S}$ whenever $\mathcal{S}$ is a model of K under μ such that A is defined in $\mathcal{S}$ under μ.

3. Let A be a wff and K a *finite* set of wff such that μA holds in $\mathcal{S}$ provided that:

   (i) $\mathcal{S}$ is a model of K under μ
   (ii) A is defined in $\mathcal{S}$ under μ.
   Prove that $K \vdash A$, assuming I.

2. Maximal-Consistent Sets

In this section we shall consider the concept of a maximal-consistent set of wff, which we shall find useful in establishing the extended completeness theorem.

We have seen that, if K is a contradictory set of wff and $K \subset L$, then L certainly is a contradictory set. On the other hand, a contradictory set may possibly possess consistent subsets. Now suppose that K is consistent; then each non-empty subset of K is of necessity a consistent set, whereas there may possibly exist a super-set of K (i.e., a set L such that $K \subset L$) that is consistent. Of course, given K we can easily construct a super-set of K that is contradictory. What interests us is a consistent set K such that L is contradictory whenever $K \subset L$ and $K \neq L$.

DEFINITION: A set of wff, say K, is said to be *maximal-consistent* iff
(1) K is consistent, and
(2) L is contradictory whenever $K \subset L$ and $K \neq L$.

To illustrate this important concept we now construct a maximal-consistent set of wff. We begin by constructing a structure $\mathcal{S}$ from the symbols of the predicate calculus. The basic set of $\mathcal{S}$ is the set of all individuals of the predicate calculus. Let **R** be any predicate of order n; then we say that "R" denotes the following n^{ary} relation of $\mathcal{S}$: $\{(a_1, \ldots, a_n) \mid (a_1, \ldots, a_n)$ is an ordered n^{tuple} of members of the basic set of $\mathcal{S}\}$. Finally, each member of the basic set of $\mathcal{S}$ is displayed as a term of $\mathcal{S}$. We need a mapping μ of symbols of the predicate Calculus into symbols of the structure $\mathcal{S}$; we choose the identity mapping. Thus, $\mu\phi = \phi$ whenever ϕ is a predicate or individual of the predicate calculus. In terms of the structure $\mathcal{S}$ and the mapping μ, we can now characterize a maximal-consistent set of wff K,

$$K = \{A \mid A \text{ is a wff and } \mu A \text{ holds in } \mathcal{S}\},$$

i.e., K is the set of all wff such that the corresponding swff holds in the structure $\mathcal{S}$. We shall now prove that K is maximal-consistent.

(1) Suppose K is contradictory. Then there is a wff B such that $K \vdash B \wedge \sim B$. Hence, there is a finite subset of K, say $\{A_1, \ldots, A_n\}$, such that $\vdash A_1 \wedge \ldots \wedge A_n \rightarrow B \wedge \sim B$. But each provable wff is true; therefore, the swff $\mu(A_1 \wedge \ldots \wedge A_n \rightarrow B \wedge \sim B)$ holds in $\mathcal{S}$; thus the swff

$$\mu A_1 \wedge \ldots \wedge \mu A_n \rightarrow \mu B \wedge \sim \mu B$$

holds in $\mathcal{S}$. By construction, $\mu A_1 \wedge \ldots \wedge \mu A_n$ holds in $\mathcal{S}$; therefore, $\mu B \wedge \sim \mu B$ holds in $\mathcal{S}$. But $\mu B \wedge \sim \mu B$ does *not* hold in $\mathcal{S}$! We have arrived at a contradiction, and so our initial assumption is false. We conclude that K is consistent.

(2) We show that L is contradictory whenever $K \subset L$ and $K \neq L$. Let A be any wff such that $A \bar{\in} K$ and $A \in L$. Then the swff μA does not hold in $\mathcal{S}$. Hence $\mu(\sim A)$ holds in $\mathcal{S}$, and so $\sim A \in K$, therefore $K \cup \{A\}$ is contradictory. Thus L is contradictory, since $K \cup \{A\} \subset L$. This demonstrates that K is maximal-consistent.

Having established the existence of a maximal-consistent set of wff, we now establish another criterion for this concept.

THEOREM 4: Suppose that K is a consistent set of wff; then K is maximal-consistent iff $K \cup \{B\}$ is contradictory whenever $B \bar{\in} K$.

Demonstration: We must show that L is contradictory whenever $K \subset L$ and $K \neq L$ iff $K \cup \{B\}$ is contradictory whenever $B \bar{\in} K$.

(a) Assume that L is contradictory whenever $K \subset L$ and $K \neq L$. But $K \subset K \cup \{B\}$ and $K \neq K \cup \{B\}$, since $B \bar{\in} K$; therefore, $K \cup \{B\}$ is contradictory.

(b) Assume that $K \cup \{B\}$ is contradictory whenever $B \bar{\in} K$. Let L be any set of wff such that $K \subset L$ and $K \neq L$. Then there is a wff, say B, such that $B \in L$ and $B \bar{\in} K$. Therefore, $K \cup \{B\}$ is contradictory; but $K \cup \{B\} \subset L$. Hence, L is contradictory.

This establishes Theorem 4.

We now establish some properties of maximal-consistent sets.

THEOREM 5: If K is maximal-consistent and $K \vdash A$, then $A \in K$.

Demonstration: Suppose that $A \bar{\in} K$; then $K \cup \{A\}$ is contradictory. Hence, $K \cup \{A\} \vdash \sim A$, and so $K \vdash \sim A$. Therefore, K is contradictory. Thus, $A \in K$.

THEOREM 6: If K is maximal-consistent and $B \bar{\in} K$, then $\sim B \in K$.

Demonstration: $K \cup \{B\}$ is contradictory; therefore, $K \cup \{B\} \vdash \sim B$. Hence, $K \vdash \sim B$. By Theorem 5, $\sim B \in K$.

COROLLARY: If K is maximal-consistent and B is any wff, then either $B \in K$ or else $\sim B \in K$.

THEOREM 7: If K is maximal-consistent, $A \in K$ and $\vdash A \rightarrow B$, then $B \in K$.

Demonstration: Clearly, $K \vdash B$; therefore, by Theorem 5, $B \in K$.

COROLLARY: If K is maximal-consistent and $A \in K$, then $A \vee B \in K$ whenever $A \vee B$ is a wff.

THEOREM 8: If K is maximal-consistent, $A \in K$, and $B \in K$, then $A \wedge B \in K$.

Demonstration: $\vdash A \wedge B \rightarrow A \wedge B$; therefore, $K \vdash A \wedge B$. Hence, by Theorem 5, $A \wedge B \in K$

THEOREM 9: If K is maximal-consistent and $\forall tC \in K$, then $S^s_t C \in K$ whenever s is not bound in $\forall tC$.

Demonstration: $\vdash \forall tC \rightarrow S^s_t C$ whenever s is not bound in $\forall tC$.

THEOREM 10: If K is maximal-consistent and $\forall tC \in K$, then $C \in K$.

Demonstration: Let s be an individual that does not occur in $\forall tC$. Then $\vdash \forall tC \rightarrow \forall s S^s_t C$. Hence, $\forall s S^s_t C \in K$ by Theorem 7. Thus, by Theorem 9, $S^t_s(S^s_t C) \in K$. But $S^t_s(S^s_t C)$ is C. Therefore, $C \in K$.

THEOREM 11: If K is maximal-consistent and $\forall tC \in K$, then $S^s_t C \in K$ whenever s is bound in C.

Demonstration: $\vdash \forall tC \rightarrow \forall s S^s_t C$; therefore, $\forall s S^s_t C \in K$ by Theorem 7; hence, $S^s_t C \in K$ by Theorem 10.

Theorems 9, 10 and 11 are summarized by

THEOREM 12: If K is maximal-consistent and $\forall tC \in K$, then $S^s_t C \in K$ whenever s is an individual.

EXERCISES

1. Given that K is consistent, prove that K is maximal-consistent iff either $A \in K$ or else $\sim A \in K$ whenever A is a wff.
2. Given that K is maximal-consistent, show that $C[K] = K$.
3. Let $\mathcal{S}$ be a structure and let μ be a mapping such that A is defined in $\mathcal{S}$ under μ whenever A is a wff.
   (a) Show that $\{A \mid \mu A \text{ holds in } \mathcal{S}\}$ is maximal-consistent.
   (b) Is $\{A \mid \mu A \text{ does not hold in } \mathcal{S}\}$ maximal-consistent?

3. ∃-Complete Sets

We need one more notion about sets of wff. Consider the following

DEFINITION: We shall say that K is ∃-*Complete* iff whenever $\exists tA \in K$ there is an individual, say s, such that $S^s_t A \in K$.

For example, $\{\exists\mathbf{xFx}, \mathbf{Fy}\}$ is $\exists$-Complete; $\{\mathbf{Fx}\}$ is $\exists$-Complete; and $\{\exists\mathbf{yGyy}, \mathbf{Gzz}, \exists\mathbf{xHxxx}, \mathbf{Hwww}\}$ is $\exists$-Complete.

We are interested primarily in $\exists$-Complete sets, which are also maximal-consistent. Suppose that K has these two properties; then K has an additional property—K possesses a model! This is our fundamental theorem about $\exists$-Complete and maximal-consistent sets, and this is why we are concerned with these two concepts. It is true, as we shall establish subsequently, that any consistent set of wff possesses a model; our point here is that we can actually *construct* a model of K by applying a fixed procedure. The model of K, say $\mathscr{M}$, is constructed as follows: The basic set of $\mathscr{M}$ is the set of all individuals of the predicate calculus. Let $\mathbf{R}$ be any predicate of order n, then we take the n^{ary} relation $\{(a_1, \ldots, a_n) \mid \mathbf{R}a_1 \ldots a_n \in K\}$ to be a term of $\mathscr{M}$. We shall denote this n^{ary} relation by "R"; thus $(a_1, \ldots, a_n) \in R$ iff $\mathbf{R}a_1 \ldots a_n \in K$. Finally, each member of the basic set of $\mathscr{M}$ is displayed as a term of the structure.

Now that we have defined our structure $\mathscr{M}$, we require a mapping μ under which the wff of K will be defined in the structure $\mathscr{M}$. Clearly, the identity mapping achieves this. Let μ, then, denote the identity mapping. Thus, μA denotes the swff A, an object that is meaningful in the structure $\mathscr{M}$. The main theorem can now be established.

THEOREM 13: A holds in $\mathscr{M}$ iff $A \in K$.

Demonstration: We apply a variant of our fundamental theorem about wff which is stated in Exercise 28 on page 159.

(1) Suppose that A is atomic. By construction, A holds in $\mathscr{M}$ iff $A \in K$.

(2) Suppose that B has the property; then B holds in $\mathscr{M}$ iff $B \in K$. We show that $\sim B$ has the property.

  (a) Assume that $\sim B$ holds in $\mathscr{M}$. This means that the swff B does not hold in $\mathscr{M}$; hence, by assumption, $B \bar{\in} K$. Therefore, by Theorem 6, $\sim B \in K$.

  (b) Assume that $\sim B \in K$. Since K is consistent, $B \bar{\in} K$; hence, by assumption, B does not hold in $\mathscr{M}$. Thus, $\sim B$ holds in $\mathscr{M}$. This establishes that $\sim B$ holds in $\mathscr{M}$ iff $\sim B \in K$.

(3) Suppose that C has the property and D has the property; then C holds in $\mathscr{M}$ iff $C \in K$, and D holds in $\mathscr{M}$ iff $D \in K$. We show that $C \vee D$ has the property.

  (a) Assume that $C \vee D$ holds in $\mathscr{M}$. Then C holds in $\mathscr{M}$ or D holds in $\mathscr{M}$. If the former, then $C \in K$, and if the latter, then $D \in K$. In either case, by Theorem 7, $C \vee D \in K$.

  (b) Assume that $C \vee D \in K$. We wish to show that $C \vee D$ holds in $\mathscr{M}$. This is so iff C holds in $\mathscr{M}$ or D holds in $\mathscr{M}$. Suppose that C does not hold in $\mathscr{M}$ and suppose D does not hold in $\mathscr{M}$.

Since C and D each has the property, it follows that $C \mathrel{\bar\in} K$ and $D \mathrel{\bar\in} K$; thus, by Theorem 6, $\sim C \in K$ and $\sim D \in K$. Hence, by Theorem 8, $\sim C \wedge \sim D \in K$, and so $\sim (C \vee D) \in K$. Thus, K is contradictory. Since K is consistent, we conclude that our assumption is false. Thus, $C \vee D$ holds in $\mathscr{M}$.

(4) Suppose $S_t^s E$ has the property whenever s is an individual—where t is free in E; then $S_t^s E$ holds in $\mathscr{M}$ iff $S_t^s E \in K$. We shall show that $\forall tE$ has the property.

(a) Assume that $\forall tE$ holds in $\mathscr{M}$. Then $S_t^s E$ holds in $\mathscr{M}$ whenever s is in the basic set of $\mathscr{M}$; therefore, $S_t^s E \in K$ whenever s is an individual. If $\forall tE \mathrel{\bar\in} K$, then $\exists t(\sim E) \in K$ by Theorem 6. But K is $\exists$-Complete; therefore, there is an individual, say a, such that $S_t^a(\sim E) \in K$, i.e. $\sim S_t^a E \in K$. However, $S_t^a E \in K$, as we have just seen. This contradiction demonstrates that our assumption, $\forall tE \mathrel{\bar\in} K$, is false; thus, $\forall tE \in K$.

(b) Assume that $\forall tE \in K$. Then $S_t^s E \in K$ whenever s is an individual, by Theorem 12. Therefore, $S_t^s E$ holds in $\mathscr{M}$ whenever s is a member of the basic set of $\mathscr{M}$, by assumption; hence, $\forall tE$ holds in $\mathscr{M}$ by definition. This establishes Theorem 13.

Notice that we have established much more than we really required. Our intention was to demonstrate that the structure $\mathscr{M}$ is a model of K under the identity mapping μ. We have established this, since Theorem 13 states, in part, that μA holds in $\mathscr{M}$ whenever $A \in K$; and so $\mathscr{M}$ is a model of K under μ. Furthermore, we have established another interesting connection between the set of wff K and the structure $\mathscr{M}$: $A \in K$ whenever μA holds in $\mathscr{M}$. In a sense, then, either of K or $\mathscr{M}$ is completely characterized by the other.

EXERCISES

1. Let $K = \{S_{\mathbf{w}}^t \mathbf{Fw} \mid t \text{ is an individual}\} \cup \{\exists \mathbf{x}(\sim \mathbf{Fx})\}$;
   (a) Show that K is not $\exists$-Complete.
   (b) Show that $(\{a, b\}, \{a\}, a)$ is a model of K under μ, where $\mu t = a$ whenever t is an individual, and $\mu \mathbf{F} = \{a\}$.
   (c) Show that K is consistent.
   (d) Show that K is not maximal-consistent.

2. Let K be a set of wff such that:
   (1) if $A \in K$ then either A is atomic or else there exists an atomic wff, say B, such that A is $\sim B$

(2) if A is atomic, then $A \in K$ or else $\sim A \in K$

(a) Construct a model of K. (*Hint:* Follow the construction of the text.)
(b) Show that K is consistent.
(c) Show that K is not maximal-consistent.
(d) Using the result of (c), construct a super-set of K which is maximal-consistent.
(e) Is the maximal-consistent set constructed in (d) also ∃-Complete?

3. Let K be a non-empty set of wff such that A is atomic whenever $A \in K$.
(a) Construct a model of K.
(b) Show that K is consistent.
(c) Show that K is not maximal-consistent.
(d) Construct a super-set of K which is maximal-consistent.
(e) Is the maximal-consistent set constructed in (d) also ∃-Complete?

4. Let $\mathcal{M}$ be any structure with basic set the set of all individuals of the predicate calculus, and involving each predicate and individual of the predicate calculus as a displayed term. Let K be a set of wff such that $\mathcal{M}$ is a model of K under the identity mapping μ, and such that μA holds in $\mathcal{M}$ iff $A \in K$. Show that:
(a) K is maximal-consistent
(b) K is ∃-Complete.

4. Proof of the Extended Completeness Theorem

We shall now prove

THE EXTENDED COMPLETENESS THEOREM: K is consistent iff K possesses a model.

It is obvious that K is consistent if K possesses a model; we shall demonstrate that K possesses a model whenever K is consistent.

Suppose that K is a consistent set and that K possesses a super-set, say K_1, which is both maximal-consistent and ∃-Complete. Then, by Section 3, there is a structure $\mathcal{S}$ and a mapping μ such that $\mathcal{S}$ is a model of K_1 under μ. Therefore, $\mathcal{S}$ is a model of K under μ.

Unfortunately, there exist consistent sets that do not possess super-sets that are both maximal-consistent and ∃-Complete. For example, consider the set $\{S^t_{\mathbf{w}}\mathbf{Fw} \mid t \text{ is an individual}\} \cup \{\exists\mathbf{x}(\sim \mathbf{Fx})\}$; clearly, this set is not ∃-Complete, though it is consistent (see Exercise 1, page 204).

A sophisticated idea presented by Henkin in his 1949 paper brilliantly overcomes the difficulty. Consider a sequence of predicate calculi—

$$C_1, C_2, C_3, \ldots, C_n, \ldots$$

such that C_{n+1} is obtained from C_n by extending the set of individuals of C_n whenever n is a natural number. In particular, let C_1 be any predicate calculus, let $u_{i,j}$, $i = 1, 2, 3, \ldots$, and $j = 1, 2, 3, \ldots$ be symbols not occurring in C_1. Then C_2 is the predicate calculus obtained from C_1 by adjoining $\{u_{1,j} \mid j \in N\}$ to the individuals of C_1. In general, the predicate calculus C_{n+1} is constructed from the predicate calculus C_n by adjoining $\{u_{n,j} \mid j \in N\}$ to the individuals of C_n. We need one more predicate calculus, which we denote by C_ω. The symbols of C_ω are the symbols that appear in any C_n; that is, the predicates of C_ω are the predicates of C_1, and the set of individuals of C_ω is the union of the set of individuals of C_1 with $\{u_{i,j} \mid i \in N \text{ and } j \in N\}$.

Now that we have constructed the predicate calculus C_ω, let us consider the wff of C_ω. Since there is a denumerable number of predicates in C_ω and a denumerable number of individuals in C_ω, and since each wff is finite in length, it follows that the number of wff in C_ω is denumerable. Let us consider a particular enumeration of the wff of C_ω, which we shall call the *standard ordering*.

Now let K be any consistent set of wff of the predicate calculus C_1. We intend to construct a super-set of K that is maximal-consistent and ∃-Complete in the predicate calculus C_ω. First, we establish that K is consistent in C_ω.

THEOREM 14: K is consistent in any predicate calculus obtained by adjoining additional symbols to the set of individuals of C_1.

Demonstration: We are given that K is consistent in the predicate calculus C_1 and wish to show that K is consistent in a predicate calculus, say C, obtained by adjoining additional symbols to the set of individuals of C_1. Suppose that K is contradictory in C; then there is a finite subset of K, say $\{A_1, \ldots, A_n\}$, such that $\vdash A_1 \wedge \ldots \wedge A_n \rightarrow \mathbf{Fx} \wedge \sim \mathbf{Fx}$. To assert that the wff $A_1 \wedge \ldots \wedge A_n \rightarrow \mathbf{Fx} \wedge \sim \mathbf{Fx}$ is provable in the predicate calculus C is to assert the existence of a proof of $A_1 \wedge \ldots \wedge A_n \rightarrow \mathbf{Fx} \wedge \sim \mathbf{Fx}$ in C. If this proof is not a proof of $A_1 \wedge \ldots \wedge A_n \rightarrow \mathbf{Fx} \wedge \sim \mathbf{Fx}$ in the predicate calculus C_1, then this proof involves individuals of C that are not individuals of C_1, say $z_1, z_2, \ldots, z_m$. Let $w_1, w_2, \ldots, w_m$ be individuals of C_1 that do not occur in the given proof; consider the syntactical transforms $I_{\mathbf{z}_1}^{\mathbf{w}_1}$, $I_{\mathbf{z}_2}^{\mathbf{w}_2}$, $\ldots$, $I_{\mathbf{z}_m}^{\mathbf{w}_m}$. Now apply these transforms to the given proof; by Theorem 8, page 171, and Exercise 10, page 173, we obtain a proof of $A_1 \wedge \ldots \wedge A_n \rightarrow \mathbf{Fx} \wedge \sim \mathbf{Fx}$ which involves only individuals of C_1. We conclude that $A_1 \wedge \ldots \wedge A_n \rightarrow \mathbf{Fx} \wedge \sim \mathbf{Fx}$ is provable in C_1; hence, $K \vdash \mathbf{Fx} \wedge \sim \mathbf{Fx}$ in C_1, and so K is contradictory in C_1. This contradiction demonstrates our theorem.

Having established that the given set K is consistent in C_ω, our purpose is to extend K, within C_ω, to a maximal-consistent set which is also ∃-Complete.

We begin by extending K to a maximal-consistent set in C_1, which we denote by "K_1". K_1 is constructed as follows: Let $K_{1,1} = K$ and let B_1 be the first wff of C_1 in the standard ordering, such that $K_{1,1} \cup \{B_1\} = K_{1,2}$ is consistent; in general, having found B_n and $K_{1,n+1}$, let B_{n+1} be the first wff of C_1 following B_n in the standard ordering, such that $K_{1,n+1} \cup \{B_{n+1}\} = K_{1,n+2}$ is consistent. Then K_1 is the set of all wff appearing in any $K_{1,i}$; that is,

$$K_1 = \{A \mid \text{there is a natural number } i \text{ such that } A \in K_{1,i}\}$$

Clearly, $K \subset K_1$.

THEOREM 15: K_1 is maximal-consistent in C_1.

Demonstration: If K_1 is contradictory, there is a finite subset of K_1 which is contradictory; hence, there is a natural number n such that $K_{1,n}$ is contradictory. This is impossible by construction; therefore, K_1 is consistent. Now suppose that A is a wff of C_1 such that $K_1 \cup \{A\}$ is consistent. Then $K_{1,n} \cup \{A\}$ is consistent for each n. Let A be the jth wff of C_1 in the standard ordering; then $A \in K_{1,j+1}$. Therefore, $A \in K_1$. This proves that K_1 is maximal-consistent in C_1.

The second step in our construction is to extend K_1 to a $\exists$-Complete set in the predicate calculus C_2. Select the first wff of K_1 in the standard ordering, which has the form $\exists tD$; now construct the wff $S_t^{u_{1,1}}D$. The set $K_1 \cup \{S_t^{u_{1,1}}D\}$ is consistent in C_2; for if this set is contradictory, then there is a finite subset of K_1, say $\{A_1, A_2, \ldots, A_n\}$, such that

$$\vdash A_1 \wedge A_2 \wedge \ldots \wedge A_n \wedge S_t^{u_{1,1}}D \rightarrow \mathbf{Fx} \wedge \sim \mathbf{Fx}$$

in the predicate calculus C_2. Therefore, $\vdash S_t^{u_{1,1}}D \dot{\rightarrow} A_1 \wedge A_2 \wedge \ldots \wedge A_n \rightarrow \mathbf{Fx} \wedge \sim \mathbf{Fx}$ in C_2, where $u_{1,1}$ does not occur in the wff

$$A_1 \wedge A_2 \wedge \ldots \wedge A_n \rightarrow \mathbf{Fx} \wedge \sim \mathbf{Fx}$$

and is free in $S_t^{u_{1,1}}D$. Hence, $\vdash \exists tD \dot{\rightarrow} A_1 \wedge A_2 \wedge \ldots \wedge A_n \rightarrow \mathbf{Fx} \wedge \sim \mathbf{Fx}$ in C_2; thus $K_1 \vdash \mathbf{Fx} \wedge \sim \mathbf{Fx}$ in C_2, and we conclude that K_1 is contradictory in the predicate calculus C_2. But K_1 is consistent in C_2 by Theorem 14. This contradiction demonstrates that $K_1 \cup \{S_t^{u_{1,1}}D\}$ is consistent in C_2.

Each wff of K_1 having the form $\exists tD$ is treated in this manner. For example, suppose that $\exists \mathbf{x}B$ is the next wff in the standard ordering, which is in K_1 and has the stipulated form. Then we adjoin the wff $S_{\mathbf{x}}^{u_{1,2}}B$ to the set $K_1 \cup \{S_t^{u_{1,1}}D\}$. Again, the resulting set, $K_1 \cup \{S_t^{u_{1,1}}D, S_{\mathbf{x}}^{u_{1,2}}B\}$, is consistent in C_2. Once each wff in K_1 possessing the form $\exists tD$ has been treated the resulting consistent set is extended to a maximal-consistent set in C_2, following the same procedure as in the case of the predicate calculus C_1. Call the resulting set K_2. Clearly, $K_1 \subset K_2$.

We have completed the first stage of our construction. Given K_1 maximal-consistent in C_1, we have extended K_1 to K_2, which is maximal-consistent in C_2 and has the property that $S_t^a D \in K_2$ for some individual a of C_2 whenever $\exists t D \in K_1$.

The same procedure is now applied to the set K_2. That is, we construct K_3 following the procedure outlined above, so that $K_2 \subset K_3$, K_3 is maximal-consistent in C_3, and $S_t^a D \in K_3$ for some individual a of C_3 whenever $\exists t D \in K_2$.

We see that moving through a predicate calculus, say C_{n+1}, involves two procedures. Given K_n maximal-consistent in C_n, we consider each wff of K_n that has the form $\exists t D$ and adjoin a wff of C_{n+1} to K_n as outlined above. Having treated each wff of K_n that begins with an existential quantifier, we next extend the resulting consistent set to a maximal-consistent set, using the construction outlined above. Denoting the resulting set by "K_{n+1}", we observe that:

(1) $K_n \subset K_{n+1}$
(2) K_{n+1} is maximal-consistent in C_{n+1}
(3) $S_t^a I \cdot \in K_{n+1}$, for some individual a of C_{n+1}, whenever $\exists t D \in K_n$.

The final step in our program involves the predicate calculus C_ω. Let "K_ω" denote the set of all wff in any K_n; that is,

$$K_\omega = \{A \mid \text{there is a natural number } n \text{ such that } A \in K_n\}$$

Then $K \subset K_\omega$, and K_ω is a set of wff of the predicate calculus C_ω. We shall now demonstrate that K_ω is maximal-consistent and $\exists$-Complete.

THEOREM 16: K_ω is maximal-consistent in C_ω.

Demonstration: Suppose that K_ω is contradictory. Then there is a finite subset of K_ω, say $\{A_1, A_2, \ldots, A_n\}$, such that $\vdash A_1 \wedge A_2 \wedge \cdots \wedge A_n \rightarrow \mathbf{Fx} \wedge \sim \mathbf{Fx}$ in C_ω. Then there is a natural number m such that $\{A_1, A_2, \ldots, A_n\} \subset K_m$. Clearly, $\{A_1, A_2, \ldots, A_n\}$ is contradictory in C_ω; therefore, by Theorem 14, $\{A_1, A_2, \ldots, A_n\}$ is contradictory in C_m, and so K_m is contradictory in C_m. This contradiction establishes that K_ω is consistent in C_ω. Now suppose that A is a wff of C_ω such that $K_\omega \cup \{A\}$ is consistent. But A is a wff of some predicate calculus, say C_j, and $K_j \cup \{A\}$ is consistent in C_j. (If $K_j \cup \{A\}$ is contradictory in C_j, then $K_j \cup \{A\}$ is contradictory in C_ω.) Therefore, $A \in K_j$, since K_j is maximal-consistent in C_j. Hence, $A \in K_\omega$. This establishes Theorem 16.

Finally, we consider

THEOREM 17: K_ω is $\exists$-Complete in C_ω.

Demonstration: Suppose that $\exists t D \in K_\omega$. Then there is a natural number m such that $\exists t D \in K_m$. Hence, there is an individual of the predicate calculus

C_{m+1}, say a, such that $S_t^a D \in K_{m+1}$. Therefore, $S_t^a D \in K_\omega$. This demonstrates that K_ω is $\exists$-Complete.

Since K_ω is maximal-consistent and $\exists$-Complete in the predicate calculus C_ω, we know that K_ω possesses a model. But $K \subset K_\omega$; therefore, K also possesses a model. This completes the demonstration of the extended completeness theorem.

5. Some Consequences of the Extended Completeness Theorem*

Having established Statement III of Section 1, we have automatically demonstrated Statements II and I (recall Theorems 1 and 3 of that section). This means that we have established two important points. First, our strictly formal notion of a *provable* wff has, indeed, completely captured the idea of a *true* wff, since the set of all provable wff *is* the set of all true wff. Second, we have demonstrated that we have constructed a theory of deduction in the following sense. Let K be the postulate-set of a mathematical theory, and let A be a statement whose truth can be deduced from K in the usual mathematical sense; i.e., A holds in each model of K. Then A can be deduced from K within our logical system without reference to the models of K—in the sense that the wff A is a *consequence* of K; i.e., $K \vdash A$. To be precise, we have established that $K \vdash A$ iff μA holds in $\mathcal{S}$ whenever $\mathcal{S}$ is a model of K under μ.

This result enables us to think of a mathematical theory in a particularly simple and effective way. Normally, one thinks of a mathematical theory; for example the theory of groups, as possessing several parts. First, there are the undefined terms or primitive concepts of the theory. (In the case of the theory of groups, the undefined terms are a set of objects B, a binary operator on B—this can be expressed by a ternary relation on B, and an equivalence relation on B, say E—and a special member of B, say 0.) Then there is the postulate-set of the theory—in the case of the example, the following set of wff:

1. $\forall x(Exx)$
2. $\forall x \forall y \forall z(Exy \wedge Eyz \rightarrow Ezx)$
3. $\forall x \forall y \forall z \forall t \forall u \forall v(Sxyz \wedge Ext \wedge Eyu \wedge Ezv \rightarrow Stuv)$
4. $\forall x \forall y \exists z \forall w(Sxyz \dot{\wedge} Sxyw \rightarrow Ezw)$
5. $\forall x \forall y \forall z \forall t \forall u \forall v(Sxyt \wedge Stzu \wedge Syzv \rightarrow Sxvu)$
6. $\forall x(Sx0x)$
7. $\forall x \exists y(Sxy0)$

You may be puzzled by the particular choice of a postulate-set for the notion of a group, since it looks somewhat different from the postulate-set presented on page 90. We shall discuss this in a moment. Returning to our main point, we observe that the given undefined terms and the given postulate-set describe a family of structures—the structures involving the undefined terms and in which the listed postulates are true. We make use of this family of structures to define the notion of a theorem. By a *theorem* of a mathematical theory, we mean a statement that is true in each structure of the family of structures described by the theory.

There are really two parts to a mathematical theory: the family of structures of the theory and the theorems of the theory. The family of structures is characterized by describing the general form of each structure in the family and then announcing the postulate-set. Clearly, the set of theorems of a theory is a super-set of the postulate-set.

The point is that the aspects of a mathematical theory described here are essentially contained within the single notion of the postulate-set of the theory. The postulate-set involves the predicates and displayed members of the basic set that are essential to the theory; therefore, the family of structures involved in the theory is the family of all models of the postulate-set which involve only the predicates and displayed members present in the postulate-set. Finally, the theorem-set of the theory is the set of all consequences of the postulate-set whose predicates are present in the postulate-set and whose free individuals are also free in the postulate-set.

For this reason, we shall regard a mathematical theory as being constituted by a set of wff—the postulate-set. Of course, a postulate-set that possesses no model is of little interest, so we restrict the notion of a mathematical theory to a *consistent* set of wff. For example, the theory of groups is characterized by the consistent set of wff displayed on page 209. Let us pause now to discuss these postulates.

Postulates 1 and 2 assert that the binary relation E is an equivalence relation on B, and Postulate 3 asserts that E is substitutive in the ternary relation S. Postulate 4 ensures that the ternary relation S can be used to define a binary operator on B, up to the equivalence relation E; note that Postulate 4 states that given any members of B, say x and y, there exists a unique member of B, say z, such that $Sxyz$; in effect, then, a unique member of B is associated with each ordered pair of members of B, and so we have a binary operator on B. Remember, the uniqueness goes only as far as the equivalence relation, but this complication is easily taken care of. Postulate 5 gives us the associative law for our binary operator; Postulate 6 asserts that the special member 0 is an identity under the binary operator—within the equivalence relation. Finally, Postulate 7 asserts the existence of an inverse under the binary operator.

It may be helpful, at this point, to establish the connection between the models of the postulate-set under discussion and groups in the normal sense. Let $(B, E, S, 0)$ be any model of the given postulate-set; we shall construct an algebraic system from this structure. First, we partition B, using the equivalence relation E; the resulting set of subsets of B is denoted by "B/E". Suppose that x is any member of B; it is useful to denote the member of B/E which contains x by "$[x]$". We want to introduce a binary operator on B/E, which we shall denote by "$+$", which is defined as follows: $[x] + [y]$ is $[z]$ iff $(x, y, z) \in S$. Since E is substitutive in S, it follows that $[a] + [b]$ is $[z]$ whenever $a \in [x]$ and $b \in [y]$; thus, our rule associates a unique member of B/E with a given ordered pair of members of B/E. In other words, $+$ is a binary operator on B/E. Finally, we note that $0 \in [0]$. We have now constructed the algebraic system

$$(B/E, +, [0])$$

from the given structure $(B, E, S, 0)$. In view of the seven postulates listed above, there is no difficulty in establishing that $(B/E, +, [0])$ is a group in the sense of page 90.

It is clear from this example that the essential notion of an operator can be characterized by a relation together with a substitutive equivalence relation. Indeed, the family of structures characterized by a given postulate-set carries with it, in the manner described above, the corresponding family of algebraic systems obtained by replacing relations by the operators they represent. Without doubt this notion of representing an operator by a relation and introducing a substitutive equivalence relation is a complication in the *mathematical* theory; however, it enables us to develop the *logical* theory in a simple and straight-forward manner; otherwise the fundamental processes of our theory of deduction would be greatly complicated.

We are now in a position to explain just why the technical notion of a "proof" is given this particular name. Let K be any consistent set of wff, and consider the mathematical theory characterized by K. We wish to demonstrate that the wff A is a theorem of this mathematical theory. In view of Statement II on page 198, it is enough to show that $K \vdash A$. Assume we have done this. Then we have found a finite subset of K, say $\{A_1, A_2, \ldots, A_n\}$, such that $\vdash A_1 \wedge A_2 \wedge \ldots \wedge A_n \rightarrow A$. In other words, we have found a "proof" of the wff $A_1 \wedge A_2 \wedge \ldots \wedge A_n \rightarrow A$. But in the usual mathematical sense of the word, our "proof" is a proof that A is a theorem! Thus, the mathematical object that we have called a "proof"—a finite sequence of wff—is itself a proof of a mathematical theorem.

Here is another important consequence of the extended completeness theorem. Consider a mathematical theory that is characterized by an *infinite* postulate-set, K. Let T be any theorem of this mathematical theory. Then $K \vdash T$. Therefore, there is a *finite* subset of K, say $\{A_1, A_2, \ldots, A_n\}$, such that $\{A_1, A_2, \ldots, A_n\} \vdash T$. Hence, by Statement II, μT holds in $\mathcal{S}$ whenever $\mathcal{S}$ is a model of $\{A_1, A_2, \ldots, A_n\}$ under μ. In other words, T is a theorem of the mathematical theory described by the postulate-set $\{A_1, A_2, \ldots, A_n\}$. Here we have a genuine mathematical result. To illustrate, observe that the notion of a field is easily characterized by a postulate-set within our language; furthermore, it is easy to express the idea of a field that has characteristic p, where p is prime. (This means that p a's added together produce the additive identity, whenever a is a member of the basic set of the field.) A field is said to have characteristic zero iff the field does not have characteristic 2, does not have characteristic 3, does not have characteristic 5, and in general, does not have characteristic p, given that p is prime. Thus, the notion of a field of characteristic zero is characterized by an infinite postulate-set. Suppose that A is true in each field of characteristic zero; then by our result, A is a consequence of a postulate-set that contains only a finite number of statements asserting that the field does not have characteristic p, for various prime numbers p. Therefore, there is a largest prime number, say q, that occurs in this postulate-set. Hence, each field with characteristic greater than q is a model of our postulate-set. Since A is a consequence of this postulate-set, we conclude that A is true in each field of characteristic greater than q. Summarizing, we see that if A is true in each field of characteristic zero, then A is true in each field of characteristic greater than q, where q is a prime number which depends upon the wff A.

In the same way, it is easy to see that the concept of an algebraically closed field, i.e., a field in which each polynomial possesses a zero, is characterized by an infinite postulate-set. Therefore, by our result, if B is true in each algebraically closed field, then B is true in any field such that each polynomial of degree less than m possesses a zero where m is a natural number which depends upon the wff B.

Here is another consequence of the extended completeness theorem of a quite different type.

THE SKOLEM-LÖWENHEIM THEOREM: If K is a set of wff that possesses a model, then there is a model of K whose basic set is denumerable.

Demonstration: Since K possesses a model, K is consistent. Now consider the predicate calculus C_ω involved in the proof of the extended completeness theorem. Clearly, the set of individuals of C_ω is denumerable; but this set is the basic set of the model of K constructed on page 203. Thus, there is a model of K whose basic set is denumerable.

The Skolem-Löwenheim theorem is of interest, because it tells us that we cannot hope to axiomatize the notion of a finite cardinal number or a non-denumerable cardinal number within our predicate calculus.

In the proof of the extended completeness theorem, we considered a predicate calculus whose set of individuals is denumerable. Though this assumption made life a little easier, it is not essential to the demonstration.

The extended completeness theorem can be established by a parallel proof, in case the predicate calculus C_1 has a basic set with cardinal $\aleph$, $\aleph \geq \aleph_0$. Notice that C_ω also has a basic set with cardinal $\aleph$. This observation permits us to extend the Skolem-Löwenheim theorem as follows.

THEOREM: Let C be any predicate calculus whose set of individuals has transfinite cardinal $\aleph$, and suppose that K is a set of wff of C that possesses a model. Then there is a model of K whose basic set has cardinal $\aleph$.

The purpose of this section has been to show how the extended completeness theorem acts as a bridge connecting mathematical logic and abstract algebra. Of course, the "iff" in the theorem means that our bridge is a two-way bridge. In particular, given a wff A and a consistent set K, we can establish that $K \vdash A$ by showing, with purely mathematical arguments, that μA holds in $\mathcal{S}$ whenever $\mathcal{S}$ is a model of K under μ such that A is defined in $\mathcal{S}$ under μ.

For example, consider the wff

$$A = \forall \mathbf{x} \forall \mathbf{y} \forall \mathbf{z} \forall \mathbf{t} \forall \mathbf{u} \forall \mathbf{v} \forall \mathbf{w}(\mathbf{Sxyt} \wedge \mathbf{Stzu} \wedge \mathbf{Syzv} \wedge \mathbf{Sxvw} \rightarrow \mathbf{Euw})$$

and the postulate-set of the theory of groups presented on page 209. Let $\mathcal{S}$ be any model under μ of the postulate-set. It is easy to see that the swff μA holds in $\mathcal{S}$. Therefore, by Statement II, the wff A is a consequence of the postulate-set.

6. Algebraic Structures *

We have observed that we cannot within our predicate calculus characterize a family of structures whose basic sets are equi-numerous. Nonetheless, it is highly important that we be able to speak, in some sense, about the cardinal number of a structure. The answer to the dilemma forced on us by the Skolem-Löwenheim theorem is obvious once we recall that we introduced the notion of a structure in order to simplify our theory of deduction. The fundamental mathematical concept is the algebraic system; each algebraic system is represented by a structure that involves a substitutive equivalence relation. The basic set of the algebraic system is obtained from the basic set of the structure by partitioning, using the given equivalence relation.

The point should now be clear. The Skolem-Löwenheim theorem refers to structures, but we are really interested in the corresponding algebraic systems. For this reason, let us consider the special kind of structure that involves a substitutive equivalence relation, say E; following A. Robinson's terminology, we shall call a structure that has this property, an *algebraic structure*.

DEFINITION: A structure, say $\mathcal{S}$, is said to be an *algebraic structure* iff $\mathcal{S}$ involves a binary relation E such that the following swff hold in $\mathcal{S}$:
(1) $\forall x(Exx)$
(2) $\forall x \forall y \forall z(Exy \land Eyz \to Ezx)$
(3) $\forall x_1 \forall x_2 \ldots \forall x_n \forall y_1 \forall y_2 \ldots \forall y_n(Rx_1x_2 \ldots x_n \land Ex_1y_1 \land Ex_2y_2 \land \ldots \land Ex_ny_n \to Ry_1y_2 \ldots y_n)$ whenever R is an n^{ary} relation of $\mathcal{S}$.

We have observed that each algebraic structure $\mathcal{S}$ with basic set B and substitutive equivalence relation E gives rise to a corresponding algebraic system whose basic set is B/E. In a very real sense, the algebraic structure $\mathcal{S}$ is illusory, since it is the algebraic system constructed from $\mathcal{S}$ that concerns us. For this reason, by the cardinal number of the algebraic structure $\mathcal{S}$, we shall mean the cardinal number of the set B/E.

DEFINITION: Let $\mathcal{S}$ be an algebraic structure with basic set B and substitutive equivalence relation E. Then by *the cardinal number of* $\mathcal{S}$, we shall mean the cardinal number of B/E.

For example, consider the algebraic structure (B, E, S) where B is the set of integers, E is a binary relation on B such that $(a, b) \in B$ iff a and b are both even or both odd, and S is a ternary relation on B such that $(a, b, c) \in S$ iff $a + b$ and c are both even or both odd. Clearly, E is an equivalence relation on B; furthermore, if $(a, b, c) \in S$, $(a, d) \in E$, $(b, e) \in E$, and $(c, f) \in E$, then $(d, e, f) \in E$; that is, E is substitutive in S. Hence, E is a substitutive equivalence relation on B. Finally, we note that B/E consists of two subsets of B: one subset contains the even integers, and the other contains the odd integers. Therefore, 2 is the cardinal number of the algebraic structure (B, E, S).

Making use of this idea, we note that the concept of a group with exactly two members is characterized by adjoining to the seven wff listed on page 209 the wff.

8. $\exists \mathbf{x} \exists \mathbf{y} \forall \mathbf{z}(\sim \mathbf{Exy} \dot{\land} \mathbf{Exz} \lor \mathbf{Eyz})$

Replacing this wff by $\exists \mathbf{x} \exists \mathbf{y}(\sim \mathbf{Exy})$, we obtain the notion of a group with at least two members.

Though we have succeeded in characterizing a family of algebraic structures each of which has cardinal n, where n is finite, it turns out that transfinite cardinals have eluded us. Consider the following

THEOREM 18: Let K be a set of wff involving at most m free individuals, such that an algebraic structure with transfinite cardinal is a model of K. Then there is an algebraic structure with cardinal $\aleph$, which is a model of K whenever $\aleph$ is transfinite and $\aleph \geq m$.

Demonstration: Let $\aleph$ be any transfinite cardinal such that $\aleph \geq m$. We shall construct an algebraic structure with cardinal $\aleph$, which is a model of K, by applying the method of Henkin's proof of the extended completeness

theorem. Let K_1 denote the set obtained by adjoining to K the following wff:
(1) $\forall \mathbf{x}(\mathbf{Exx})$
(2) $\forall \mathbf{x} \forall \mathbf{y} \forall \mathbf{z}(\mathbf{Exy} \wedge \mathbf{Eyz} \rightarrow \mathbf{Ezx})$
(3) $\forall \mathbf{x}_1 \forall \mathbf{x}_2 \ldots \forall \mathbf{x}_n \forall \mathbf{y}_1 \forall \mathbf{y}_2 \ldots \forall \mathbf{y}_n(\mathbf{Rx}_1\mathbf{x}_2 \ldots \mathbf{x}_n \wedge \mathbf{Ex}_1\mathbf{y}_1 \wedge \mathbf{Ex}_2\mathbf{y}_2 \wedge \ldots \wedge \mathbf{Ex}_n\mathbf{y}_n \rightarrow \mathbf{Ry}_1\mathbf{y}_2 \ldots \mathbf{y}_n)$ whenever n is a natural number and R is a predicate of order n which occurs in K.

Since K possesses a model which is an algebraic system, we see that K_1 possesses the same model, and so is consistent.

Next, let M be a set with cardinal $\aleph$ and such that no symbol of the predicate calculus is a member of M. Now consider the predicate calculus obtained from the given predicate calculus by adjoining the members of M to the set of individuals. Then K_1 is consistent in the resulting predicate calculus. Let us show that the set of wff

$$K_2 = K_1 \cup \{\sim \mathbf{E}\alpha\beta \mid \alpha \in M \text{ and } \beta \in M - \{\alpha\}\}$$

is also consistent in our enlarged predicate calculus. But K_2 is consistent iff each finite subset of K_2 is consistent. Since K_1 possesses an infinite model, it follows that each finite subset of K_2 possesses a model—the same model. Therefore, K_2 is consistent.

Now consider the model of K_2 obtained by carrying out Henkin's method. Since there are at most m free individuals occurring in K, and since $m \leq \aleph$, we see that K_2 involves exactly $\aleph$ free individuals. Therefore, in carrying out Henkin's method, we may restrict ourselves to a family of predicate calculi involving exactly $\aleph$ individuals. Hence, the model of K_2 that results possesses a basic set with exactly $\aleph$ members, and so the cardinal number of this algebraic structure is at most $\aleph$. But this algebraic structure is a model of $\{\sim \mathbf{E}\alpha\beta \mid \alpha \in M \text{ and } \beta \in M - \{\alpha\}\}$; therefore, the cardinal of this algebraic structure is not less than $\aleph$. We conclude that our model of K has cardinal $\aleph$. This establishes our theorem.

Notice that there is no restriction on the cardinal number m involved in Theorem 18; m may be either a finite cardinal number or a transfinite cardinal number.

Clearly, Theorem 18 asserts the impossibility of characterizing a family of algebraic structures each of which has the same transfinite cardinal number. Furthermore, Theorem 18 tells us there is no consistent set of wff whose only model is the real number system; indeed, there is no consistent set of wff whose only model is the natural number system.

The following corollary to Theorem 18 is useful:

COROLLARY: Let K be a set of wff with cardinal m such that an algebraic structure with transfinite cardinal is a model of K. Then there is an algebraic structure with cardinal $\aleph$ which is a model of K whenever $\aleph$ is transfinite and $\aleph \geq m$.

EXERCISES

1. (a) Characterize the concept of a semi-group, using a set of wff that involves a predicate of order two, say **E**, and a predicate of order three, say **S**.
(b) Show that the structure (B, E, S) is a model of your set of wff under the identity mapping, where $B = \{a, b\}$, $E = \{(a, a), (b, b)\}$

and $$S = \{(a, a, a), (a, b, a), (b, a, a), (b, b, b)\}.$$

(c) Show that the structure (B, E, S) is a model of your set of wff under the identity mapping, where

$$B = \{a, b, c\}$$

$$E = \{(a, a), (b, b), (c, c), (b, c), (c, b)\}$$

and

$$S = \{(a, a, a), (a, b, a), (a, c, a), (b, a, a), (b, b, b), (b, c, b), (c, a, a), (c, b, b), (c, c, b), (c, b, c), (b, b, c), (b, c, c), (c, c, c)\}.$$

(d) By partitioning the basic set of the structure of (c) using the equivalence relation of that structure and then constructing the binary operator represented by the relations E and S of the given structure, construct an algebraic system that involves a basic set and a binary operator on that set. Show that this algebraic system is a semi-group.

2. (a) Characterize the notion of a field, using a set of wff that involves a predicate of order two, say **E**, two predicates of order three, say **S** and **P**, and two free individuals, say **0** and **1**.
(b) Show that the structure $(B, E, S, P, 0, 1)$ is a model of your set of wff under the identity mapping, where

$$B = \{0, 1\},$$
$$E = \{(0, 0), (1, 1)\},$$
$$S = \{(0, 0, 0), (0, 1, 1), (1, 0, 1), (1, 1, 0)\},$$
and $$P = \{(0, 0, 0), (0, 1, 0), (1, 0, 0), (1, 1, 1)\}.$$

(c) By applying the method of the text, construct an algebraic system from the structure of (b); show that this algebraic system is a field. What is the cardinal number of the given structure?
(d) Show that the notion of a field with characteristic two is characterized by adjoining the wff **∀x(Sxx0)** to the set of (a).

(e) Show that the notion of a field with characteristic three is characterized by adjoining the wff **∀x∀y(Sxxy → Sxy0)** to the set of (a).
(f) Characterize the notion of a field with characteristic five.
(g) Characterize the notion of a field with characteristic zero.
(h) Show that **∀x(Sxxx → Ex0)** is a consequence of the set of (a).

3. Characterize the notion of an ordered field.

4. Characterize the notion of a Boolean Algebra.

5. By a *loop* one means any algebraic system, say $(B, +, 0)$ where $+$ is a binary operator on B and $0 \in B$ such that $\forall x(x + 0 = 0 + x = x)$ and the equation $x + y = z$ has a unique solution given any two of x, y, and z. Characterize the concept of a loop within the predicate calculus.

6. Let K denote the set of wff characterizing a group displayed on page 209. Show that
(a) $K \vdash$ **∀x∀v∀u∀w(Sxvu ∧ Sxvw → Euw)**
(b) $K \vdash$ **∀x∀y∀z∀t∀u∀v∀w(Sxyt ∧ Stzu ∧ Syzv ∧ Sxvw → Euw)**

7. Let K be a set of wff that characterizes the concept of a field in terms of predicates **E**, **S**, and **P**.
(a) Show that the concept of a field in which each polynomial of degree two has a zero is characterized by adjoining to K the wff

∀a∀b∀c∃x∃y∃t∃u∃v(Pxxy ∧ Payt ∧ Pbxu ∧ Stuv → Svc0)

(b) Characterize the concept of a field in which each polynomial of degree three has a zero.
(c) Characterize the concept of an algebraically closed field.

8. An ordered field such that
(1) each polynomial of odd degree possesses a zero
(2) the polynomial of degree two, $x^2 + a$, possesses a zero whenever $a < 0$
is said to be a *real-closed* ordered field.

Characterize the concept of a real-closed ordered field within the predicate calculus.

9. (a) Characterize the concept of an Abelian group.
(b) Characterize the concept of an Abelian group whose basic set contains at least two members.
(c) An Abelian group is said to be *torsion-free* iff the result of adding x to itself any finite number of times is different from the additive identity, provided that x is not the additive identity. Characterize the notion of a torsion-free Abelian group.
(d) An Abelian group is said to be *completely divisible* iff given x and

any natural number, say n, y exists such that

$$x = \underbrace{y + y + \ldots + y}_{\text{ny's}}.$$

Characterize this concept within the predicate calculus.

10. Let K be a set of wff such that given any natural number n, there is an algebraic structure with cardinal at least n, which is a model of K. Prove that K possesses a model which is an algebraic structure and whose cardinal is transfinite.

7. The Diagram of a Structure*

We have seen (see page 203) that a model of a set K of wff can be constructed from the atomic wff of K provided that K is maximal-consistent and $\exists$-Complete. Consider the related problem: given a structure $\mathcal{S}$, characterize the set of all swff that hold in $\mathcal{S}$. The important concept that helps us with this problem is the notion of the *Diagram* of a structure, an idea due to A. Robinson (ref. 4). To simplify our notation, we shall assume that the symbols of the predicate calculus have been chosen as follows: The set of individuals of the predicate calculus is the basic set of the given structure, and the predicates of the predicate calculus are the relations that occur in the given structure. This means there is no longer any distinction between wff and swff; in particular, we may speak of a wff holding in $\mathcal{S}$.

We now define the diagram of $\mathcal{S}$. This is a set of wff, which is denoted by "D", such that $A \in D$ iff A holds in $\mathcal{S}$, and either A is atomic or else $A = \sim B$ and B is atomic.

Our problem is to characterize, within the predicate calculus, the set of all wff that hold in $\mathcal{S}$. Consider the following theorem.

THEOREM 19: $\{A \mid A \text{ holds in } \mathcal{S}\}$ is maximal-consistent and $\exists$-Complete.

Demonstration: If $B \overline{\in} \{A \mid A \text{ holds in } \mathcal{S}\}$, then $\sim B \in \{A \mid A \text{ holds in } \mathcal{S}\}$; hence, $\{A \mid A \text{ holds in } \mathcal{S}\} \cup \{B\}$ is contradictory. But $\{A \mid A \text{ holds in } \mathcal{S}\}$ is consistent, by the extended completeness theorem; therefore, $\{A \mid A \text{ holds in } \mathcal{S}\}$ is maximal-consistent.

Now suppose that $\exists tC \in \{A \mid A \text{ holds in } \mathcal{S}\}$. But $\exists tC$ holds in $\mathcal{S}$ iff there is a member of the basic set of $\mathcal{S}$, say a, such that $S_t^a C$ holds in $\mathcal{S}$. Hence, $S_t^a C \in \{A \mid A \text{ holds in } \mathcal{S}\}$. Thus, $\{A \mid A \text{ holds in } \mathcal{S}\}$ is $\exists$-Complete.

We now display the connection between the diagram of $\mathcal{S}$ and the set of all wff that hold in $\mathcal{S}$.

THEOREM 20: Let K be any super-set of D, within the given predicate calculus, which is both maximal-consistent and $\exists$-Complete. Then A holds in $\mathcal{S}$ iff $A \in K$.

Demonstration: Apply Theorem 13, page 203.

COROLLARY: Within the given predicate calculus, there is exactly one super-set of D which is both maximal-consistent and $\exists$-Complete.

THEOREM 21: $\{A \mid A \text{ holds in } \mathcal{S}\}$ is *the* maximal-consistent super-set of D that is also $\exists$-Complete.

In general, it is not necessarily the case that each wff that holds in $\mathcal{S}$ is a consequence of D, the diagram of $\mathcal{S}$. However we shall show that wff which hold in $\mathcal{S}$ and possess a special form are necessarily consequences of D.

THEOREM 22: $D \vdash A$ whenever A is quantifier-free and A holds in $\mathcal{S}$.

Demonstration: Assuming that there is a quantifier-free wff which holds in $\mathcal{S}$ and is not a consequence of D, let A be the shortest such wff. It is easy to see that A is not atomic, and that A does not have length one; i.e., A is neither $\sim B$ nor $B \vee C$, where B is atomic and C is atomic. Consider the main connective of A.

(1) Suppose that $A = \sim B$. Since B is not atomic, there are two possibilities:
   (a) $A = \sim(\sim C)$; then C holds in $\mathcal{S}$ and so $D \vdash C$, since C is shorter than A. Hence, $D \vdash A$.
   (b) $A = \sim(E \vee F)$; then $E \vee F$ does not hold in $\mathcal{S}$. Thus, $\sim E$ holds in $\mathcal{S}$, and $\sim F$ holds in $\mathcal{S}$. It follows that $D \vdash \sim E$ and $D \vdash \sim F$; therefore, $D \vdash \sim E \wedge \sim F$, and so $D \vdash A$.

(2) Suppose that $A = B \vee C$. Then B holds in $\mathcal{S}$ or C holds in $\mathcal{S}$. If the former is true, then $D \vdash B$; if the latter, $D \vdash C$. In either case, $D \vdash B \vee C$; i.e., $D \vdash A$. This establishes the Theorem.

THEOREM 23: $D \vdash A$ whenever A is in prenex normal form, $\forall$ does not appear in the prefix of A, and A holds in $\mathcal{S}$.

Demonstration: If it is assumed that there is a wff possessing the stated properties which is not a consequence of D, then there is a "shortest" such wff (i.e., the length of its prefix is minimum), say A. We denote A by "$\exists tB$". Since $\exists tB$ holds in $\mathcal{S}$, there is an individual, say a, such that $S_t^a B$ holds in $\mathcal{S}$. Either $S_t^a B$ is quantifier-free, or $S_t^a B$ is in prenex normal form. In the former case, $D \vdash S_t^a B$ by Theorem 22. In the latter case, $\forall$ does not appear in the prefix of $S_t^a B$, and the prefix of $S_t^a B$ is shorter than the prefix of $\exists tB$; therefore, $D \vdash S_t^a B$ by assumption. Hence, in either case, $D \vdash S_t^a B$. But $\vdash S_t^a B \to \exists tB$; thus, $D \vdash \exists tB$. This establishes the theorem.

It is vital that we extend the scope of Theorems 22 and 23. We shall achieve this by constructing the structure involved from the symbols of a given predicate calculus, rather than constructing a predicate calculus from a given structure. Consider a predicate calculus such that the cardinal number of its set of individuals is transfinite; our purpose is to select a set of wff of the given predicate calculus, which we shall use to construct our structure $\mathcal{S}$. Consider the following definition.

DEFINITION: We shall say that a set of wff, say D, is *diagrammatic* provided that

(1) D is non-empty
(2) if $A \in D$, then either A is atomic or else $A = \sim B$, and B is atomic
(3) let R be a predicate which occurs in D, and suppose that R has order n; then either $Rt_1t_2 \ldots t_n \in D$, or else $\sim Rt_1t_2 \ldots t_n \in D$—whenever $t_1, t_2, \ldots, t_n$ are individuals occurring in D.

For example, each of the following sets is diagrammatic:

$\{\mathbf{Fx}\}$, $\{\mathbf{Fy}, \sim \mathbf{Fz}\}$, $\{\mathbf{Gxx}, \mathbf{Gxy}, \sim \mathbf{Gyx}, \sim \mathbf{Gyy}\}$

$\{\mathbf{Fx}, \sim \mathbf{Fy}, \sim \mathbf{Gxx}, \sim \mathbf{Gxy}, \mathbf{Gyx}, \mathbf{Gyy}\}$

$\{\mathbf{G}st \mid s \text{ is an individual and } t \text{ is an individual}\}$

$\{\mathbf{G}st \mid s \text{ and } t \text{ are distinct individuals}\} \cup \{\sim \mathbf{G}ss \mid s \text{ is an individual}\}$

Notice that a diagrammatic set D involves a set of individuals, say S, and a set of predicates such that $A \in D$ iff there is a predicate in the given set, say R of order n, and an ordered n^{tuple} of members of S, say $(t_1, t_2, \ldots, t_n)$, such that either $A = Rt_1t_2 \ldots t_n$ or else $A = \sim Rt_1t_2 \ldots t_n$.

Given a diagrammatic set D, it is easy to construct a structure $\mathcal{S}$ from the symbols appearing in D by following the procedure on page 200. This means that the basic set of $\mathcal{S}$ consists of the individuals that occur in D; furthermore, let n be any natural number and let R be any predicate of order n that occurs in D, then $\{(t_1, t_2, \ldots, t_n) \mid Rt_1t_2 \ldots t_n \in D\}$ is an n^{ary} relation of $\mathcal{S}$. Finally, each member of the basic set of $\mathcal{S}$ is displayed as a term of the structure.

Thus, each diagrammatic set of wff describes a structure in a natural way.

Now that we have constructed $\mathcal{S}$ from the given diagrammatic set D, let us consider the diagram of $\mathcal{S}$. This means that we must first construct a predicate calculus from the symbols of $\mathcal{S}$. Clearly, the resulting predicate calculus is contained within the given predicate calculus; furthermore, the diagram of $\mathcal{S}$, as is easily seen, is D, the given diagrammatic set. This comment, together with Theorems 22 and 23, establishes the following extension of Theorems 22 and 23.

THEOREM 24: Let D be any diagrammatic set; then $D \vdash A$ whenever A is quantifier-free and the swff A holds in $\mathcal{S}$, the structure constructed from D.

THEOREM 25: Let D be any diagrammatic set; then $D \vdash A$ whenever A is in prenex normal form, $\forall$ does not appear in the prefix of A, and the swff A holds in $\mathcal{S}$ the structure constructed from D.

We shall now establish a result that we shall find useful in the Appendix.

THEOREM 26: Let D be any diagrammatic set, and let $\mathcal{S}$ be the structure constructed from D. Suppose there is a wff A defined in $\mathcal{S}$ under the identity mapping such that neither $D \vdash A$ nor $D \vdash \sim A$. Then, there is a wff in prenex normal form, say C, and an individual t free in C, such that C is defined in $\mathcal{S}$ under the identity mapping, and neither $D \vdash \exists tC$ nor $D \vdash \sim \exists tC$; furthermore, the swff $\exists tC$ does not hold in $\mathcal{S}$.

Demonstration: Consider the given wff A; since A is defined in $\mathcal{S}$ under the identity mapping, either A holds in $\mathcal{S}$, or else $\sim A$ holds in $\mathcal{S}$. We may as well assume that the swff A holds in $\mathcal{S}$. If A is quantifier-free, then $D \vdash A$ by Theorem 24; hence, A is not quantifier-free. We may assume, then, that A is in prenex normal form (see page 192); furthermore, by Theorem 25, the prefix of A involves both $\forall$ and "$\exists$". It follows that there is a wff defined in $\mathcal{S}$ under the identity mapping which has the form $\exists tC$ and is such that neither $D \vdash \exists tC$ nor $D \vdash \sim \exists tC$. We may also assume there is no wff that possesses these properties and has a shorter prefix than has $\exists tC$.

We want to show that the swff $\exists tC$ does not hold in $\mathcal{S}$. Assume, for the moment, that $\exists tC$ holds in $\mathcal{S}$; then there is an individual a such that $S_t^a C$ holds in $\mathcal{S}$. But $S_t^a C$ is in prenex normal form, has a shorter prefix than $\exists tC$, and is defined in $\mathcal{S}$ under the identity mapping. Therefore, $D \vdash S_t^a C$ or $D \vdash \sim S_t^a C$. Since $S_t^a C$ holds in $\mathcal{S}$, a model of D under the identity mapping, it follows that $D \vdash S_t^a C$. But $\vdash S_t^a C \rightarrow \exists tC$. We conclude that $D \vdash \exists tC$, which is a contradiction. Therefore, the swff $\exists tC$ does not hold in $\mathcal{S}$. This establishes our theorem.

Appendix

*Complete theories**

1. Introduction

The purpose of this appendix is to indicate the power of the results obtained so far in this book. In particular, we wish to make clear the impact on mathematics of the two-way bridge linking abstract algebra and mathematical logic, described in Chapter 6.

One of the properties of a maximal-consistent set of wff, say T, is that $T \vdash A$ or else $T \vdash \sim A$ whenever A is a wff. It turns out that there are important mathematical theories that possess a similar property. Let K be a set of wff such that $K \vdash A$ or else $K \vdash \sim A$ whenever A is a wff *defined* in K; i.e., each predicate of A occurs in a wff of K, and each free individual of A is also free in a wff of K; then we shall say that K is *complete*.

DEFINITION: K is *complete* iff $K \vdash A$ or else $K \vdash \sim A$ whenever A is defined in K.

For example, consider a set of wff K which characterizes the concept of an algebraically closed field of fixed characteristic. In Section 2 we shall prove that this set is complete. This result is significant for the following reason. Suppose that by a purely mathematical argument, we are able to demonstrate that a certain swff, say A, holds in a particular model of K; i.e., the swff A holds in a certain algebraically closed field which possesses the stated characteristic. Since K is complete and the wff A is defined in K, either $K \vdash A$ or else $K \vdash \sim A$. If the latter, then the swff $\sim A$ holds in each model of K. But A holds in one model of K; therefore, $\sim A$ is not a consequence of K, and so $K \vdash A$. Hence, by II, the swff A holds in each algebraically closed field possessing the stated characteristic.

Notice that the mathematical result (that A holds in a particular algebraically closed field possessing the stated characteristic) is used to demonstrate that the wff A is a consequence of K, a result within our theory of deduction. In turn, this purely logical result is used to obtain a purely mathematical result, which in fact is a generalization of the original mathematical result—namely, A holds in *each* algebraically closed field that possesses the stated characteristic.

2. Vaught's Test

In this section we shall demonstrate, once again, the power of our extended completeness theorem and its consequences. Our purpose is to establish an easily-applied test for determining that a given set of wff is complete. This test was developed by R. L. Vaught and presented to the world in a 1954 research paper*.

VAUGHT'S TEST: K is complete if
(1) K possesses a model
(2) each model of K is an algebraic structure with transfinite cardinal
(3) there is a transfinite cardinal, say $\aleph$, such that $\aleph \geq \bar{\bar{K}}$ and any two algebraic structures with cardinal $\aleph$ which are models of K, are isomorphic,
(4) given an algebraic structure $\mathcal{S}$ and two mappings μ_1 and μ_2 such that $\mathcal{S}$ is a model of K under both μ_1 and μ_2, then $\mu_1 F$ is $\mu_2 F$ whenever F is a predicate appearing in K, and $(\mu_1 t, \mu_2 t) \in E$ whenever t is a free individual of K, where E is the substitutive equivalence relation of $\mathcal{S}$.

Demonstration: Let K be a set of wff satisfying the four conditions of Vaught's test; suppose that K is *not* complete. Then there is a wff, say A, which is defined in K and such that neither $K \vdash A$ nor $K \vdash \sim A$. Then $K \cup \{\sim A\}$ is consistent and $K \cup \{A\}$ is consistent. By the extended completeness theorem, each of these sets possesses a model; let $\mathcal{M}_1$ be a model of $K \cup \{\sim A\}$, and let $\mathcal{M}_2$ be a model of $K \cup \{A\}$. Since $\mathcal{M}_1$ and $\mathcal{M}_2$ are models of K, it follows from (2) that $\mathcal{M}_1$ and $\mathcal{M}_2$ are algebraic structures with transfinite cardinal. Let $\aleph$ be a cardinal which possesses the properties stated in (3); then by the Corollary to Theorem 18, page 215, there are algebraic structures $\mathcal{S}_1$ and $\mathcal{S}_2$ each with cardinal $\aleph$, such that $\mathcal{S}_1$ is a model of $K \cup \{\sim A\}$, and $\mathcal{S}_2$ is a model of $K \cup \{A\}$. (Note that $\bar{\bar{K}} + 1 \leq \aleph$, since $\aleph$ is transfinite.)

Therefore, by (3), $\mathcal{S}_1$ and $\mathcal{S}_2$ are isomorphic; i.e., there is a one-one mapping λ of the basic set of $\mathcal{S}_1$ onto the basic set of $\mathcal{S}_2$ such that $\lambda\mathcal{S}_1$ is $\mathcal{S}_2$. In other words, $\mathcal{S}_1$ and $\mathcal{S}_2$ are algebraically the same. It follows from this

* R. L. Vaught: "Applications of the Löwenheim-Skolem-Tarski theorem to problems of completeness and decidability", Indagationes Math. **16,** 1954, pp. 467–472.

that $\mathcal{S}_1$ is a model of both $K \cup \{\sim A\}$ and $K \cup \{A\}$. Since $\mathcal{S}_1$ is a model of K, it follows from (4) that there is essentially (i.e., within the given equivalence relation of $\mathcal{S}_1$) only one mapping, say μ, such that $\mathcal{S}_1$ is a model of K under μ. Therefore, $\mathcal{S}_1$ is a model of $K \cup \{\sim A\}$ under μ, and $\mathcal{S}_1$ is a model of $K \cup \{A\}$ under μ. In particular, this means that the swff $\mu(\sim A)$ holds in $\mathcal{S}_1$, and the swff μA holds in $\mathcal{S}_1$. This is impossible! Therefore, our initial assumption that K is not complete is false; we conclude that K *is* complete. This establishes Vaught's test.

Now that we have established this important test, it is time to look at it from a general point of view. Vaught's test asserts that a mathematical theory is complete provided that certain algebraic conditions are satisfied. We say the conditions of the test are *algebraic* because they refer directly to the models of the theory. Thus, by demonstrating that a given theory possesses the algebraic properties mentioned in Vaught's test, one in fact has established the completeness of the theory. Here, then, is a striking example of the powerful methods that result from the fusion of two distinct disciplines.

To illustrate the application of Vaught's test, let us establish our assertion of Section 1—that the postulate-set characterizing the theory of algebraically closed fields with fixed characteristic, is complete. Denoting the usual postulate-set for this theory by "K", let us show that the conditions of the test are fulfilled. Clearly, there exists an algebraically closed field with characteristic p, whenever p is a prime number or zero. Thus, K possesses a model. Second, it is easy to see that no algebraically closed field is finite; in fact, a field in which each polynomial of degree two possesses a zero, of necessity is infinite. Referring to (3), let $\aleph$ be any non-countable transfinite cardinal; since $\bar{\bar{K}} = \aleph_0$, we see that $\aleph \geq K$. But Steinitz* has shown that two algebraically closed fields are isomorphic if they possess the same characteristic and the same degree of transcendence over their prime field. Since the degree of transcendence of a non-countable field over its prime field is the cardinal number of the field, it follows that any two algebraically closed fields which possess the same characteristic and have cardinal $\aleph$ also have the same degree of transcendence over their prime field and so are isomorphic. This establishes (3). Finally, we point out that the postulate-set for the concept of a field has property (4). The conditions of Vaught's test have been satisfied, so K is complete.

Notice that by purely algebraic observations we have established the important logical result: The postulate-set characterizing the theory of algebraically closed fields with fixed characteristic is complete.

* E. Steinitz: "Algebraische Theorie der Körper," Journal für reine und angewandte Mathematik, **137,** 1910, pp. 167–309.

3. On Simplifying the Concept of a Model

Our notion of a diagrammatic set enables us to express the important concept of a *model* of a consistent set of wff within the language of the predicate calculus. First, recalling Henkin's proof of the extended completeness theorem, let us say that a predicate calculus, say C', is an *extension* of a predicate calculus, say C, iff C and C' involve the same predicates, and each individual of C is also an individual of C'.

Henkin's proof points out that, given a consistent set of wff, say K, there is a structure $\mathcal{S}$ such that $\mathcal{S}$ is a model of K under the identity mapping, and the diagram of $\mathcal{S}$ is a set of wff within an extension of the given predicate calculus. For this reason we may restrict the notion of a model of a non-empty set of wff by restricting the mapping involved to the identity mapping. But any such structure is characterized by its diagram; therefore, the notion of a model of a non-empty set of wff can be characterized within the language of the predicate calculus. Let K denote any non-empty set of wff.

DEFINITION: We shall say that *D is a model of K* iff there is an extension of the given predicate calculus in which D is diagrammatic, and the structure constructed from D is a model of K under the identity mapping.

For example, $\{\mathbf{Fy}\}$ is a model of the set $\{\forall \mathbf{yFy}, \exists \mathbf{zFz}\}$. Here, the extension of the predicate calculus is the given predicate calculus; clearly, $\{\mathbf{Fy}\}$ is diagrammatic, and the structure constructed from $\{\mathbf{Fy}\}$ is $(\{\mathbf{y}\}, \{\mathbf{y}\})$. Again, let "$I$" denote the set of individuals of a predicate calculus, and suppose that $\mathbf{a}$ is a symbol that does not occur in the given predicate calculus; then the diagrammatic set

$$\{\mathbf{F}t \mid t \in I\} \cup \{\sim \mathbf{Fa}\}$$

is a model of the set of wff

$$\{\mathbf{F}t \mid t \in I\} \cup \{\exists \mathbf{y}(\sim \mathbf{Fy})\}$$

Here, the extension of the given predicate calculus is constructed by adjoining $\mathbf{a}$ to the set of individuals I of the given predicate calculus. The structure constructed from the above diagrammatic set has basic set $I \cup \{\mathbf{a}\}$, and one unary operator on $I \cup \{\mathbf{a}\}$—namely, I; furthermore, each member of I is displayed.

The preceding observations regarding Henkin's proof of the extended completeness theorem enable us to establish an important simplification of this theorem, which we shall make use of subsequently.

THEOREM 1: K is consistent iff K possesses a model (in the sense of the preceding definition).

The following theorems are easily established. Let "D" denote any diagrammatic set, and suppose that the wff A and B are defined in D; then

THEOREM 2: D is a model of D.

THEOREM 3: D is a model of $\{\sim A\}$ iff D is not a model of $\{A\}$.

THEOREM 4: D is a model of $\{A \vee B\}$ iff D is a model of $\{A\}$ or D is a model of $\{B\}$.

THEOREM 5: D is a model of $\{\forall tA\}$ iff D is a model of $\{S^s_t A \mid s$ is an individual that occurs in $D\}$.

Since we are expressing the algebraic notion of a structure by means of a diagrammatic set of wff, a notion of the predicate calculus, we may as well characterize the algebraic notion of *isomorphic* structures within our predicate calculus.

DEFINITION: Let D and D^* be any diagrammatic sets; we shall say that D and D^* are *isomorphic* iff there exists a one-one mapping, say μ, of the free individuals of D onto the free individuals of D^*, such that $\mu D = D^*$. By "μD" we denote the set of wff obtained from D by replacing each free individual occurring in a wff of D by its image under μ.

For example, let

$$D = \{\mathbf{Gxy}, \mathbf{Gyy}, \mathbf{Gxx}, \mathbf{Gyx}\}$$

and

$$D^* = \{\mathbf{Gyt}, \mathbf{Gtt}, \mathbf{Gyy}, \mathbf{Gty}\}.$$

Then $\mu D = D^*$ where $\mu\mathbf{x} = \mathbf{y}$ and $\mu\mathbf{y} = \mathbf{t}$. Note that D is a model of $\{\mathbf{Gxy}, \mathbf{Gyy}\}$, while D^* is not a model of $\{\mathbf{Gxy}, \mathbf{Gyy}\}$. However, the structure constructed from D^*—namely, $(\{\mathbf{y}, \mathbf{t}\}, \{(\mathbf{y}, \mathbf{t}), (\mathbf{t}, \mathbf{t})\}, \mathbf{y}, \mathbf{t})$, is a model of $\{\mathbf{Gxy}, \mathbf{Gyy}\}$ under the mapping μ.

The following theorems are important.

THEOREM 6: Let D and D^* be any isomorphic diagrammatic sets, and let μ be any one-one mapping of the individuals of D onto the individuals of D^*, such that $\mu D = D^*$. Let A be any wff; then D is a model of $\{A\}$ iff D^* is a model of $\{\mu A\}$.

Demonstration: Apply the variant of the fundamental theorem about wff contained in Exercise 28, page 159.

COROLLARY: Let D and D^* be isomorphic diagrammatic sets such that $\mu D = D^*$; and let $\mathcal{S}^*$ be the structure constructed from D^*. Then $\mathcal{S}^*$ is a model of K under μ whenever D is a model of K.

Demonstration: D^* is a model of μK, by Theorem 6; therefore, $\mathcal{S}^*$ is a model of K under μ.

THEOREM 7: $K \vdash A$ iff D is a model of $\{A\}$ whenever D is a model of K, and A is defined in D.

Demonstration: (1) Suppose that $K \vdash A$; then by statement II, D is a model of $\{A\}$ whenever D is a model of K and A is defined in D.

(2) Suppose that D is a model of $\{A\}$ whenever D is a model of K, and A is defined in D. If A is not a consequence of K, then $K \cup \{\sim A\}$ is consistent and, hence, has a model D' by Theorem 1. Thus, D' is a model of K, and A is defined in D'. Therefore, D' is a model of $\{A\}$. This contradiction establishes Theorem 7.

DEFINITION: Let K be any non-empty set of wff, let B and B' be any sets of individuals, and let μ be any one-one mapping of B onto B'. We shall say that μ is a *K-mapping* iff $\mu t = t$ whenever t is an individual that occurs free in a wff of K.

For example, $\mu = \{(\mathbf{x}, \mathbf{s}), (\mathbf{y}, \mathbf{t}), (\mathbf{z}, \mathbf{z})\}$ is a K-mapping, given that $K = \{\mathbf{Fz}, \forall\, \mathbf{yGyy}\}$. Here, $B = \{\mathbf{z}, \mathbf{y}, \mathbf{x}\}$ and $B' = \{\mathbf{t}, \mathbf{z}, \mathbf{s}\}$.

DEFINITION: We shall say that D is a *prime* model of K iff D is a model of K, and given any model of K, say D', there is a K-mapping μ such that $\mu D \subset D'$.

We can interpret this notion algebraically as follows: A structure $\mathscr{P}$ is a prime model of a theory K iff each model of K (in the algebraic sense), contains a substructure that is isomorphic with $\mathscr{P}$. In other words, $\mathscr{P}$ is a prime model of a theory K iff each model of K is essentially an extension of $\mathscr{P}$.

THEOREM 8: $K \vdash A$ whenever $K \cup D \vdash A$, D is a prime model of K, and A is defined in K.

Demonstration: Since $K \cup D \vdash A$, there is a finite subset of D, say

$$\{Z_1, Z_2, \ldots, Z_m\},$$

such that $K \vdash Z_1 \wedge Z_2 \wedge \ldots \wedge Z_m \rightarrow A$. Let $x_1, x_2, \ldots, x_t$ be the individuals that occur in the wff $Z_1 \wedge Z_2 \wedge \ldots \wedge Z_m$ and are not free in K. Let $Y = \exists x_1 \exists x_2 \ldots \exists x_t(Z_1 \wedge Z_2 \wedge \ldots \wedge Z_m)$; then $K \vdash Y \rightarrow A$. Furthermore, D is a model of $\{Y\}$. Next, let D' be any model of K. Since D is a prime model of K, there is a K-mapping μ such that $\mu D \subset D'$. Hence, $\mu Y = Y$; but by Theorem 6 μD is a model of $\{\mu Y\}$; hence μD is a model of $\{Y\}$. Therefore, by Theorem 25, page 220, $\mu D \vdash Y$. But D' is a model of μD, since $\mu D \subset D'$; therefore, D' is a model of $\{Y\}$. We have established that D' is a model of $\{Y\}$ whenever D' is a model of K. Hence, by Theorem 7, $K \vdash Y$. Since $K \vdash Y \rightarrow A$, it follows that $K \vdash A$.

The ideas of this section are due to A. Robinson (ref. 4); in Section 4 we shall see how he uses these notions to develop a useful test for the completeness of a theory.

EXERCISES

1. Find a diagrammatic set which is a model of $\{\exists \mathbf{y}\mathbf{F}\mathbf{y}, \exists \mathbf{y}(\sim \mathbf{F}\mathbf{y})\}$.
2. Find a diagrammatic set which is a model of $\{\forall \mathbf{x}\mathbf{F}\mathbf{x}, \exists \mathbf{y}(\mathbf{G}\mathbf{y}\mathbf{y})\}$.
3. Find a diagrammatic set which is a model of $\{\exists \mathbf{y}\mathbf{F}\mathbf{y}, \sim (\mathbf{F}\mathbf{w} \vee \mathbf{G}\mathbf{x}\mathbf{t}), \exists \mathbf{z}\mathbf{G}\mathbf{z}\mathbf{t}\}$.
4. Find a diagrammatic set which is a model of $\{\mathbf{G}tt \mid t \text{ is an individual}\} \cup \{\sim \forall \mathbf{x}\mathbf{G}\mathbf{x}\mathbf{x}\}$.
5. Show that D is a model of $\{A \wedge B\}$ iff D is a model of $\{A\}$, and D is a model of $\{B\}$, given that $A \wedge B$ is defined in D.
6. Show that D is a model of $\{\exists \mathbf{w}A\}$ iff there is an individual t occurring in D, such that D is a model of $\{S^t_{\mathbf{w}}A\}$, given that $\exists \mathbf{w}A$ is defined in D.
7. Show that D is a model of $\{A\}$ whenever $D \vdash A$ and A is defined in D, a diagrammatic set.
8. Show that D is a model of K whenever $K \subset D$ and D is a diagrammatic set.
9. Show that μD is diagrammatic whenever D is diagrammatic, and μ is a mapping of the individuals of D onto a set of individuals.
10. (a) Show that $\{\mathbf{F}\mathbf{x}, \mathbf{F}\mathbf{y}\}$ is diagrammatic.
    (b) Show that $\{\mathbf{F}\mathbf{x} \vee \mathbf{F}\mathbf{y}\} \cup \{\mathbf{F}\mathbf{x}, \mathbf{F}\mathbf{y}\} \vdash \mathbf{F}\mathbf{x}$.
    (c) Show that "$\{\mathbf{F}\mathbf{x} \vee \mathbf{F}\mathbf{y}\} \vdash \mathbf{F}\mathbf{x}$" is false.
    (d) Is $\{\mathbf{F}\mathbf{x}, \mathbf{F}\mathbf{y}\}$ a model of $\{\mathbf{F}\mathbf{x} \vee \mathbf{F}\mathbf{y}\}$?
    (e) Is $\{\mathbf{F}\mathbf{x}, \mathbf{F}\mathbf{y}\}$ a *prime* model of $\{\mathbf{F}\mathbf{x} \vee \mathbf{F}\mathbf{y}\}$?
11. Let

$$\begin{aligned} K = \{&\forall \mathbf{x}\mathbf{E}\mathbf{x}\mathbf{x}, \forall \mathbf{x}\forall \mathbf{y}\forall \mathbf{z}(\mathbf{E}\mathbf{x}\mathbf{y} \wedge \mathbf{E}\mathbf{y}\mathbf{z} \rightarrow \mathbf{E}\mathbf{z}\mathbf{x}),\\ &\forall \mathbf{x}\forall \mathbf{y}\forall \mathbf{z}\forall \mathbf{w}(\mathbf{G}\mathbf{x}\mathbf{y} \wedge \mathbf{E}\mathbf{x}\mathbf{z} \wedge \mathbf{E}\mathbf{y}\mathbf{w} \rightarrow \mathbf{G}\mathbf{z}\mathbf{w}),\\ &\forall \mathbf{x}\exists \mathbf{y}(\mathbf{G}\mathbf{x}\mathbf{y}), \qquad \forall \mathbf{x}\forall \mathbf{y}(\mathbf{G}\mathbf{x}\mathbf{y} \rightarrow \sim \mathbf{G}\mathbf{y}\mathbf{x}),\\ &\forall \mathbf{x}\forall \mathbf{y}(\sim \mathbf{E}\mathbf{x}\mathbf{y} \rightarrow \mathbf{G}\mathbf{x}\mathbf{y} \vee \mathbf{G}\mathbf{y}\mathbf{x}),\\ &\forall \mathbf{x}\forall \mathbf{y}\forall \mathbf{z}(\mathbf{G}\mathbf{x}\mathbf{y} \wedge \mathbf{G}\mathbf{y}\mathbf{z} \rightarrow \mathbf{G}\mathbf{x}\mathbf{z})\}, \end{aligned}$$

and let

$$\begin{aligned} D = &\{\mathbf{G}st \mid s \in N \text{ and } t \in N \text{ and } s < t\}\\ &\cup \{\sim \mathbf{G}st \mid s \in N \text{ and } t \in N \text{ and } t \leq s\}\\ &\cup \{\mathbf{E}st \mid s \in N \text{ and } t \in N \text{ and } s = t\}\\ &\cup \{\sim \mathbf{E}st \mid s \in N \text{ and } t \in N \text{ and } s \neq t\} \end{aligned}$$

where N is the set of natural numbers.

(a) Show that D is diagrammatic.
(b) Show that D is a model of K.
(c) Show that {**Eaa**, **Gaa**} is *not* a model of K.
(d) Show that D is a prime model of K.
(e) Show that $K \cup D \vdash \exists$**x**(~ **Gxx**). (*Hint:* use Theorem 25, page 220)
(f) Show that $K \vdash \exists$**x**(~ **Gxx**). (*Hint:* use Theorem 8, page 228)
(g) Show that $K \vdash \forall$**x**(~ **Gxx**). (*Hint:* use Theorem 7, page 227)

12. Given that D is a prime model of K and $K \vdash A$, show that A is not necessarily a consequence of D.

13. State and prove Vaught's test, using the definition of a model of K given in this section.

4. Robinson's Test

An ingenious and useful test for the completeness of a theory has been developed by A. Robinson (ref. 4); we shall devote this section to a study of Robinson's method.

First, we need the notion of a *model-complete* theory.

DEFINITION: A non-empty set K is said to be *model-complete* iff $K \cup D$ is complete whenever D is a model of K.

Our first goal is to characterize the notion of a model-complete theory. To this purpose, we require the notion of a *primitive* wff.

DEFINITION: A wff, say Y, is said to be *primitive* iff Y is in prenex normal form, $\forall$ does not appear in the prefix of Y, and the matrix of Y has the form $A_1 \wedge A_2 \wedge \ldots \wedge A_m$ where each A_i is atomic, or $A_i = \sim B_i$ and B_i is atomic.

THEOREM 9: If K is model-complete, then $D \vdash Y$ whenever D and D' are models of K such that:

(1) $D \subset D'$
(2) Y is primitive and Y is defined in D
(3) $D' \vdash Y$

Demonstration: Since D is a model of K, $K \cup D$ is complete. But Y is defined in $K \cup D$; therefore, $K \cup D \vdash Y$ or else $K \cup D \vdash \sim Y$. If the latter is true, then D' is a model of $\{\sim Y\}$, since D' is a model of $K \cup D$. But $D' \vdash Y$; therefore, D' is a model of $\{Y\}$, which is a contradiction. Thus, $K \cup D \vdash Y$. But D is a model of $K \cup D$; hence, D is a model of $\{Y\}$. Applying Theorem 25, page 220, we see that $D \vdash Y$. This establishes the theorem.

THEOREM 10: If K is not model-complete, there is a primitive wff Y and models of K, say D and D', such that

(1) $D \subset D'$
(2) $D' \vdash Y$
(3) Y is defined in D
(4) not $D \vdash Y$

Demonstration: We shall construct a wff Y and models of K, D, and D', possessing the stated properties.

Since K is not model-complete, there exists a model of K, say D_1, and a wff A defined in D_1, such that neither $K \cup D_1 \vdash A$ nor $K \cup D_1 \vdash \sim A$. Considering the demonstration of Theorem 26, page 221, there is a wff in prenex normal form with shortest prefix, say $\exists tC$, such that neither $K \cup D_1 \vdash \exists tC$ nor $K \cup D_1 \vdash \sim \exists tC$. Furthermore, D_1 is not a model of $\{\exists tC\}$. Next, consider *all* pairs (D, B) such that D is a model of K, and B is a wff defined in D and in prenex normal form, such that neither $K \cup D \vdash B$ nor $K \cup D \vdash \sim B$. Choose a pair from this collection of pairs such that the wff involved has a prefix of minimum length; for example, the pair $(D, \exists sE)$. This means that $K \cup D^* \vdash B^*$ or $K \cup D^* \vdash \sim B^*$ whenever D^* is a model of K, B^* is defined in D^* and is in prenex normal form, and the prefix of B^* is shorter than the prefix of $\exists sE$.

Since $\sim \exists sE$ is not a consequence of $K \cup D$, $K \cup D \cup \{\exists sE\}$ is consistent; hence, has a model D', by Theorem 1, page 226. Thus, $D \subset D'$. Since D' is a model of $\{\exists sE\}$, there is an individual occurring in D', say a, such that D' is a model of $\{S^a_s E\}$. Consider the pair $(D', S^a_s E)$; D' is a model of K, $S^a_s E$ is defined in D' and has prefix shorter than that of $\exists sE$. (Recalling the proof of Theorem 26, page 221, we see that $S^a_s E$ is in prenex normal form.) Therefore, $K \cup D' \vdash S^a_s E$ or $K \cup D' \vdash \sim S^a_s E$; since D' is a model of $K \cup D' \cup \{S^a_s E\}$, we conclude that $K \cup D' \vdash S^a_s E$. But $\vdash S^a_s E \rightarrow \exists sE$; thus, $K \cup D' \vdash \exists sE$.

It follows that there is a finite subset of D', say $\{Z_1, Z_2, \ldots, Z_m\}$, such that

$$K \vdash Z_1 \wedge Z_2 \wedge \ldots \wedge Z_m \rightarrow \exists sE.$$

Let $x_1, x_2, \ldots, x_t$ be the individuals occurring in the wff $Z_1 \wedge Z_2 \wedge \ldots \wedge Z_m$ which do not occur in D. Then $K \vdash Y \rightarrow \exists sE$, where

$$Y = \exists x_1 \exists x_2 \ldots \exists x_t (Z_1 \wedge Z_2 \wedge \ldots \wedge Z_m).$$

Since D is a model of K, we see that D is a model of $\{Y \rightarrow \exists sE\}$. Clearly, Y is primitive, $D' \vdash Y$ (by Theorem 25, page 220, since D' is a model of $\{Y\}$), and Y is defined in D. If $D \vdash Y$, then D is a model of $\{Y\}$; hence, D is a model of $\{\exists sE\}$. But, by Theorem 26, page 221, D is *not* a model of $\{\exists sE\}$! This contradiction demonstrates that Y is not a consequence of D.

COROLLARY: K is model-complete iff $D \vdash Y$ whenever D and D' are models of K such that:
(1) $D \subset D'$
(2) Y is primitive and is defined in D
(3) $D' \vdash Y$.

Note: $D \vdash Y$ iff D is a model of $\{Y\}$, by Theorem 25, page 220.

Robinson uses the criterion expressed in this Corollary to demonstrate that various theories are model-complete (see ref. 4).

Now, we examine the connection between model-completeness and completeness.

ROBINSON'S TEST: K is complete if K is model-complete, and K possesses a prime model.

Demonstration: Let A be any wff defined in K, and let D be a prime model of K. Since $K \cup D$ is complete, either $K \cup D \vdash A$ or else $K \cup D \vdash \sim A$. If the former is true, then $K \vdash A$ by Theorem 8, page 228; if the latter is true, then $K \vdash \sim A$. Hence, K is complete.

One point needs to be emphasized. Both conditions of Robinson's test are, in fact, *algebraic* conditions. This is because our notion of a *model* of a set of wff (see page 226), corresponds to the usual algebraic notion of a model (or realization) of a theory. Furthermore, the condition that K possesses a *prime* model corresponds to the algebraic notion of a theory such that each model of the theory is essentially—i.e., up to isomorphism—an extension of a given model of the theory.

Examining the criterion for model-completeness from a purely algebraic point-of-view, we see that a theory K is model-complete iff each primitive wff Y that is meaningful in M, where M is a given model of K (in the algebraic sense), holds in M if Y holds in some extension of M that is also a model of K (again, in the algebraic sense).

To illustrate, let K be the concept of an algebraically closed field. Then a primitive wff Y of this theory, which is meaningful in M, a given model of K, asserts the existence of a solution of a given set of equations and inequalities; these equations and inequalities involve certain unknowns and possibly certain members of the basic set of the algebraically closed field M. Robinson has shown (ref. 4) that by a simple trick the inequalities can be replaced by equations; hence, Y asserts the existence of a solution of a finite system of polynomial equations. But any system of polynomial equations with coefficients in a field M possesses a solution in the algebraic closure of M, provided the system has a solution in some extension of M. Since we are assuming that Y possesses a solution in M', an extension of M which is also a model of

K, we conclude that Y has a solution in M—since M is algebraically closed. Thus, the concept of an algebraically closed field is model-complete.

It is clear that the concept of an algebraically closed field is not complete, since there exist algebraically closed fields with differing characteristic; therefore, if "K" denotes a set of wff characterizing the concept of an algebraically closed field, K does not possess a prime model—by Robinson's test.

Moreover, it is well-known that the concept of an algebraically closed field of characteristic p possesses a prime model; clearly, this concept is model-complete, since the concept of an algebraically closed field is model-complete. Applying Robinson's test, we conclude that the concept of an algebraically closed field of characteristic p is complete.

Robinson has applied his test to demonstrate the completeness of many other important theories (ref. 4).

References

Books and Articles which Influenced This Book Directly

1. Henkin, L., "The completeness of the first-order functional calculus", *Journal of Symbolic Logic*, Vol. 14, 1949, pp. 159–166.

2. Hilbert, D., and W. Ackermann, *Principles of Mathematical Logic*. New York: Chelsea Publishing Co., 1950.

3. Lightstone, A. H., and A. Robinson, "Syntactical Transforms", *Trans. American Math. Society*, Vol. 86, 1957, pp. 220–245.

4. Robinson, A., *Complete Theories*. Amsterdam: North-Holland Publishing Co., 1956.

A Selection of Books of General Interest

5. Arnold, B. H., *Logic and Boolean Algebra*. Englewood Cliffs, N.J.: Prentice-Hall, Inc., 1962.

6. Basson, A. H., and D. J. O'Connor, *Introduction to Symbolic Logic*. London: University Tutorial Press, 1953.

7. Curry, H. B., *Outlines of a Formalist Philosophy of Mathematics*. Amsterdam: North-Holland Publishing Co., 1951.

8. Curry, H. B., *Foundations of Mathematical Logic*. New York: McGraw-Hill, 1963.

9. Kleene, S. C., *Introduction to Metamathematics*. Princeton, N.J.: Van Nostrand, 1952.

10. Robinson, A., *Introduction to Model Theory and to the Metamathematics of Algebra.* Amsterdam: North-Holland Publishing Co., 1963.

11. Rosenbloom, P. C., *The Elements of Mathematical Logic.* New York: Dover 1950.

12. Stoll, R. R., *Sets, Logic and Axiomatic Theories.* San Francisco: Freeman, 1961.

13. Suppes, P., *Introduction to Logic.* Princeton, N.J.: Van Nostrand, 1957.

Answers

Chapter I

Section 1: 1. $\sim\sim s$ 3. $s \rightarrow p$ 5. $(\sim s) \wedge (\sim p)$ 7. Neither mathematics nor logic is easy 9. Logic is easy iff mathematics is easy 11. Logic is easy iff mathematics is easy

13.

p	q	neither p nor q
T	T	F
T	F	F
F	T	F
F	F	T

15.

p	q	not both of p, q
T	T	F
T	F	T
F	T	T
F	F	T

17. p and q take the same truth-value in each possible truth-value case

Section 2:

1(a).

p	q	$(p \wedge q) \vee p \rightarrow \sim q$		
T	T	T	F	
T	F	T	T	
F	T	F	T	
F	F	F	T	

3. No

5.

p	q	r	$(p \rightarrow r) \wedge (q \rightarrow r) \rightarrow (p \leftrightarrow q)$		
T	T	T	T	T	T
T	T	F	F	T	T
T	F	T	T	F	F
T	F	F	F	T	F
F	T	T	T	F	F
F	T	F	F	T	F
F	F	T	T	T	T
F	F	F	F	T	T

7(a). The instructor is kind.

(b). This course is easy, or the instructor is kind and the course is not easy iff the instructor is not kind and the course is easy.

Section 3: 3(a). 8 3(b). 256 3(c). 65,536 5(a). T 5(b). T 5(c). T 5(d). F

Section 4: 1(a). $(p_1 \wedge \sim p_2 \wedge \sim p_3) \vee (\sim p_1 \wedge p_2 \wedge p_3)$
1(b). $(p_1 \wedge p_2 \wedge p_3) \vee (\sim p_1 \wedge p_2 \wedge \sim p_3)$ 1(c). $p_1 \wedge \sim p_2 \wedge p_3$
3. Let $q_1 \wedge q_2 \wedge \cdots \wedge q_n$ be a disjunct of the given proposition, where q_i is p_i or $\sim p_i$. Then a truth-value case under which the given proposition is true, is such that p_i is true iff $q_i = p_i$.

Section 5: 19. Not a tautology 21. Not a tautology 23. Not a tautology 25. Tautology 27. Tautology 29. Not a tautology 31. Tautology 33. Tautology 35. Invalid 37. Invalid 39. Invalid 41. Invalid 43. Valid 45. Valid

Section 6: 3. f 5. t 7. $p \vee q$ 9. $p \vee q$ 11. $p \wedge q$ 13. $(p \vee \sim q) \wedge r$

Section 7: 1. $p \wedge q$ 3. $(p \wedge \sim q) \vee (\sim p \wedge \sim r) \vee (q \wedge r)$ 5. $p \wedge q$

Section 8: 1. Everyone is a Canadian 3. Everyone is dishonest 5. All Canadians are honest 7. Canadians, and only Canadians, are honest 17. No

Section 9. 1. Valid 3. Valid 5. Invalid 7. Valid 13. $\exists !x[P(x)] = \exists x \forall y[P(x) \wedge (P(y) \rightarrow y = x)]$

Section 10: 1. $\forall x(x = x)$ True 3. $\forall x \forall y \forall z[x = y \wedge y = z \rightarrow x = z]$ True 5. $\forall x \exists y[x = y]$ True 7. $\exists x[x + x = x]$ True 9. $\forall x \forall y[x + y = y + x]$ True 15. True 17. True 19. False for integers, true for natural numbers 21. True 23. True for rational numbers, false for integers 25. True

Chapter II

Section 1: 13. The even integers 15. The odd, positive primes 17. $\{2, -2\}$ 19. $\{1\}$ 27. $x \in \{x\}$ is true

Section 5: 3. $\{(a, b)\}$ 5. $\{(a, d), (b, d), (c, d)\}$ 7. No 11. The set of all ordered pairs whose terms are members of A or of B 13. $\{\{a\}\}$

Section 6: 1(a). Associate the center of the circle with the circle 1(b). With each point associate the unit circle with center at the origin 1(c). Yes

Section 7: 1(a). No 1(b). The set of all real numbers other than 0.

Section 8: 1. $(1, -2, 2)$ 3. $(3, 2, 1)$ 5. $(-2, 4, 4)$ 13. $\mathbf{R}$ is a unary relation on A iff $\mathbf{R} \subset A$

Section 9: 9. $\{\{a, c, d\}, \{b\}\}$
11. $\{(a, a), (b, b), (c, c), (d, d), (e, e), (a, b), (b, a), (a, c), (c, a), (d, e), (e, d)\}$

Section 10: 1(a). S has exactly one member iff $\exists x \forall y[x \in S \dot{\wedge} y \in S \rightarrow y = x]$
1(c). S has exactly four members iff

$$\exists x \exists y \exists z \exists w \forall t[x \in S \wedge y \in S \wedge z \in S \wedge w \in S \dot{\wedge} t \in S \rightarrow t = x \veebar t = y \veebar t = z \veebar t = w]$$

Chapter III

Section 1: 5(a). True 5(c). False 5(e). True 5(g). True 5(i). True
5(k). True

Section 2: 1(b). $(\{0, 1\}, \{(0, 1), (1, 0)\})$ 3(b). $(\{0, 1, 2\}, \{(0, 1), (1, 2), (0, 2)\})$

Section 3: 1. $(\{0, 1, 2\}, \{(0, 0, 0), (0, 1, 1), (0, 2, 2), (1, 0, 1), (1, 1, 2), (1, 2, 0), (2, 0, 2), (2, 1, 0), (2, 2, 1)\})$
5. $1 \mathbin{?} (2 \mathbin{?} 3) = 1 \mathbin{?} 10 = 11$, $(1 \mathbin{?} 2) \mathbin{?} 3 = 3 \mathbin{?} 3 = 18$

Section 5: 1. (S, o) where S consists of the six possible permutations of $\{a, b, c\}$ and "$p \, o \, q$" denotes the result of applying first q, then p

Note that $\begin{pmatrix} a & b & c \\ b & c & a \end{pmatrix} o \begin{pmatrix} a & b & c \\ b & a & c \end{pmatrix} = \begin{pmatrix} a & b & c \\ c & b & a \end{pmatrix}$

whereas $\begin{pmatrix} a & b & c \\ b & a & c \end{pmatrix} o \begin{pmatrix} a & b & c \\ b & c & a \end{pmatrix} = \begin{pmatrix} a & b & c \\ a & c & b \end{pmatrix}$

7. $(R, +, \cdot, >, 0, 1)$

Section 6: 13. $(B, \cup, \cap, (0, 0, 0), (1, 1, 1))$ where

$B = \{(0, 0, 0), (1, 0, 0), (0, 1, 0), (0, 0, 1), (0, 1, 1), (1, 0, 1), (1, 1, 0), (1, 1, 1)\}$,
$(a_1, a_2, a_3) \cup (b_1, b_2, b_3) = (\max\{a_1, b_1\}, \max\{a_2, b_2\}, \max\{a_3, b_3\})$,
$(a_1, a_2, a_3) \cap (b_1, b_2, b_3) = (a_1 \cdot b_1, a_2 \cdot b_2, a_3 \cdot b_3)$

Chapter IV

Section 2: 1. (*a*), (*b*), (*c*), (*d*), (*g*) are expressions, whereas (*e*), (*f*), and (*h*) are not expressions
7. No 9. l counts the connectives occurring in a wff
11. n counts the instances of $\sim$ in a wff
13. p counts the parentheses occurring in a wff
15. r counts the instances of **(X)** in a wff

Section 3: 1. $\sim X \vee \sim Z$ 3. $X \vee \sim Y \rightarrow W$ 5. $(X \rightarrow Y) \leftrightarrow (\sim Y \rightarrow \sim X)$
7. $X \rightarrow (X \vee X)$ 9. $(X \wedge Y) \rightarrow Z$ 11. $X \rightarrow (Y \leftrightarrow Z)$ 13. $X \wedge Y \dot{\vee} Y \wedge X$
15. $X \rightarrow Y \dot{\rightarrow} Z \rightarrow W$

Section 5: 5. $Y, \sim X, X$

Section 6: 4, 6, 7, 8, 11, 12, 13, 15, 16 are in normal form; 5, 9, 10, 14 are not in normal form

Section 7: 1. $\sim Y \vee \sim X \dot{\vee} W \vee X$ 3. $X \vee Y \dot{\vee} \sim X \vee Y$
5. $(\sim X \vee \sim Y) \wedge W$ 7. $Y \wedge X \dot{\wedge} \sim W \wedge \sim X$ 9. $X \wedge Y \dot{\vee} \sim W$
11. $X \wedge \sim Y$ 13. $Y \vee \sim X \dot{\vee} \sim W \vee X$
15. $(\sim W \wedge \sim X \dot{\wedge} \sim Y) \wedge (\sim X \wedge \sim Y \dot{\wedge} \sim Z)$ 21. $Y \dot{\wedge} W \wedge Z$
23. $X \wedge Y \dot{\vee} \sim Y \wedge \sim X$ 25. $X \wedge Y \dot{\vee} \sim Y \wedge \sim X$ 33(a). $\sim X \rightarrow Y$
33(b). $X \wedge Y \dot{\wedge} \sim Z$ 33(d). $\mathcal{S}$ replaces any disjunction by its first disjunct
35(a). $\sim Y \vee X \dot{\vee} \sim (\sim \sim Y \vee X)$ 35(b). $Y \vee Y \wedge X \vee \sim Y$ 35(c). Each atomic wff to which $\sim$ is affixed, is replaced by **Y**; all other atomic wff are replaced by **X**
35(d). $Z \vee \sim Z$

Section 8: 7. The "by duality" refers to Theorem 42, which has been applied incorrectly.

Chapter V

Section 2: 1. (a), (b), (c), (e), (f), (i) are expressions; (d), (g), (h) are not expressions
2. (a) Is not a wff (c) Is not a wff (e) Is not a wff (g) Is a wff
(i) Is not a wff (k) Is a wff (m) Is not a wff (o) Is not a wff
(q) Is not a wff (s) Is a wff (u) Is not a wff (w) Is a wff
3. (a) Free (c) Bound (e) Free (g) Free (i) Free (k) Bound
7. $\mathcal{L}$ counts the instances of $\forall$

Section 3: 1. $(\forall y(Fz \vee Gxy)) \rightarrow \exists zFz$ 3. $(\forall z(Fz \rightarrow Gxx)) \vee Fy$
5. $\exists y(\exists x(Fy \leftrightarrow Fx))$ 7. $(\forall xGxy) \vee (\forall z(Fz \wedge Fz))$
9. $Gxy \vee (Fz \rightarrow \forall wHxyw)$ 11. $(\sim (\forall x(\sim ((\sim (Fx)) \vee (Fy)))))$
13. $(\forall x(\sim (\forall y(\sim (Gxy)))))$ 15. $(\sim ((\sim (\forall y(Gyy))) \vee (\sim (\sim (\forall x(\sim (Fx)))))))$
17. $(\sim ((\sim ((\sim (\sim (\forall x(\sim (Fx))))) \vee (\sim (\forall y(\sim (Fy)))))) \vee$
$(\sim ((\sim (\sim (\forall y(\sim (Fy))))) \vee (\sim (\forall x(\sim (Fx)))))))))$
19. $\forall yFy$ 21. $\forall z(Fz \vee Gyz)$ 23. $\exists yFy$ 25. $\forall y(Gyx \rightarrow \forall zFz)$

Section 4: 1. $Fy \vee \sim (Gyx \vee Hzxy)$ 3. $\forall w(Hxyw \vee Fz)$
5. $Fy \vee \forall x(Gyx \vee \forall z(Hyxz))$ 11. $Fw \wedge \exists y\forall x\exists zHyxzw$
13. $\forall x\forall y\exists w\forall zHxywz$ 15. $\forall x\forall y\exists z\forall wHxyzw$ 25(v). $B = \forall y\forall xGxy$

Section 7: 9. $A = \forall xFx \vee \forall yFy$ 11. $A = \forall x\forall yGxy \rightarrow \forall yGwy$

Section 8: 1. $\exists x(Fx \vee Gxy)$, $\forall x(\sim(Fx \vee Gxy))$, $\sim(Fx \vee Gxy)$, $Fx \vee Gxy$, Fx, Gxy
3. $\forall y \exists x(Fx \wedge Gxy)$, $\exists x(Fx \wedge Gxy)$, $\forall x(\sim(Fx \wedge Gxy))$, $\sim(Fx \wedge Gxy)$, $Fx \wedge Gxy$, $\sim Fx \vee \sim Gxy$, $\sim Fx$, Fx, $\sim Gxy$, Gxy
7. $((Fx) \vee (Fy))$ is a wff 9. yes

Section 9: 1. $\sim Fx \vee \forall yGyy$, 3. $\exists y(Fy \vee Gyy)$ 5. $Fx \wedge \exists y(\sim Fy)$
7. $\forall y(\sim Fy \wedge \sim Gyy)$ 9. $\exists y(\sim Fy \vee \sim Gyy)$ 11. $\sim Fx \wedge \exists y(Fy \wedge Gyy)$
13. $Fx \wedge Gyy$ 15. $\forall y(Fx \wedge Gyy)$ 17. $\forall y(Fx \wedge Gyy)$ 27. $A = \sim Fx \vee Fy$

Section 10: 1. $\forall x(Fy \vee Gxy)$ 3. $\exists y \forall x(Fy \vee Gxx)$ 5. $\forall x \forall y(Fx \vee Gyy)$
7. $\forall x \forall y \exists z \forall w(Fx \wedge Gyz \dot{\vee} Hwww)$ 9. $\forall x(Fz \wedge (Fx \vee \sim Fx))$
11. $\forall x((Fz \wedge \sim Fz) \wedge (Fx \vee \sim Fx))$ 13. Yes

Section 11: 13. No 17. $\{Fx \wedge \sim Fx\}$

Index